The Geological Society of America

MEMOIR 94

BIBLIOGRAPHY AND INDEX OF FOSSIL
DINOFLAGELLATES AND ACRITARCHS

CHARLES DOWNIE

Department of Geology, University of Sheffield, England

WILLIAM ANTONY S. SARJEANT

Department of Geology, University of Nottingham, England

NEW YORK • DECEMBER 1964

Published by
The Geological Society of America, Inc.
Library of Congress catalog card number 64-8209

Address all communications to
The Geological Society of America, Inc.
231 East 46th Street, New York, N. Y. 10017

THE MEMOIR SERIES
OF THE GEOLOGICAL SOCIETY OF AMERICA
IS MADE POSSIBLE THROUGH THE BEQUEST OF
RICHARD ALEXANDER FULLERTON PENROSE, JR.

CONTENTS

FOREWORD

This volume attempts to give a complete, annotated bibliography of two groups of microfossils with organic shell walls, the dinoflagellates and the acritarchs. Although bibliographies of these groups are known to have been prepared for private use by commercial organisations and although partial bibliographies have been appended to papers treating with these micro-organisms, no complete bibliography has been published to date. In view of the considerable importance these micro-fossils are assuming in stratigraphy, such a bibliography is regarded by the authors as likely to prove a useful tool for the extension of geological knowledge.

Two principal groups of microfossils are dealt with, the dinoflagellates and the acritarchs. The former group comprises unicellular algae of marine and fresh waters, usually represented in the fossil state by cysts, ruptured or unruptured. The latter group is defined in Evitt (1963, p. 300-2) and in Downie, Evitt and Sarjeant (1963, p.7); it comprises unicellular, or apparently unicellular, micro-fossils of unknown or doubtful affinity. Both groups occur together in microscopic preparations; the attribution of certain genera to one or the other group is doubtful. For these reasons they are treated together. Certain genera considered by the authors to be attributable to a family of the Chlorophy-ceae, the Tasmanaceae (see Downie, Evitt and Sarjeant, 1963, p.15) are also included, since they have for long been treated as acritarchs and are still so regarded by some authorities: however, references dealing wholly with Tasmanaceae are so distinguished.

The study of these micro-organisms commenced around 1836, when a paper by the great micro-scopist, Christian Gottfried Ehrenberg, was read to the Berlin Akademie der Wissenschaften describing dinoflagellates, dinoflagellate cysts and acritarchs, although only the first named group was immediately recognised. Unfortunately, a criticism of Ehrenberg's views by the French microscopist, Turpin, was published before Ehrenberg's paper reached press, so the German did not have the honour of first publication.

The subsequent development of the study of this group is shown in the accompanying figure (text - fig. 1). There was a brief burst of publication in the 1840's, and the Tasmanaceae were first described in 1871. However, serious attention began to be paid to the group, from a stratigraphical and systematic view-point, only as late as 1931: research declined during the war years, but recovered thereafter and is today growing steadily as the importance of these organisms as strati-graphical indices is increasingly realised. The increasing rates at which taxa are being erected is well portrayed in text - figures 2 and 3.

The plan adopted in presenting this bibliography is tripartite. First of all, a list of all books and articles treating with these organisms, arranged alphabetically and chronologically under the author's name, is given. Secondly, the geological horizons studied to date are indexed. Thirdly, the taxa erected for these organisms are indexed, names currently considered to be valid and names not so considered being listed separately. The bibliography covers the period from 1837, when Turpin's paper was published, to 1963; the authors hope in the future to bring it up to date by periodic publication of supplements and in this connection they will welcome information, comments and criticisms. The format adopted corresponds with that used in the journal "Micropaleontology", which is likely to be familiar to specialists using this bibliography.

Although every endeavour has been made to attain completeness, some omissions are in-evitable. Particular difficulty has been experienced with Russian literature, not only in terms of coverage but also in terms of systematics. In the choice and rejection of taxa, the authors have provisionally included as valid a number of genera and species apparently not validly published in terms of the current "International Code of Botanical Nomenclature", since they are not in all cases sure that coverage of literature is complete.

In preparing the lists of valid species, it has been found necessary to reattribute a number of species from invalid or wrongly used genera; these reattributions have been kept to a minimum. Inclusion of a species in the list of valid taxa in no way implies personal endorsement of its validity by the authors: the list is intended merely to represent the present status of opinion.

The species published by Naumova presented considerable additional problems. A large number of these were stated to show trilete marks; in all such cases, the species in question have been excluded from consideration, although the authors suspect that the alleged marks may in many cases have been merely fortuitous associations of ridges. Species without trilete marks have been re-allocated where necessary to genera to which they correspond in morphology. In several instances, e.g. in the genus Trachydiacrodium, species proposed by Timofeyev have become secondary homonyms as a result; new names are not, however, here proposed, since the status of the species erected by both these authors is considered in general to be suspect.

Where fossil species are attributed to modern genera, citation in detail of the original description and the description of the type species is not attempted, since it is considered outside the scope of this work. Hard and fast distinction between fossil and modern species did not prove always easy. The principle adopted with post-Pleistocene records was inclusion of reference to genera and species recorded from sediment samples, and exclusion of records from living plankton. Descriptions of plankton from sediment samples are at present scarce and are in themselves of definite geological interest.

The system of abbreviations adopted in the editions of the "World List of Scientific Periodicals" (of which the third edition, published in 1952 and covering the period 1900-1950, is current) has been followed in the listing of names of scientific publications. In transliteration of the names of Russian scientists and periodicals, the system adopted by Professor Raymond C. Moore and his Committee, for the "Lexique Stratigraphique International", has been followed. The scheme of stratigraphic sub-divisions adopted in the latter work has likewise been followed.

Work on this bibliography has extended over a number of years. The authors are particularly indebted to Professor L. R. Moore, for the use of the bibliographic facilities of the Micropalaeontology Laboratory of the University of Sheffield, and to the Librarians of the Geological Society of London and of the Palaeontology, Zoology, Botany and General Libraries of the British Museum (Natural History) for their unstinting assistance. Help has also been received on particular matters from Dr. Lucy M. Cranwell (Geochronology Laboratories, Tucson, Arizona), Professor G. Deflandre (École Pratique des Hautes Études, Paris), Professor A. Eisenack (Reutlingen, Germany), Dr. W. R. Evitt (Stanford University, California), Herr H. Gocht and Mr. N. Creel (Geologisches Institut, Tubingen, Germany), Dr. P. Kaye and Mr. D. Williams (Sedimentology Research Laboratory, Reading), and from numerous authors of papers. One of us (W. A. S. S.) would like further to acknowledge the help of Professor P. Allen and the Research Board of Reading University during the earlier stages of preparation of the manuscript, which was commenced under tenure of a Reading University Research Fellowship, and of Professor W. D. Evans (University of Nottingham) during the later stages.

CHARLES DOWNIE

WILLIAM ANTONY S. SARJEANT

January, 1964.

LIST OF NEW TAXONOMIC COMBINATIONS HERE PROPOSED

Acanthodiacrodium aciferum (Naumova, 1950); A. brevispinum (Naumova, 1950); A. curvispinum (Naumova, 1950); A. denticulatum (Naumova, 1950); A. echinatum (Naumova, 1950); A. hirtum (Naumova, 1950); A. meonanthum (Naumova, 1950); A. quadrangularis (Naumova, 1950: A. simplissimum (Naumova, 1950); A. spinellosum (Naumova, 1950); A. subrotundum (Naumova, 1950); A. subscarbum (Naumova, 1950); A. varium (Naumova, 1950).

Baltisphaeridium anticum (Naumova, 1950); B. ashdodensis (Rossignol, 1962); B. conspersum (Naumova, 1950); B. denticulatum (Courteville in Deflandre, 1946a); B. duvernayensis (Staplin, 1961); B. excisum (Naumova, 1950); B. israelianum (Rossignol, 1962); B. mutabilis (Naumova, 1950); B. ohioensis (Winslow, 1962); B. paucifurcatum (Cookson and Eisenack, 1961b); B. scaber (Naumova, 1950); B. serratum (Naumova, 1950); B. spectatissimum (Naumova, 1950); B. spinellosum (Naumova, 1950); B. spiralisetum (de Wit, 1942); B. sylheti (Baksi, 1962); B. tschunensis (Timofeyev, 1962); B. veliferum (Downie, 1958).

Cannosphaeropsis scaffoldi (Baksi, 1962).

Cymatiogalea membrasnacea (Naumova, 1950).

Dasydiacrodium argutum (Naumova, 1950); D. imperfectum (Naumova, 1950); D. singulare (Naumova, 1950).

Leiosphaeridia belloyense (Jansonius, 1962); L. communis (Naumova, 1950); L. disca (Timofeyev, 1962); ? L. globosa (White, 1842); L. muitscha (Timofeyev, 1962); L. pestovi (Timofeyev, 1962); L. punctulosa (Naumova, 1950).

Lophodiacrodium aculeatum (Naumova, 1950); L. gibberosum (Naumova, 1950); L. notatum (Naumova, 1950); L. parvimammum (Naumova, 1950); L. parvispinum (Naumova, 1950); L. sinuoitum (Naumova, 1950); L. subspinellosum (Naumova, 1950); L. torulosum (Naumova, 1950); L. tuberculatum (Naumova, 1950).

Membranilarnacia liradiscoides (O. Wetzel, 1933); ?M. marina (Kufferath, 1950); ?M. pira (Deunff, 1958); ?M. pterospermoides (O. Wetzel, 1933).

Tasmanites primigenus (Naumova, 1950).

Trachydiacrodium dentatum (Naumova, 1950).

SECTION I: BIBLIOGRAPHY

BIBLIOGRAPHY

An asterisk * marks those articles in which new taxa are proposed or which are of taxonomic interest for other reasons. Articles dealing with Tasmanites and related genera, but not with these groups in general, are distinguished by the word "(Tasmanaceae)". Where a book passed through several editions, only the first is included except where significant alterations were later made to the relevant section.

ABUZYAROVA, R.,
    1962   Palynological data on the Eocene flora of Kazakhstan. Abstr., International Conference on Palynology, Tucson, Arizona, 1962. Pollen et Spores, vol. 4, no. 2, p. 328.

ALBERTI, G.,
  * 1959a   Uber Pseudodeflandrea n.g. (Dinoflag.) aus dem Mittel-Oligozän von Norddeutschland. Geol. Staatsinst. Hamburg, Mitt., vol. 28, pp. 91-2, text-fig. 1.

  * 1959b   Zur Kenntnis der Gattung Deflandrea Eisenack (Dinoflag.) in der Kreide und im Alttertiär Nord und Mitteldeutschlands. Geol. Staatsinst. Hamburg, Mitt., vol. 28, pls. 8 - 9, text - fig. 1.

  * 1961   Zur Kenntnis mesozoischer und alttertiärer Dinoflagellaten und Hystrichosphaerideen von Nord - und Mitteldeutschland sowie einigen anderen europäischen Gebieten. Palaeontographica, ser. A, vol. 116, pp. 1 - 58, pls. 1 - 12, 1 tab.

ALYUSHINSKIY, Y.A., KIRICHENKO, G.I., and TIMOFEYEV, B.V.,
    1957   Spores of the Sinian deposits of the Yenisei Block (in Russian). Akad. Nauk. S.S.S.R., Dokl., vol. 117, no. 1, pp. 111-4.

ANDREYEVA, E.M.
    1961   Spore complexes of the Upper Proterozoic and Lower Palaeozoic of the Russian Platform. (in Russian). Geol. Kongr., XXI Sess., Mezhd., 1960. Doklad. Soviet Geol., pp. 172-6.

    1962   Spore and pollen complexes in Upper Proterozoic and Paleozoic deposits of some regions of the U.S.S.R. Abst., International Conference on Palynology, Tucson, Arizona, 1962. Pollen et Spores, vol. 4, no. 2, pp. 329-30.

ARMSTRONG, T.A.
    1953   New exploration tool - fossil pollen and spores used in new approach to job of determining age of rock formations cut by drillers' bit. Oil and Gas J., vol. 51, no. 44, pp. 64-5.

AVERDIECK, F.R.
    1958   Pollen vom Chenopodiaceen-Typ im Flöz Frimmersdorf --- ein Hinweis auf seine strandnahe Entstehung. Fortschr. Geol. Rheinld. Westf., vol.1, pp. 101-12, text - fig. 1, tabs. 1-2 (pp. 105, 107 relevant).

BAKSI, S.K.
  * 1962   Palynological investigation of Simsang River Tertiaries, South Shillong Front, Assam. Geol. Min. Met. Soc. India, Bull., no. 26, pp. 1-22, pls. 1-5, text - figs. 1-2, tabs. 1-2.

BALME, B.E.
  * 1957   Spores and pollen grains from the Mesozoic of Western Australia. Commonwealth of Australia Fuel. Res., Phys. & Chem. Surv. Nat. Coal. Res. 48 pp.,11 pl., 128 text-figs. (p.32, pl.8, figs. 88-90 relevant).

1963   Plant microfossils from the Lower Triassic of Western Australia. Palaeontology, vol. 6, pt. 3, pp. 12-40, pls. 4-6, text-figs. 1-2. (pp. 32-4 relevant).

BALTEŞ, N.   see Venkatachala, B.S., and Balteş.

BANERJI, D.   see Ghosh, A.K., and Banerji.

BARBOSA, O.
1949   Vegetais fosseis do Devoniano do Brasil e da Bolivia. Mineraç. Metall., Rio de Janeiro, vol. 14, no. 81, pp. 8-4 (Tasmanaceae).

BARGHOORN, E.S., and TYLER, S.A.
1962   Microfossils from the Middle Precambrian of Canada. Abstr., International Conference on Palynology, Tucson, Arizona, 1962. Pollen et Spores, vol. 4, no. 2, p. 331. See also Tyler, S.A., and Barghoorn.

BARNARD, T.
1957   News reports: Great Britain. Micropaleontology, vol. 3, No. 4, pp. 415-6.

BASCHNAGEL, R.A.
1942   Some microfossils from the Onondaga Chert of Central New York State. Buffalo Soc. Nat. Sci., Bull., vol. 17 no. 3, pp. 1-8, pl.1.

BEJU, D.   see Venkatachala, B.S., and Beju.

BENTALL, R.   see Schopf, J.M., Wilson, L.R., and Bentall.

BERMUDEZ, P.J.
see Riveiro, F. - Ch. de, and Bermudez.

BITTERLI, P.
1960   Bituminous Posidonienschiefer (Lias Epsilon) of Mount Terri, Jura Mountains. Ver. Schweizer. Petrol. - Geol. u. - Ing., Bull., vol. 26, no. 71, pp.41-8, text-fig. 1. (Tasmanaceae, p. 42).
See also Brosius M, and Bitterli.

BLACKWELDER, R.E. and R.M.
1961   Directory of zoological taxonomists of the world. Soc. System. Zool., Carbondale, Ill.: Southern Illinois Univ. Press, 404 pp. (pp. 1 and 3 relevant).

BOEKEL, N.M. van
see Sommer, F.W., and Boekel.

BOWERBANK, J.S.
1841a   On the siliceous bodies of the Chalk, Greensands and Oolite. Geol. Soc. Lond., Proc., vol. 3, pp. 278-81.

1841b   On the siliceous bodies of the Chalk, Greensands and Oolite. Microsc. J. Struct. Rec., vol. 1, pp. 99-103, 113-15, 131-35, text-figs. 1-2 + 1-2.

1841c   On the siliceous bodies of the Chalk, Greensands and Oolite. Geol. Soc. Lond., Trans., vol. 2. pt. 6, pp. 181-94, pls. 18-19.

BRELIE, G. von der
1958   Sporen und Pollen im marinen Tertiär der Niederrheinischen Bucht. Fortschr. Geol. Rheinld. Westf., vol. 1, pp. 185-204, pl.1, text-figs. 1-2, tab. 1.

BRELIE, G. von der, and WOLTERS, R.
    1958   Das Alttertiär von Gürzenich. Fortschr. Geol. Rheinld. Westf. vol. 1,
            pp. 473-7, text-fig. 1. (pp. 473, 476 relevant).

BRONN, H. G.
    1838   Lethaea geognostica; oder, Abbildungen und Beschriebungen der für die
            Gebirgs - Formationen bezeichendsten Versteinerungen. Stuttgart:
            E. Schweizerbart. 2 vols., 1346 pp., 2 pl. (p. 803 relevant).

    1848   Handbuch einer Geschichte der Natur. Vol. 3.   Index
            palaeontologicus. Stuttgart: E. Schweizerbart. 1382 pp. (p.1375 relevant).

BROSIUS, M.
   * 1963   Plankton aus dem nordhessischen Kasseler Meeressand (Oberoligozan).
            Deutsch. Geol. Ges., Z., vol. 114, pt. 1, pp. 32-56, pls. 1-8,
            text-figs. 1-2, tabs. 1-2.

BROSIUS, M., and BITTERLI, P.
   * 1961   Middle Triassic hystrichosphaerids from salt-wells Riburg - 15 and - 17,
            Switzerland. Ver. Schweizer. Petrol. - Geol. u. - Ing., Bull.,
            vol. 28, no. 74. pp. 33-49, pls. 1-2. text-figs. 1-8, tabs. 1-2.

BROSIUS, M., and GRAMANN, F.
    1959   Die stratigraphische Reichweite des Heskemer Pollenbildes in Borken
            (Tertiär, Niederhessen). Deutsch. Geol. Ges., Z., vol. 3, pt. 1,
            pp. 182-97, pls. 6-7, text-figs. 1-5.

BROTZEN, F.
    1941   Några bidrag till Visingsoformationens stratigrafi och tektonik. Geol. Foren.
            Forh., vol. 63, pt. 3, pp. 245-61, text-figs. 1-5.

BROWN, C.W. and PIERCE, R.L.
    1962   Palynologic correlations in Cretaceous Eagle Ford Group, northeast Texas.
            Amer. Assoc. Petrol. Geol., Bull., vol. 46, pp. 2133-47, text-figs. 1-19.

BUREAU DE RECHERCHE DU PÉTRÔLE
    1959   Contribution a l'étude du Cambrien et de l'Ordovicien du Sahara. Soc. Géol.
            Fr., C.R. Somm., no. 7, pp. 194-5.

BURSA, A.
    1962   Some morphogenetic factors in taxonomy of dinoflagellates. Abstr., Inter-
            national Conference on Palynology, Tucson, Arizona, 1962. Pollen et Spores,
            vol. 4, no. 2, pp. 337-8.

CAMPAU, D. E.
            see Jodry, R.L.,and Campau.

CARPENTER, W. B.
    1875   The microscope and its revelations. London: Churchill. 848 pp., 25 pls.,
            449 text-figs, (pp. 297, 797 relevant).

CARPENTIER, A.
    1932   Etude de végétaux à structuré conserve. Silex Stéphanien de Grand'Croix
            (Loire). Facultés Cath. de Lille, Mém. et Trav., vol. 40, pp.1-30,
            pl. 1-15 (pl. 15, pp. 21-2 relevant).

CAYEUX, L.
    1894   Les preuves de l'existence d'organisens dans le terrain précambrien. Premier
            note sur les Radiolaires précambriens. Soc. Géol. Fr., Bull., vol. 22, no. 4,
            pp. 197-228, pl. 11, text-figs. 1-2.

CHACHIA, N.G.
> see Vladimirskaya, I.V., Timofeyev, B.V., and Chachia.

CHEPIKOV, K.R. and MEDVEDEVA, A.M.
> 1963   Recent data on organic micro-residues in the oils of the European part of the
> U.S.S.R. (in Russian).   Akad. Nauk. S.S.S.R., Dokl., vol. 153, no. 2,
> pp. 444-5.

CHEPILOVA, I.K.
> see Medvedeva, A.M. and Chepilova.

CHOUX, J. and DURAND, S.
> 1961   Etude minéralogique et micropaléontologique d'un sédiment toarcien des environs
> de Liguqé (Vienne).   Bur. Rech. Géol. Minières, Mém., no. 4,   Colloque
> sur le Lias français, pp. 163-9, text-figs. 1-2 (p. 167 relevant).

CHOUX, J., DURAND, S. and MILON, Y.
> 1961a   Le dépôt des argiles conservés au Sud de Quimper (Finistère), sous les formations
> marines pliocènes, s'est terminé au début de l'Oligocène.   Acad. Sci. Paris,
> C.R., vol. 252, pp. 3833-5.

> 1961b   Observations nouvelles sur la constitution et l'évolution de la Cuvette de
> Toulven (Finistère).   Soc. Géol. Min. Bretagne, Bull., new ser., vol. 1,
> pp. 19-69, text-figs. 1-17.   (text-fig. 11 relevant).

CHRONIC, J.
> see McKee, E.D., Chronic and Leopold, E.B.

CHURCHILL, D.M.
> 1960   Living and fossil unicellular algae and aplanospores.   Nature, vol. 186,
> no. 4723, pp. 493-4, text-fig. 1.

CHURCHILL, D.M. and SARJEANT, W.A.S.
> 1962   Fossil dinoflagellates and hystrichospheres in Australian freshwater deposits.
> Nature, vol. 194, no. 4833, p. 1094, fig. 1.

> * 1963   Freshwater microplankton from Flandrian (Holocene) peats of south western
> Australia.   Grana Palynologica, vol. 3, no. 3, pp. 29-53, pls. 1-2,
> text-figs. 1-17.

CIZANCOURT, M. de
> 1947   News: France.   The Micropaleontologist,   vol. 1, no. 2, pp. 2-4.

> 1950   News: France.   The Micropaleontologist,   vol. 4, no. 3, pp. 9-11.

CLARKE, J.M.
> 1885   On Devonian spores.   Amer. J. Sci., ser. 3, vol. 29,   pp. 284-9, text.
> figs. 1-3 (Tasmanaceae).

CLOUGH, C.T.
> see Peach, B.N., Horne, J., Gunn, W., Clough and Hinxman, W.

COLLINSON, C.
> 1963   Collection and preparation of Conodonts through mass production techniques.
> Illinois State Geol. Surv., Circulars, no. 343, 16 pp., 6 text-figs.
> (p. 12 relevant).

10

COLLINSON, C. and SCOTT, A. J.
    1958   Chitinozoan faunule of the Devonian Cedar Valley Formation.   Illinois Geol.
              Surv., Circulars, no. 247, 34 pp., 3 pls., 13 text-figs. (p. 11 relevant).

COMBAZ, A.
    * 1962   Sur un nouveau type de microplanctonte cénobial fossile du Gothlandien de Libye.
             Deflandrastrum nov. gen.   Acad. Sci., Paris, C.R., vol. 255, pp. 1977-9,
             text-figs. 1-7.

CONRAD, W.
    * 1941   Notes protistologiques XIX.   Quelques microfossiles des silex crétacés.
             Mus. Roy. Hist. Nat. Belg., Bull., vol. 17, no. 36, pp. 1-10,   pl. 1,
             text-figs. 1-3.

COOKSON, I. C.
    * 1953   Records of the occurrence of Botryococcus braunii,   Pediastrum and the
             Hystrichosphaeridae in Cainozoic deposits of Australia.   Nat. Mus.
             Melbourne. Mem., no. 18, pp. 107-23, pls. 1-2.

    * 1956   Additional microplankton from Australian late Mesozoic and Tertiary sediments.
             Aust. J. Mar. Freshw. Res., vol. 7, No. 1, pp. 183-91, pls. 1-2.
             See also Deflandre, G. and Cookson; Eisenack, A. and Cookson.

COOKSON, I. C. and EISENACK, A.
    * 1958   Microplankton from Australian and New Guinea Upper Mesozoic sediments.
             Roy. Soc. Vict., Proc., vol. 70, pt. 1, pp. 19-79, pls. 1-12, text-figs.1-20.

    * 1960a   Microplankton from Australian Cretaceous sediments.   Micropaleontology,
             vol. 6, no. 1, pp. 1-18, pls. 1-3, text-figs. 1-6.

    * 1960b   Upper Mesozoic microplankton from Australia and New Guinea.
             Palaeontology, vol. 2, pt. 2, pp. 243-61, pls. 37-9, text-figs. 1-4.

    * 1961a   Upper Cretaceous microplankton from the Belfast no. 4 bore, South-Western
             Australia.   Roy. Soc. Vict.,Proc., vol. 74, no. 1,   pp. 69-76,
             pls. 11-12, text-fig. 1.

    * 1961b   Tertiary microplankton from the Rottnest Island bore, Western Australia.
             Roy. Soc. W. Aust., J., vol. 44, pt. 2, pp. 39-47, pls. 1-2, text-fig. 1.

    * 1962a   Some Cretaceous and Tertiary microfossils from Western Australia.   Roy. Soc.
             Vict., Proc., vol. 75, no. 2, pp. 269-73, pl. 37.

    * 1962b   Additional microplankton from Australian Cretaceous sediments.
             Micropaleontology, vol. 8, no. 4, pp. 485-507, pls. 1-7, text-figs. 1-2.

COOKSON, I. C. and MANUM, S.
    * 1960   On Crassosphaera, a new genus of microfossils from Mesozoic and Tertiary
             deposits. Nytt Mag. Bot., vol. 8, pp. 5-8, pls. 1-2.   (Tasmanaceae).

COUPER, R.A.
    1960   New Zealand Mesozoic and Cainozoic plant microfossils.   Paleont. Bull. N.Z.
             no. 32.   87 pp.   12 pl., 4 text-figs., 3 tabs.

COUPER, R. A. and HARRIS, W. F.
    1960   Pliocene and Pleistocene plant microfossils from drillholes near Frankton, New
             Zealand.   N. Z. J. Geol. Geophys., vol. 3, no.   pp.   (p. 17 relevant)

COURTEVILLE, H.
             See Deflandre, G. and Courteville.

COUSMINER, H.L.
    1961   Palynology, paleofloras and paleoenvironments.   Micropaleontology vol. 7,
            no. 3, pp. 365-8, text-figs. 1-5, (p. 368 relevant).

CRANWELL, L.M.
    1962   Antarctica, cradle or grave for Nothofagus? Pollen et Spores vol. 4, pt. 1,
            pp. 190-2.

CRANWELL, L.M., HARRINGTON, H.J., and SPEDEN, I.G.
    1960   Lower Tertiary microfossils from McMurdo Sound, Antarctica.   Nature, vol. 186,
            no. 4726, pp. 700-2, text-figs. 1-2.

CRESPIN, I.
    1955   News reports: Australia. Micropaleontology, vol. 1, no. 1, pp. 106-7.

    1958a   News reports: Australia. Micropaleontology, vol. 4, no. 1, p. 116.

    1958b   Microfossils in Australian and New Guinea stratigraphy.   Roy. Soc. N.S.W.,
            J., vol. 92, pp. 133-47.

    1959   News reports: Australia. Micropaleontology, vol. 5, no. 2, p. 261.

    1961   News reports: Australia. Micropaleontology, vol. 7, no. 4, pp. 499-500.

CUVILLIER, J.
    1957   News reports: France. Micropaleontology, vol. 3, no. 4, pp. 411-5.

    1958   News reports: France. Micropaleontology, vol. 4, no. 4, pp. 442-7.

    1959   News reports: France. Micropaleontology, vol. 5, no. 4, pp. 502-6.

    1961   News reports: France. Micropaleontology, vol. 7, no. 1, pp. 119-24.

    1962a   News reports: France. Micropaleontology, vol. 8, no. 1, pp. 116-21.

    1962b   News reports: France, Micropaleontology, vol. 8, no. 4, pp. 528-32.

DALE, B.
            see Neves, R. and Dale.

DANGWAL, A.K.
            see Varma, C.P. and Dangwal.

DARRAH, W.C.
    1937   Spores of Cambrian plants. Science, vol. 86, no. 2224, pp. 154-5.

DAVID, Sir T.W. EDGEWORTH
    1950   The geology of the Commonwealth of Australia.   vol. 2. London: Arnold,
            618 pp. 372 text-figs. (Tasmanaceae, p. 500).

DAWSON, J.W.
    1863   Synopsis of the flora of the Carboniferous period in Nova Scotia.   Canadian
            Naturalist, new ser., vol. 8, no. 6, pp. 431-57 (Tasmanaceae).

    1866   On the conditions of the deposition of coal, more especially as illustrated by the
            Coal-formation of Nova Scotia and New Brunswick.   Geol. Soc. London,
            Quart. J., vol. 22, pp. 95-169, pls. 5-12 (Tasmanaceae).

    1871a   On spore cases in coals. Amer. J. Sci., ser.3, vol. 1, no. 4, pp. 256-63,
            text-figs. 1-4 (Tasmanaceae).

1871b   On spore cases in coals.   Canadian Naturalist, vol. 5, pp. 369-77, text-figs. 1-4
        (Tasmanaceae).

1871c   The fossil plants of the Devonian and Upper Silurian formations of Canada.
        Canad. Geol. Surv. 92 pp., 20 pls.   (p. 79, pl. 19, Tasmanaceae).

1884a   On rhizocarps in the Palaeozoic period.   Canad. Rec. Sci., vol. 1, no. 1,
        pp. 19-27, text-figs. a-d (Tasmanaceae).

1884b   On rhizocarps in the Palaeozoic period.   Amer. Assoc. Adv. Sci., Proc.,
        32nd. Meeting, pp. 260-4, text-figs. a-d (Tasmanaceae).

1886   On rhizocarps in the Erian (Devonian) period in America.   Chicago Acad. Sci.,
        Bull.,vol. 1, no. 9, pp. 105-18, text-figs. 1-12. (Tasmanaceae).

1888a   On sporocarps discovered by Prof. E. Orton in the Erian Shale of Columbus,
        Ohio.   Canad. Rec. Sci.,   vol. 3, pp. 137-40, text-fig. 1. (Tasmanaceae).

1888b   The geological history of plants.   London: Kegan Paul, 290 pp., 79 text-figs.
        (Tasmanaceae, pp. 84-6).

DEANE, H.
    1849   On the occurrence of fossil Xanthidia and Polythalamia in Chalk.   Microsc. Soc.
           Lond., Trans., vol. 2, pp. 77-9, pl. 9.

DEFLANDRE, G.
  * 1933   Note préliminaire sur un péridinien fossile.   Lithoperidinium oamaruense n.g.n.
           sp. Soc. Zool. Fr., Bull., vol. 58, pp. 265-73, text-figs. 1-7.

  * 1934   Sur les microfossiles d'origine planctonique conservés a l'état de matière organique
           dans les silex de la craie.   Acad. Sci. Paris, C.R., vol. 199, pp. 966-8,
           text-figs. 1-11.

  * 1935a Considérations biologiques sur les micro-organismes d'origine planctonique
           conservés dans les silex de la craie.   Bull. Biol. Fr. Belg., vol. 69, pp. 213-44,
           pl. 5-9, text-figs. 1-11.

    1935b Technique micropaléontologique appliquée a l'etude des silex.   Soc. Fr. Microsc.,
           Bull., vol. 4, no. 2, pp. 104-11.

    1935c Revue; Les microfossiles des silex de la craie.   Soc. Fr. Microsc., Bull., vol. 4,
           no. 3, pp. 116-20, text-figs. 1-3.

  * 1936a Les Flagellés fossiles.   Aperçu biologique et paléontologique.   Rôle géologique.
           Actual. scient. et ind., no. 335, 98 pp., 135 text-figs.

    1936b Isolement et coloration in vitro de certains des microfossiles des silex.   Soc. Fr.
           Microsc., Bull., vol. 5, p. 71.

  * 1936c Microfossiles des silex crétacés. 1. Generalités. Flagellés.   Ann.   Paléont.,
           vol. 25, pp. 151-91, pl. 11-20.

    1937a Les microfossiles de la craie et des silex.   La Nature, no. 3010, pp. 314-20,
           text-figs. 1-17.

  * 1937b Phanerodinium, genre nouveau de Dinoflagellé fossile des silex.   Soc. Fr.
           Microsc., Bull., vol. 6, no. 3, pp. 109-15, text-figs. 1-5.

* 1937c   <u>Microfossiles des silex crétacés 11.   Flagellés incertae sedis.   Hystricho-</u>
<u>sphaeridées.   Sarcodinés.   Organismes divers.</u>   Ann Paléont, vol. 26,
pp. 51-103, pl. 8-18.

1938a   <u>Micropaléontologie des silex crétacés.</u>   Soc. Géol. Fr., C.R., no. 3, pp. 33-5.

* 1938b   <u>Sur le microplancton des mers jurassiques conservé a l'état de matière organique</u>
<u>dans les marnes de Villers - sur - Mer.</u>   Acad. Sci. Paris, C.R., vol. 206,
pp. 687-9, text-figs. 1-6.

* 1938c   <u>Etat des matières organiques constituant certains micro-organismes planctoniques</u>
<u>fossiles.   Essais d'analyse microchimique.</u>   Acad. Sci. Paris, C.R., vol. 206,
pp. 854-6.

1938d   <u>Microplancton à Dinoflagellés conservé dans les schistes bitumineux kiméridgiens</u>
<u>d'Orbagnoux (Jura).</u>   Acad. Sci. Paris, C.R., vol. 207, pp. 590-1.

* 1938e   <u>Microplancton des mers jurassiques conservé dans les marnes de Villers-sur-Mer</u>
<u>(Calvados).   Étude liminaire et considérations générales.</u>   Stat. Zool.
Wimereux, Trav., vol. 13, Vol. jubilaire M. Caullery, pp. 147-200, pls. 5-11,
text-figs. 1-10.

1938f   <u>Revue: Microplancton des mers jurassiques conservé dans les marnes de Villers-</u>
<u>sur-Mer (Calvados).</u>   Soc. Fr. Microsc., Bull., vol. 7, no. 4, pp. 147-50,
text-figs. 1-6.

1939a   <u>L'étude micropaléontologique des silex.</u>   Sciences Naturelles, vol. 1,
pp. 259-64, text-figs. 1-24.

* 1939b   <u>Sur les dinoflagellés des schistes bitumineux d'Orbagnoux (Jura).</u>   Soc. Fr.
Microsc., Bull., vol. 8, no. 4, pp. 141-5, pl. 6.

1940a   <u>Microfossiles de quelques silex de la craie blanche de Vendôme.</u>   Soc. Hist.
Nat. Toulouse, Bull., vol. 75, pp. 155-9, text-figs. 1-4.

* 1940b   <u>Sur un nouveau Péridinien fossile à thèque originellement siliceuse.</u>   Acad.
Sci. Paris, C.R., vol. 211, pp. 265-8, text-figs. 1-4.

1941a   <u>La vie créatrice de roches.   Le rôle bâtisseur des êtres microscopiques et</u>
<u>la genèsedes houilles et des pétrôles.</u>   Paris: Presses Universitaires de France.
Coll. Que sais - je?   128 pp., 25 text-figs.

* 1941b   <u>Le microplancton kiméridgien d'Orbagnoux et l'origine des huiles sulfurées</u>
<u>naturelles.</u>   Acad. Sci. Paris, Mém., no. 65, pp. 1-32, pls. 1-7,
text-figs. 1-7.

1942a   <u>Des roches sont nées.</u>   L'Illustration, no. 5268, p. 218, text-figs. 1-6.

* 1942b   <u>Sur les Hystrichosphères des calcaires siluriens de la Montagne Noire.</u>   Acad.
Sci. Paris, C.R., vol. 215,   no. 20, pp. 475-6, text-figs. 1-16.

* 1943a   Sur quelques nouveaux Dinoflagellés des silex crétacés.   Soc. Géol. Fr.,
           Bull., ser. 5, vol. 13, pp. 499-509, pl. 17.

* 1943b   Dinoflagellés 1. Peridiniales.   Fichier micropaléont., ser. 1. Arch. Orig.
           Serv. Docum. C. N. R. S., no. 155, parts. 1-1V, cards 001-094.

* 1944   Hystrichosphaeridés 1.   Fichier micropaléont. ser. 3. Arch. Orig. Serv. Docum.
           C. N. R. S., no. 159, parts 1-111, cards 186-254.

* 1945a   Microfossiles des calcaires siluriens de la Montagne Noire.   Ann. Paléont.
           vol.31 (1944-5), pp. 41-76, pls. 1-3.

* 1945b   Dinoflagellés II.   Gymnodiniales et Dinoflagellés incertae sedis.   Flagellés
           incertae sedis.   Fichier micropaléont. ser. 5. Arch. Orig. Serv. Docum.
           C. N. R. S., no. 235, parts 1-12, cards 752-859.

* 1946a   Hystrichosphaeridés II.   Espèces du Secondaire et du Tertiaire.   Fichier micro-
           paléont. ser. 6. Arch. Orig. Serv. Docum. C. N. R. S., no. 235, parts 1-V,
           cards 860-1019.

* 1946b   Remarques sur la systématique des Hystrichosphaeridés.   Soc. Géol. Fr., C. R.
           Somm., no. 7, pp. 110-11.

* 1946c   Hystrichosphaeridés III.   Espèces du primaire.   Fichier micropaléont., ser. 8.
           Arch. Orig. Surv. Docum. C. N. R. S., no. 257, parts 1-V, cards 1096-1185.

* 1946d   Radiolaires et Hystrichosphaeridés du Carbonifère de la Montagne Noire.   Acad.
           Sci. Paris, C. R., vol. 223, pp. 515-7, text-figs. 1-10.

* 1947a   Sur une nouvelle Hystrichosphère des silex crétacés et sur les affinitiés du genre
           Cannosphaeropsis O. We. Acad. Sci. Paris, C. R., vol. 224, pp. 157416,
           text-figs. 1-5.

* 1947b   Calciodinellum nov. gen., premier representant d'une famille nouvelle de Dino-
           flagellés fossiles à thèque calcaire.   Acad. Sci. Paris, C. R., vol. 224,
           pp. 1781-2, text-figs. 1-6.

* 1947c   Le problème des Hystrichosphères.   Inst. Oceanogr. Monaco, Bull., no. 918,
           pp. 1-23, text-figs. 1-61.

* 1947d   Sur quelques micro-organismes planctoniques des silex jurassiques.   Inst. Oceanogr.
           Monaco, Bull., no. 921, pp. 1-10, text-figs. 1-23.

  1948a   Microscopic pratique. Le microscopie et ses applications.   La faune et la flore
           microscopique des eaux.   Les microfossiles.   Paris: P. Lechevalier (ed.).
           Encyclopédie pratique du Naturaliste, vol. 25. 441 pp, 158 pls. (pp. 386-99,
           pls. 117-21 relevant).

  1948b   Les Dinoflagellés à thèque mineralisée.   XIII Congr. Intern. Zool., Paris, 1948,
           Communic., pp. 210-11.

* 1948c   Les Calciodinellidés: Dinoflagellés fossiles à thèque calcaire.   Le Botaniste,
           vol. 34, pp. 191-219, text-figs. 1-37.

  1948d   The flagellates.   The Micropaleontologist, vol. 2, no. 4, pp. 14-15.

  1949   Les soi-disant Radiolaires du Précambrien de Bretagne et la question de l'existence
           de Radiolaires embryonnaires fossiles.   XIII Congr. Intern. Zool., Paris, 1948,
           Communic. Soc. Zool. Fr., Bull., vol. 74, pp. 351-2.

1952a   Protistes.Généralités.   Sous-embranchement des Flagellés.   Groupes Incertae Sedis.   In J. Piveteau (ed.): Traité de Paléontologie, vol. 1, Paris: Masson. (pp. 89-95, 99-130, text-figs. 322-9 relevant).

1952b   Dinoflagellés fossiles.   In P.P. Grassé (ed.): Traité de Zoologie. vol. 1. Paris: Masson. 1071 pp., 830 text-figs. (pp. 391-406, text-figs. 300-39 relevant).

* 1954   Systématique des Hystrichosphaeridés: sur l'acception du genre Cymatiosphaera O. Wetzel.   Soc. Géol. Fr., C.R. Somm., no. 12, pp. 257-8.

* 1955   Palaeocryptidium n.g. cayeaxi n. sp., micro-organismes incertae sedis des phtanites briovériens bretons.   Soc. Géol. Fr., C.R. Somm., nos. 9-10, pp. 182-4.

* 1957a   Remarques sur deux genres de Protistes du Précambrien(Arnoldia Hovasse, 1956, Cayeuxipora Graindor 1957).   Acad. Sci. Paris, C.R., vol. 244, pp. 2640-1.

1957b   Annotated bibliography of micropaleontology in France, 1952-56.   (exclusive of Foraminifera and Ostracoda).   Micropaleontology, vol. 3, no. 3, pp. 263-7.

1959   Paléoplanctologie du Crétacé superieur français.   84e Congr. Soc. Savantes, Dijon 1959, Proc., Section des Sciences, pp. 57-60.

1960   Micro-organismes du Précambrien: une mise au point.   Soc. Géol. Fr., C.R. Somm., no. 5, pp. 119-02.

1961   G. Deflandre: Catalogue des taxons introduits dans la systématique.   Liste chronologique des traveux publiés.   Paris: Multicop. Lab. Micropaléont. E.P.H.E., pp. 1-11, 1-58 & 1-21.

1962   Palynologie, micropaléontologie et semantique.   Pollen et Spores, vol. 4, no. 1, pp. 181-8.

1963   État actuel de nos connaissances sur la répresentation, au Trias, de quelques groupes de microfossiles.   Protistes, autres que Foraminifères.   Colloque sur le Trias de la France et des régions limitrophes, Montpellier 1961.   Bur. Rech. Géol. Min., Mém., no. 15, pp. 541-2.
    See also Wetzel, W., Wetzel, O. and Deflandre.

DEFLANDRE, G., and COOKSON, I.C.
* 1954   Sur le microplancton fossile conservé dans diverses roches sédimentaires australiennes s'étageant du Crétacé inférieur au Miocène supérieur.   Acad. Sci. Paris, C.R., vol. 239, no. 19, pp. 1235-8, text-figs. 1-17.

* 1955   Fossil microplankton from Australian late Mesozoic and Tertiary sediments.   Aust. J. Mar. Freshw. Res., vol. 6, no. 2, pp. 242-313, pls. 1-9, text-figs. 1-59.

DEFLANDRE, G. and COURTEVILLE, H.
* 1939   Note préliminaire sur les microfossiles des silex crétacés du Cambrésis.   Soc. Fr. Microsc., Bull., vol. 8, pp. 95-106, pls. 1-3.

DEFLANDRE, G. and DEFLANDRE-RIGAUD, M.
1943   Constitution et diffusion d'un fichier micro-paléontologique général.   Soc. Géol. Fr., C.R., no. 14, pp. 186-8.

* 1958   Hystrichosphaeridés IV et Genres incertae sedis.   Espèces du Secondaire et du Tertiaire (Supplément 1).   Fichier micropaléont, ser. 10. Arch. Orig. Centre Docum. C.N.R.S., no. 366, parts I-XX, cards 1293-1750.

1959   Fichier micropaléontologique général. Catalogue des fiches des Séries 1 à 10
(1943-1958) dans l'ordre chronologique de parution. Paris: Multicop. Lab.
Micropaléont. E. P. H. E. , 21 pp.

* 1961   Nomenclature et systématique des Hystrichosphères (s. l.). Observations et
recrifications. Paris: Multicop. Lab. Micropaléont. E. P. H. E. 14 pp. ,
11 text-figs.

* 1962   Nomenclature et systématique des Hystrichosphères (s. l.). Observations et
rectifications. Rev. Micropaléont. vol. 4, no. 4, pp. 190-6, text-figs. 1-11.

DEFLANDRE - RIGAUD, M.
* 1954   Microfossiles des silex sénoniens du Bassin de Paris. Soc. Géol. Fr. , C. R. Somm.
no. 3, pp. 58-9, text-figs. 1-3.

1955   Microfossiles des silex sénoniens du Tréport (Seine-Maritime). Soc. Géol. Fr. ,
C. R. Somm. nos. 1-2, pp. 19-20.
See also Deflandre G. , and Deflandre-Rigaud.

DELCOURT, A. and SPRUMONT, G.
1955   Les spores et grains de pollen du Wéaldien du Hainaut. Soc. Géol. Belg. , Mém. ,
new ser. , no. 5, 73 pp. , 4 pls. , 15 text-figs. (p. 57, pl. 4, fig. 9 relevant).

1957   Quelques microfossils du Wéaldien de Féron - Glageon. Soc. Géol. Belg. , Bull. ,
vol. 6, pt. 1, pp. 57-68, pls. 1-3.

1959   Spores, grains de pollen, Hystrichosphères et Péridiniens dans le Wéaldien de Féron -
Glageon. Soc. Géol. Nord, Ann. , vol. 79, pp. 29-64, pls. 3-7.

DEUNFF, J.
1951   Sur la présence de micro-organismes (Hystrichosphères) dans les schistes ordoviciens
du Finistère. Acad. Sci. Paris, C. R. , vol. 233, pp. 321-3, text-figs. 1-6.

1954a   Sur le microplancton du Gothlandien armoricain. Soc. Géol. Fr. , C. R. Somm. ,
no. 3, pp. 54-5.

* 1954b   Micro-organismes planctoniques (Hystrichosphères) dans le Dévonien du Massif
armoricain. Soc. Géol. Fr. , C. R. Somm. , no. 11, pp. 239-42, text-figs. 1-8.

* 1954c   Veryhachium, genre nouveau d'Hystrichosphères du Primaire. Soc. Géol. Fr. , C. R.
Somm. , no. 13, pp. 305-6.

* 1954d   Sur un microplancton du Dévonien du Canada recélant des types nouveaux
d'Hystrichosphaeridés. Acad. Sci. Paris, C. R. , vol. 239, pp. 1064-6,
text-figs. 1-16.

* 1955a   Un microplancton fossile dévonien à Hystrichosphères du Continent Nord-Americain.
Bull. Microsc. Appliqué, ser. 2, vol. 5, nos. 11-12, pp. 138-47, pls. 1-4,
text-figs. 1-28.

* 1955b   Aremoricanium, genre nouveau d'Hystrichosphères du Silurien breton. Soc. Géol.
Fr. , C. R. Somm. , nos. 11-12, pp. 227-9, text-figs. 1-3.

1956   Progrès récents de nos connaissances sur les microplanctons fossiles à hystrichosphères des mers primaires. Grana Palynologica, vol. 1, no. 2, pp. 79-84,
text-figs. 1-19.

* 1957   Micro-organismes nouveaux (Hystrichosphères) du Dévonien de l'Amerique du Nord.
Soc. Géol. Min. Bretagne, Bull. , new ser. , vol. 2, pp. 5-14. 2 un-numbered pls.

* 1958   Micro-organismes planctoniques du Primaire armoricain 1. Ordovicien du Veryhac'h (Presqu' île de Crozon). Soc. Géol. Min. Bretagne, Bull., new ser., vol. 2, pp. 1-41, pl. 1-12.

1959   Formations recifales et Hystrichosphères. Soc. Géol. Fr., Bull., 7th ser., vol. 1, pp. 409-10.

* 1961a   Un microplancton à Hystrichosphères dans le Tremadoc du Sahara. Rev. Micropal., vol. 4, no. 1, pp. 37-52, pls. 1-3.

1961b   Quelques précisions concernant les Hystrichosphaeridées du Devonien du Canada. Soc. Géol. Fr., C.R. Somm., no. 8, pp. 216-8.

DÖRING, H.
    * 1961   Planktonartige Fossilien des Jura/Kreide Grenzbereichs der Bohrungen Werle (Mecklenburg). Geologie, Jg. 10, Beih. 32, pp. 110-17, pls. 16-17, text-figs. 1.

DOUGLAS, J. G.
    * 1960a   Microplankton of the Deflandreidae group in Western District sediments. Min. Geol. J., vol. 6, no. 4, pp. 17-32, pls. 1-4, text-fig. 1.

    1960b   Preliminary identification of microplankton and microflora. Min. Geol. J., vol. 6, no. 4, p. 45.

DOWNIE, C.
    * 1957   Microplankton from the Kimeridge Clay. Geol. Soc. London, Quart. J., vol. 112, pp. 413-34, pl. 20, text-figs. 1-6.

    * 1958   An assemblage of microplankton from the Shineton Shales (Tremadocian). Yorks. Geol. Soc., Proc., vol. 31, pt. 4, no. 12, pp. 331-49, pls. 16-17, text-figs. 1-5, tab. 1.

    * 1959   Hystrichospheres from the Silurian Wenlock Shale of England. Palaeontology, vol. 2, pt. 1, pp. 56-71, pls. 10-12, tab. 1.

    * 1960   Deunffia and Domasia, new genera of hystrichosphères. Micropaleontology, vol. 6, no. 2, pp. 197-202, pl. 1, text-figs. 1-5, tab. 1.

    1962   So-called spores from the Torridonian: Report of demonstration. Geol. Soc. London, Proc., no. 1600, pp. 127-8.

    * 1963   'Hystrichosphères' (acritarchs) and spores of the Wenlock Shales (Silurian) of Wenlock, England. Palaeontology, vol. 6, pt. 4, pp. 625-52, pls. 91-2, text-figs. 1-4, tabs. 1-15.
        See also Wall, D., and Downie.

DOWNIE, C., EVITT, W.R., and SARJEANT, W.A.S.
    1963   Dinoflagellates, hystrichosphères and the classification of the acritarchs. Stanford Univ. Publ., Geol. Sciences. vol. 7, no. 3, pp. 1-16.

DOWNIE, C. and SARJEANT, W.A.S.
    * 1963   On the interpretation and status of some Hystrichosphère genera. Palaeontology, vol. 6, no. 1, pp. 83-96.

DOWNIE, C., WILLIAMS, G.L. and SARJEANT, W.A.S.
    * 1961   Classification of fossil microplankton. Nature, vol. 192, no. 4801, p. 471.

DRICOT, E.M.
    1962   Microstratigraphie des Argiles de Campine. Soc. Belg. Géol., Bull., vol. 70, pt. 2, pp. 113-41, pls. 1-3, text-figs. 1-7 (pp. 121-2, 136, 138 relevant).

DUBOIS, G.
   1933   Cadre systématique pour l'étude des flagellates fossiles.   Assoc. Amicale de l'Inst.
           Sciences Gen., Strasbourg, Bull. no. 2, pp. 23-31.

DULHUNTY, J.A. and R.
   1949a   Notes on microspore types in Tasmanian Permian coals.   Abstract.   Linn. Soc.
           N.S.W., Abs. Proc., no. 601.   (Tasmanaceae).

   1949b   Notes on microspore types in Tasmanian Permian coals.   Linn. Soc. N.S.W., Proc.,
           vol. 74, pts. 3-4, pp. 132-9, text-fig. 1, tabs 1-4.   (Tasmanaceae).

DURAND, S.
   1958   Présence de deux microfossiles incertae sedis du Lutétien du Bassin de Paris,
           Calcicarpinum   (? Calciodinellidae) et Neanthozoites (? Anthozoa), dans les
           sables de Campbon (L.A.).   Soc. Géol. Min. Bretagne, Bull., new ser., vol. 1,
           pp. 66-9, text-figs. 1-4.

   1960   Le Tertiaire de Bretagne.   Étude stratigraphique, sédimentologique et tectonique.
           Soc. Géol. Min. Bretagne, Mém., vol. 12, pp. 1-389, text-figs. 1-93, 1 map.
           (pp. 13-14, 70, 100, 102 relevant).
           See also Choux, J., and Durand: Choux, J., Durand and Milon, Y.

EAGAR, S.H. and SARJEANT, W.A.S.
   1963   Fossil Hystrichospheres concentrated by sieving techniques.   Nature, vol. 198,
           no. 4875, p. 81.

ECHOLS, D.J.
   1959   News reports: United States - Mid Continent region.   Micropaleontology, vol. 5,
           no. 3, pp. 384-6.

   1961   News reports: United States - Mid Continent region.   Micropaleontology, vol. 7,
           no. 2, pp. 251-5.

   1962   News reports: United States - Mid Continent region.   Micropaleontology, vol. 8,
           no. 2, pp. 283-7.

   1963   News reports: United States - Mid Continent region.   Micropaleontology, vol. 9,
           no. 3, pp. 353-8.

EHRENBERG, C.G.
   * 1838a   Uber das Massenverhaltnis der jetzt labenden Kieselinfusorien und über ein neues
           Infusorien - Conglomerat als Polierschiefer von Jastraba in Ungarn.   Akad. Wiss.
           Berlin, Abh. (1836), vol. 1, pp. 109-35, pl. 1.

   1838b   Uber die Bildung der Kreidefelsen und des Kreidemergels durch unsichtbare Organism-
           en. Akad. Wiss. Berlin, Abh. (1838), pp. 59-148, pls. 1-4, tab. 1-2(p.70 relevant).

   1840   Uber noch jetzt zahlreich lebende Tierarten der Kreidebildung und den Organismus
           der Polythalamien.   Akad. Wiss. Berlin, Abh., pp. 81-174, pls. 1-4.

   1843   Uber einige Jura - Infusorien Arten des Corallrags bei Krakau.   Akad. Wiss. Berlin,
           Mber., pp. 61-3.

   * 1854   Mikrogeologie: das Erden und Felsen schaffende Wirken des unsichtbar kleinen
           selbständigen Lebens auf der Erde.   Leipzig: Voss.   374 + 31 + 88 pp.,
           41 pls.

   1875   Die Sicherung der Objektivität der selbständiger mikroskopischen Lebensformen und
           ihrer Organisation durch eine zweckmassige Aufbewahrung.   Akad. Wiss. Berlin,
           Mber., pp. 71-81.

EISENACK, A.
* 1931   Neue Mikrofossilien des baltischen Silurs I.   Paläont. Z., vol. 13, Nos. 1-2,
         pp. 74-118, pls. 1-5, text-figs. 1-5.

  1932   Neue Mikrofossilien des baltischen Silurs II.   Paläont. Z., vol. 14, No. 4,
         pp. 257-77, pls. 11-12, text-figs. 1-13.

* 1934   Neue Mikrofossilien des baltischen Silurs III und neue Mikrofossilien des böhmischen
         Silurs I.   Paläont. Z., vol. 16, pp. 52-76, pls. 4-5, text-figs. 1-35.

* 1935   Mikrofossilien aus Doggergeschieben Ostpreussens.   Z. Geschiebeforsch., vol. 11,
         pp. 167-84, pls. 4-5, text-figs. 1-9.

* 1936a Dinoflagellaten aus dem Jura.   Ann. Protist., vol. 5, pp. 59-64, pl. 4,
         text-figs. 1-5.

* 1936b Eodinia pachytheca n.g.n.sp., ein primitiver Dinoflagellat aus einem Kelloway -
         Geschiebe Ostpreussens.   Z. Geschiebeforsch., vol. 12, pt. 2, pp. 72-5, text-
         figs. 1-6.

  1937   3 Protozoa.   a) Protozoa exkl. Foraminifera.   Fortschr. Paläont., vol. 1, pp. 58-6

  1938a Hystrichosphaerideen und verwandte Formen in baltischen Silur.   Z. Geschiebeforsch
         vol. 14, pp. 1-30, pls. 1-4, text-figs. 1-7.

* 1938b Neue Mikrofossilien des baltischen Silurs IV.   Paläont Z., vol. 19, Nos. 3-4,
         pp. 217-43, pls. 15-16, text-figs. 1-22.

* 1938c Die Phosphoritknollen der Bernsteinformation als Uberlieferer tertiären Planktons.
         Phys. -Ökon. Ges. Königsb., Schr., vol. 70, no. 2, pp. 181-8, text-figs. 1-6.

  1939a Die Wandung fossiler Dinoflagellaten.   Arch. Protistenk., vol. 93, pt. 1, pp. 81-6

* 1939b Chitinozoen und Hystrichosphaerideen im Ordovizium des Rheinischen Schieferge-
         birges.   Senckenbergiana, vol. 21, nos. 1-2, pp. 135-52, pls. A-B, text-figs.
         1-20.

  1944   Uber einige pflanzliche Funde in Geschieben nebst Bemerkungen zum Hystricho-
         sphaerideen - Problem.   Z. Geschiebeforsch., vol. 19, pp. 103-24, pls. 1-3,
         text-figs. 1-16.

  1948   Mikrofossilien aus Kieselknollen des böhmischen Ordoviziums.   Senckenbergiana,
         vol. 28, nos. 4-6, pp. 105-17, pl. 1, text-figs. 1-20.

* 1951   Uber Hystrichosphaerideen und andere Kleinformen aus baltischen Silur und
         Kambrium.   Senckenbergiana, vol. 32, nos. 1-4, pp. 187-204, pls. 1-4,
         text-figs. 1-6.

  1953   Die Bestimmung des Alters von Kieselschiefer - Gevollen mittels Mikrofossilien.
         Senckenbergiana, vol. B. 34, pp. 99-103, pl. 1, text-fig. 1.

* 1954a Hystrichosphären aus dem baltischen Gotlandium.   Senckenbergiana, vol. B.34,
         pp. 205-11, pl. 1, text-figs. 1-7.

* 1954b Mikrofossilien aus Phosphoriten des samlandischen Unter - Oligozäns und über die
         Einheitlichkeit der Hystrichosphaerideen.   Palaeontographica, ser. A, vol. 105,
         nos. 3-6, pp. 49-95, pls. 7-12, text-figs. 1-6.

  1954c Hystrichosphaerideen, Sporen oder Plankton?   Paläont. Z., vol. 28, nos. 1-2, p. 9

1955   Chitinozoen, Hystrichosphären und andere Mikrofossilien aus dem Beyrichia - Kalk.
        Senck. Leth., vol. 36, pp. 157-88.

1956   Probleme der Vermehrung und des Lebenraumes bei der Gattung Leiosphaera
        (Hystrichosphaeridea).   Neu. Jb. Geol. Pal., Abh., vol. 102, no. 3, pp. 402-8,
        pl. 16, text-figs. 1-2.

* 1957   Mikrofossilien in organische Substanz aus dem Lias Schwabens (Suddeutschland).
          Neu. Jb. Geol. Pal., Abh., vol. 105, no. 3, pp. 239-49, pls. 19-20, text-
          figs. 1-2.

* 1958a   Tasmanites Newton 1875 und Leiosphaeridia n. g. als Gattungen der Hystricho-
           sphaeridea.   Palaeontographica, ser. A., vol. 110, pp. 1-19, pls.1-2, text-figs
           1-3.

* 1958b   Mikrofossilien aus dem Ordovizium des Baltikums.   I. Markasitschicht, Dictyonema
           Schiefer, Glaukonitsand, Glaukonitkalk.   Senck. Leth., vol. 39, nos. 5-6,
           pp. 389-405, pl.

* 1958c   Mikroplankton aus dem norddeutschen Apt nebst einigen Bemerkungen über fossile
           Dinoflagellaten.   Neu Jb. Geol. Paläont., Abh., vol. 106, pt. 3, pp. 383-422,
           pls. 21-7, text-figs. 1-10.

* 1959a   Neotypen baltischer Silur - Hystrichosphären und neue Arten.   Palaeontographica,
           ser. A, vol. 112, pp. 193-211, pls. 15-17, text-figs. 1-11.

1959b   Fossile Dinoflagellaten.   Arch. Protistenk., vol. 104, pt. 1, pp. 43-50, pl. 3.

* 1959c   Was ist Membranilarnax ?   Neu. Jb. Geol. Paläont., Mh., no. 7, pp. 327-32.

1961a   Hystrichosphären als Nahrung ordovizischer Foraminiferen.   Neu. Jb. Geol.
         Paläont., Mh., no. 1, pp. 15-19, text-figs. 1-4.

* 1961b   Einige Erörterungen über fossile Dinoflagellaten nebst Ubersicht über die zur Zeit
           bekannten Gattungen.   Neu. Jb. Geol. Paläont., Abh., vol. 112, no. 3,
           pp. 281-324, pls. 33-7, text-figs. 1-7.

1962a   Mitteilungen über Leiosphären und über das Pylom bei Hystrichosphären.   Neu. Jb.
         Geol. Paläont., Abh., vol. 114, pt. 1, pp. 58-80, pl. 2-4, text-figs. 1-2.

* 1962b   Einige Bemerkungen zu neueren Arbeiten über Hystrichosphären.   Neu. Jb. Geol.
           Paläont., Mh., no. 2, pp. 92-101.

1962c   Mikrofossilien aus dem Ordovizium des Baltikums.
         2. Vaginatenkalk bis Lyckholmer Stufe.   Senck. Leth., vol. 43, no. 5,
         pp. 349-66, pl. 44, text-figs. 1-7.

* 1962d   Neue problematische Mikrofossilien.   Neu. Jb. Geol. Paläont., Abh., vol. 114,
           no. 2, pp. 135-141, pl. 5, text-fig. 1.

* 1963a   Hystrichosphären.   Biol. Reviews, vol. 38, pp. 107-39, text-figs. 1-4.

* 1963b   Zur Membranilarnax-Frage.   Neu. Jb. Geol. Paläont., Mh., no. 2, pp. 98-103.

1963c   Sind die Hystrichosphären Zysten von Dinoflagellaten?   Neu. Jb. Geol. Palaont.,
         Mh., no. 5, pp. 225-31.

* 1963d   Uber einige Arten der Gattung Tasmanites Newton 1875.   Grana Palynologica,
           vol. 4, Erdtman 65th Anniv. vol., pt. 2, pp. 204-16, 1 un-numbered pl.

* 1963   Mitteilungen zur Biologie der Hystrichospharen und über neue Arten. Neu Jb. Geol. Paläont., Abh., vol. 118, no. 2, pp. 207-16, pls. 19.20.

* 1963f   Cordosphaeridium n.g., ex Hystrichosphaeridium, Hystrichosphaeridea. N. Jb. Geol. Paläont., Abh., vol. 118, no. 3, pp. 260-5, pl. 29.
See also Cookson, I.C. and Eisenack.

EISENACK, A., and COOKSON, I.C.
* 1960   Microplankton from Australian Lower Cretaceous sediments. Roy. Soc. Vict., Proc., vol. 72, pt. 1, pp. 1-11, pls. 1-3.

EISENACK, A., and GOCHT, H.
* 1960   Neue Namen fur einige Hystrichosphären der Bernsteinformation Ostpreussens. Neu. Jb. Geol. Paläont., Mh., no. 11, pp. 511-18, text-figs. 1-4.

ELLISON, S.P., Jnr.
1951   Microfossils as environment indicators in black shales. J. Sed. Pet., vol. 21, no. 4, pp. 214-25, text-figs. 1-7.

ERDTMAN, G.
1950   Fynd av Hystrichosphaera furcata i Gullmarn. Geol. Fören. Stockh.,Förh., vol. 72, no. 2, p. 221.

1954   On pollen grains and dinoflagellate cysts in the Firth of Gullmarn, S.W. Sweden. Botan. Not. Jg., Lund (1954), pp. 103-11, text-figs. 1-4, tabs. 1-2.

1955   On pollen grains and dinoflagellate cysts in the Firth of Gullmarn, S.W. Sweden. Grana Palynologica, vol. 1, no. 1, pp. 103-11, text-figs. 1-4, tabs. 1-2.

EVITT, W.R.
* 1961a   The dinoflagellate Nannoceratopsis Deflandre; morphology, affinities and infra-specific variability. Micropaleontology, vol. 7, no. 3, pp. 305-16, pls. 1-2, text-figs. 1-17.

* 1961b   Dapcodinium priscum n. gen.n.sp., a dinoflagellate from the Lower Lias of Denmark. J. Paleont., vol. 35, no. 5, pp. 996-1002, pl. 119, text-figs. 1-20.

* 1961c   Observations on the morphology of fossil Dinoflagellates. Micropaleontology, vol. 7, no. 4, pp. 385-420, pls. 1-9, text-figs. 1-8.

1962a   Fossil dinoflagellates and the affinities of certain hystrichospheres; abstract. Geol. Soc. Amer. Spec. Paper no. 68, p. 172.

1962b   Wall structure in hystrichospheres Hystrichosphaera and Hystrichosphaeridium. Geol. Soc. Amer., Spec. Paper no. 68, pp. 172-3.

1962c   Dinoflagellates and their use in petroleum geology; abstract. Amer. Assoc. Petrol. Geol., Bull., vol. 46, pt. 1, no. 2, p. 266.

1962d   Dinoflagellate synonyms: Nannoceratopsis deflandrei Evitt junior to ?N. gracilis Alberti. J. Paleont., vol. 36, no. 5, pp. 1129-30.

1962e   Arrangement and structure of processes in Hystrichosphaeridium and its allies. Abstr. Int. Conf. on Palynology, Tucson, Arizona, 1962. Pollen et Spores vol. 4, no. 2, pp. 343-4.

*1963a   A discussion and proposals concerning fossil Dinoflagellates, Hystrichospheres and Acritarchs. Nat. Acad. Sci., Proc., vol. 49, pp. 158-64, 298-302, text-figs. 1-4.

1963b   Occurrence of freshwater alga Pediastrum in Cretaceous marine sediments. Amer. J. Sci., vol. 261, no. 9, pp. 890-93, pl. 1
See also Downie, C., Evitt and Sarjeant, W. A. S.

FAEGRI, K., and IVERSEN, J.
1950   Textbook of modern pollen analysis. Copenhagen: Munksgaard. 168 pp., 5 pls., 151 text-figs., 3 tabs. (pp. 123-4 relevant).

FELIX, C. J.
1959   Ecological significance of Tasmanites in Tertiary and Recent sediments. Geol. Soc. Amer., Program. Stratigraphic and ecologic interpretations of plant microfossils in petroleum geology. (Tasmanaceae).

1963   Mechanical sample disaggregation in palynology. Micropaleontology, vol. 9, no. 3, pp. 337-8, text-figs. 1-6.

FENTON, C. L. and M. A.
1958   The fossil book. New York; Doubleday. 482 pp., 8 pl., numerous un-numbered text-figs. (pp. 55-6 relevant).

FIRTION, F.
*1952   Le Cenomanien inférieur du Nouvion-en-Thiérache: examen micropaléontologique. Soc. Geol. Nord, Ann., vol. 72, pp. 150-64, pls. 8-10.

FISHER, D.W.
1953   A microflora in the Maplewood and Neahga Shales. Buffalo Soc. Nat. Sci., Bull., vol. 21, no. 2, pp. 13-8, pl. 7.

FRENGUELLI, J.
* 1940   Consideraciones sobre los Silicoflagelados fossiles. Mus. La Plata, Rev., new ser., vol. 2. Ser. Palaeont., no. 7, pp. 37-112, pls. 1-4, text-figs. 1-38.

FREY, D.G.
1953   Regional aspects of the late-Glacial and post-Glacial pollen succession of Southeastern North Carolina. Ecol. Monographs, vol. 23, pp. 289-313.

FRIES, M.
1951   Pollenanalytiska vittnesbörd om senkvartär vegetationsutveckling, särskilt skogshistoria, i Nordvästra Götaland. Acta Phytogeogr. Suev., no. 29, pp. 1-219, pls. 1-8, text-figs. 1-43. (pp. 169-72, text-fig. 41 relevant).

1962   Pollen profiles of late Pleistocene and Recent sediments from Weber Lake, northeastern Minnesota. Ecology, vol. 43, no. 2, pp. 295-308, text-figs. 1-10. (p. 301, text-fig. 9 relevant).

FUCHS, T.
1905   Uber die Natur von Xanthidium Ehrenberg. Cbl. Mineral. u.s.w., pp. 340-2.

GEMEINHARDT, K.
1931   Organismenformen auf der Grenze zwischen Radiolarien und Flagellaten. Deutsch. Botan. Ges., Ber., vol. 49, no. 2, pp. 103-10, pl. 10.

GERLACH, E.
*1961   Mikrofossilien aus dem Oligozän und Miozän Nordwestdeutschlands, unter besonderer Berucksichtigung der Hystrichosphaerideen und Dinoflagellaten. Neu. Jb. Geol. Paläont., Abh., vol. 112, pt. 2, pp. 143-228, pls. 25-9, text-figs. 1-23,

GHOSH, A.K.
1963   Importance of palynology in oil exploration. Univ. Gauhati, J., vol. 13, no. 2, Science, pp. 19-28. (p. 21 relevant).

GHOSH, A.K. and BANERJI, D.
    1963   Internati onal conference on palynology.   J. Scient. Ind. Res., vol. 22, no. 2, pp. 69-72.   (pp. 69-70 relevant).

GLAESSNER, M.F.
    1945   Principles of micropalaeontology.   Melbourne; University Press.   296 pp., 14 pls.,62 text-figs, 7 tabs.   (pp. 18, 20, 203, 257, 259 relevant).

GLASS, H.D.
            See Pryor, W.A., and Glass.

GOCHT, H.
    * 1952 Hystrichosphaerideen und andere Kleinlebewesen aus Oligozänablagerungen Nord - und Mitteldeutschlands.   Geologie, vol. 1, no. 4, pp. 301-20, pls. 1-2.

    * 1955 Rhombodinium und Dracodinium, zwei neue Dinoflagellaten-Gattungen aus dem norddeutschen Tertiär.   Neu. Jb. Geol. Paläont., Mh., no. 2, pp. 84-92, text-figs. 1-5.

    * 1957 Mikroplankton aus dem nordwestdeutschen Neokem 1.   Paläont. Z., vol. 31, nos. 3-4, pp. 163-85, pls. 18-20, text-figs. 1-14.

    * 1959 Mikroplankton aus dem nordwestdeutschen Neokom II.   Paläont. Z., vol. 33, nos. 1-2, pp. 50-89, pls. 3-8.

    * 1960 Die Gattung Chiropteridium n. gen. (Hystrichosphaeridea) im deutschen Oligozän.   Paläont. Z., vol. 34, nos. 3-4, pp. 221-32, pls. 17-18, text-figs. 1-28.   See also Eisenack, A., and Gocht.

GÓRKA, H.
    * 1963 Coccolithophoridés, Dinoflagellés, Hystrichosphaeridés et microfossiles incertae sedis du Crétacé supérieur de Pologne.   Acta Palaeont. Polon., vol. 8, no. 1, pp. 3-90, pl. 1-11, text-figs. 1-8.

GRAINDOR, M.J.
    1956   Note préliminaire sur les micro-organismes du Briovérien.   Soc. Géol. Fr., C.R. Somm., no. 11, pp. 207-10, text-figs. 1-15.

    * 1957 Cayeuxidae nov. fam., organismes à squelette du Briovérien.   Acad. Sci., Paris, C.R., vol. 244, pp. 2075-7, text-figs. 1-4.

GRAMANN, F.
            See Brosius, M. and Gramann.

GRAY, J.
    1960   Temperate pollen genera in the Eocene (Claiborne) flora, Alabama.   Science, vol. 132, no. 3420, pp. 808-10, text-fig. 1, tab. 1.
            See also Martin, P.S. and Gray.

GRIFFITH, J.W., and HENFREY, A.
    1856   The micrographic dictionary: a guide to the examination and investigation of the structure and nature of microscopic objects.   London: Van.Voorst.   696 pp., 41 pls., 812 text-figs. (p. 692, pl. 19 relevant).

GRIPP, K.
    1925   Uber das Alttertiär von Hemmoor: ein Beitrag zur Stratigraphic Nordwestdeutsch- lands.   Niedersächs. Geol. Ver., Jber., vol. 17, pp. 127-37.

GROOT, J.J. and C.R.
    1962   Some plant microfossils from the Brightseat Formation (Paleocene) of Maryland.   Palaeontographica, ser. B., vol. 111, pp. 161-71, pls. 29-31. (p. 162 relevant).

24

GUISE, W. V.
    1886   <u>Presidential address to the Cotteswold Naturalists' Field Club.</u> Cotteswold
              Naturalists' Field Club, Proc., vol. 8, pp. 225-45. (Tasmanaceae, pp. 237-40).

GUNN, W.
              See Peach, B. N., Horne, J., Gunn, Clough, C. T., and Hinxman, W.

HARRINGTON, H. J.
              See Cranwell, L. M., Harrington and Speden, I. G.

HARRIS, W. F.
              See Couper, R. A., and Harris.

HEDLUND, R. W.
    1960   <u>Microfossils of the Sylvan Shale (Ordovician) of Oklahoma.</u> Univ. Oklahoma,
              Abstr., no. 184, 1 p., 1 text-fig, 8 pls.
              See also Wilson, L. R., and Hedlund.

HENFREY, A.
              See Griffith, J. W., and Henfrey.

HESSLAND, I.
    1958   <u>News reports: Scandinavia.</u> Micropaleontology, vol. 4, no. 2, pp. 220-4.

    1962   <u>News reports: Scandinavia.</u> Micropaleontology, vol. 8, no. 3, pp. 414-8.

HIEBENTHAL, F.
    1930   <u>Chemische - petrographische Studien an norddeutschen Bitumengesteine verschiedenen</u>
              <u>Alters.</u> Chemie der Erde, vol. 4, pt. 2, pp. 343-68. (p. 363 relevant).

HILTERMANN, H.
    1958   <u>News reports: Germany.</u> Micropaleontology, vol. 4, no. 2, pp. 218-19.

    1959   <u>News reports: Germany.</u> Micropaleontology, vol. 5, no. 2, pp. 266-8.

    1960   <u>News reports: Germany.</u> Micropaleontology, vol. 6, no. 3, pp. 335-7.

    1962   <u>News reports: Germany.</u> Micropaleontology, vol. 8, no. 3, pp. 411-3.

    1963   <u>News reports: Germany.</u> Micropaleontology, vol. 9, no. 3, pp. 347-8.

HINXMAN, W.
              See Peach, B. N., Horne, J., Gunn, W., Clough, C. T., and Hinxman.

HOFFMEISTER, W. S.
              See Wilson, L. R., and Hoffmeister.

HOFFMEISTER, W. S., STAPLIN, F., and MALLOY, R. E.
    1955   <u>Geologic range of Paleozoic plant spores in North America.</u> Micropaleontology.
              vol. 1, no. 1, pp. 9-27, pls. 1-4 (Tasmanaceae).

HOGG, J.
    1854   <u>The microscope: its history, construction and application, being a familiar</u>
              <u>introduction to the use of the instrument and the study of microscopical science,</u>
              London: Illustrated London Library, 440 pp., 15 pls., 169 text-figs.
              (pp. 239-41 relevant).

HOLLINGWORTH, S. E.
    1962   <u>Speech on presentation of a moiety of the Lyell Fund to Dr. C. Downie.</u> Geol.
              Soc. Lond., Proc., no. 1599, pp. 115-6.

HOLM, G.
    1885   Om Vettern och Visingsöformationen. K. Svensk. Vetensk - Akads. Handl.,
              Bih., vol. 11, no. 7, pp. 1-49, text-figs. 1-5.

HOOKER, J.
    1852   On the spheroidal bodies, resembling Seeds, from the Ludlow Bone Bed. Geol.
              Soc. Lond., Quart, J., vol. 9, no. 1, p. 12 (Tasmanaceae).

HORNE, J.
              See Peach, B. N., Horne, Gunn, W., Clough, C. T., and Hinxman, W.

HORNIBROOK, N. de B.
    1962   News reports: New Zealand. Micropaleontology. vol. 8, no. 4, pp. 534-5.

HOUGH, J.
    1934   Redeposition of microscopic Devonian plant fossils. J. Geol., vol. 42, no. 6,
              pp. 646-8 (Tasmanaceae).

HOUSE, M. R.
    1963   Dorset geology, 1950-1960. Dorset Nat. Hist. Arch. Soc., Proc., vol. 84,
              pp. 77-91, text-figs. 1-3. (pp. 84-5 relevant).

HOVASSE, R.
    * 1956   Arnoldia antiqua gen. nov., sp. nov., Foraminifère probable du Précambrien de la
              Côte - d'Ivoire. Acad. Sci. Paris, C.R., vol. 242, pp. 2582-4, text-figs. 1-5.

HUCKE, K.
    1932   Uber die Gewinnung von Mikrofossilien aus Geschieben. Z. Geschiebeforsch.,
              vol. 8, pp. 42-8, text-figs. 1-3.

    1954   Uber Mikrofossilien in norddeutschen Diluvialgeschieben.Der Aufschluss, vol. 5,
              pt. 3, pp. 49-53, 1 pl.

HUDSON, J. D.
    1963   The recognition of salinity-controlled mollusc assemblages in the Great Estuarine
              Series (Middle Jurassic) of the Inner Hebrides. Palaeontology, vol. 6, pt. 2,
              pp. 318-26, text-fig. 1, tab. 1. (p. 324 relevant).

HUGHES, N. F.
    1960   Distribution of Lower Cretaceous microplankton. Int. Geol. Cong. XXI Sess.,
              Norden. Vol. of Abstracts, p. 235.

HUNDT, R.
    1939   Das Mitteldeutsche Graptolithenmeer. Halle; Martin Boerner-Verlag. 395 pp.
              565 un-numbered text-figs. (pp. 207, 227, 233-5, 363, text-figs. 1-2 on p. 326
              relevant).

ISAGULOVA, E.
    1963   Hystrichosphaeridia in Jurassic deposits of the Lvov-Wolyu coal-bearing basin
              (in Russian). Akad. Nauk. S.S.S.R., Dokl., vol. 148, no. 5, pp. 1156-8,
              text-fig. 1.

IVANOVA, I. A.
              See Maliavkina, V.S., Samoilovitch, S. A., Voitziel, Z. A., Klumko, S. A.
              Rovana, L. V., Ivanova; Markova, L. G., and Mtchedlishvili, N. D.

IVERSEN, J.
    1936   Sekundares Pollen als Fehlerquelle. Eine Korrektions-methode zur Pollenan-
              alyse minerogener Sediment. Danmarks Geol. Unders., ser. 4, vol. 2, no. 15,
              pp. 1-24, pl. 1, text-figs. 1-2, tabs. 1-4. (p. 7, text-fig. 1 relevant).

1937   Undersøgelser over Litorinatransgressioner i Danmark. Medd. Dansk. Geol. Foren., vol. 9, part 2, pp. 223-32, text-figs. 1-4 (p. 231 relevant).

1942   En pollenanalytisk Tidsfaestelse af Ferskvandslagene ved Nørre Lyngby.   Med. Bemaerkinger om de senglaciale Naturforhold i Danmark. Medd. Dansk. Geol. Foren., vol. 10, pt. 2, pp. 130-151.
See also Faegri, K. and Iversen.

JACOB, A.

See Jekhowsky, B. de, and Jacob.

JARDINÉ, S.

See Vachey, G., and Jardiné.

JANSONIUS, J.
  * 1962   Palynology of Permian and Triassic sediments, Peace River area, Western Canada. Palaeontographica, ser. B., vol. 110, pp. 35-98, pls. 11-16, text-figs. 1-2, tabs. 1-4.

JEKHOWSKY, B. de
    1958   Méthodes d'utilisation stratigraphique des microfossiles organiques dans les problemes pétroliers. Inst. Fr. Pétrôle, Rev., no. 10, pp. 1391-1418.

    1959a   Une technique standard de préparation des roches pour l'étude des microfossiles organiques. Inst. Fr. Pétrôle, Rev., vol. 14, no. 3, pp. 315-20.

    1959b   Quelques aspects du développement de la palynologie stratigraphique dans l'Antéquaternaire. Bull. Trimestrial Serv. d'Information Géol. (S.I.G.) du B.R.G.G.M., no. 43, pp. 1-7, text-figs. 1-7.

    1960   Bibliographie palynologique du Lias européen. Colloque sur le Lias Français, Proc., pp. 155-62.

  * 1961   Sur quelques hystrichosphères permo-triasiques d"Europe et d'Afrique. Rev. Micropaléont., vol. 3, no. 4, pp. 207-12, pls. 1-2.

JEKHOWSKY, B. de, and JACOB, A.
    1961   Aperçu palynologique sommaire sur le Paléogene du Bassin de Paris. Soc. Géol. Fr., C.R. Somm., no. 7, p. 184.

JEKHOWSKY, B. de, SAH, S.C.H., and LETULLIER, A.
    1960   Reconnaissance palynologique du Permien, Trias et Jurassique des sondages effectués par la Société des Pétrôles de Madagascar dans le bassin de Morondava. Soc. Géol. Fr., C.R. Somm., no. 7, p. 166.

JERSEY, N.J. de,
  * 1962   Triassic spores and pollen grains from the Ipswich Coalfield. Geol. Surv. Queensland, Publ. no. 307, pp. 1-8, pls. 1-6. (p. 15, pl. 5 relevant).

JODRY, R.L., and CAMPAU, D.E.
    1960   Small pseudochitinous and resinous microfossils: new tools for the subsurface geologist. Rocky Mountain Section Annual Meeting, Billings, Montana, February 7-10: Abstracts. Amer. Assoc. Petrol. Geol., Bull., vol. 44, pt. 1, no. 6. p. 958.

    1961   Small pseudochitinous and resinous microfossils: new tools for the subsurface geologists. Amer. Assoc. Petrol. Geol., Bull., vol. 45, pt. 2, no. 8, pp. 1378-91, pls. 1-3, text-figs. 1-5.

JOHNSON, H.A. and THOMAS, B.W.
    1884   The microscopic organisms in the Bowlder Clay of Chicago and vicinity.   Chicago
            Acad. Sci., Bull., vol. 1, pp. 35-40   (Tasmanaceae).

JOHNSON, J.H., and KONISHI, K.
    1958   A review of Devonian algae.   Quart.   Colorado School of Mines, vol. 53, no. 2
            pp. 1-84, pls. 1-26, maps 1-6.   (Tasmanaceae, pp. 76-8, pl. 26).

JONES, D.J.
    1956   Introduction to microfossils.   New York: Harper.   406 pp., 101 text-figs.
            (pp. 21-2, 34, 45-6, text-figs. 4-4 and 4-6 relevant).

    1961   News reports: United States - Rocky Mountain region.   Micropaleontology,
            vol. 7, no. 4, pp. 382-4.

KARA - MURZA, E.N.
    1957   Upper Cretaceous and Triassic Hystrichosphaeridae of the Soviet Arctic (in
            Russian).   Leningrad, Inst. Res. Sci. Geol. Arctic, Palaeontology and Biostratig.
            no. 4, pp. 64-9, pl. 1.

KATZ, H.R.
    1961   Descubrimiento de una microflora neocomiana en la Formacion Agua Fresca
            (Eocena) de Magallanes y su significado con respecto a la evolucion tectonica
            de la zona.   Ann. Fac. Fis. Mat., Santiago, Chile, vol. 18,   no. 21,
            pp. 132-41, 1 text-fig.

KEDVES, M.
    1960   Études palynologiques dans le bassin de Dorog I.   Pollen et Spores, vol. 2, no. 1
            pp. 89-118, pls. 1-10, text-figs. 1-5, (p. 111, pl. 10 relevant).

    1961   Études palynologiques dans le bassin de Dorog II.   Pollen et spores, vol. 3,
            no. 1, pp. 101-53, pls. 1-10.   (p. 150 relevant).

    1962   Noremia, a new microfossil genus from the Hungarian Eocene, and systematical and
            stratigraphical problems about the Crassosphaeridae.   Acta. Miner. Petr. Szeged.
            vol. 15, pp. 19-27, pls. 1-2.
    1963   Contribution à la flore Eocène Inférieure de la Hongrie sur la base des examens
            palynologiques des couches houillières du puits III d'Oroszlány et du puits XV/B
            de Tatabánya.   Acta Bot. Acad. Scient. Hung., vol. 9, Nos. 1-2, pp. 31-66,
            pls. 1-8, text-figs. 1-4.   (Tasmanaceae, p. 41).
            See also Simoncsics, P., and Kedves.

KENT, D.M.
    1963   The stratigraphy of the Upper Devonian Saskatchewan Group of southwestern
            Saskatchewan.   Saskatch. Dep. Min. Res., Rep., no. 73, pp. 1-51, pls. 1-4,
            text-figs. 1-11.   (pp. 1-32, pls. 1-4 relevant).

KIRCHHEIMER, F.
    1950   Mikrofossilien aus Salzablagerungen des Tertiärs.   Palaeontographica, ser. B.,
            vol. 90, pp. 127-60, pl. 20, tabs. 1-5.

KIRICHENKO, G.I.
            See Alyushinskiy, Y.A., Kirichenko, and Timofeyev, B.V.

KIRKPATRICK, R.
    1916   The Nummulosphere.   Part III :   The ocean floor or benthoplankton.
            London; Lamley.   319 pp., 24 pls.   (pp. 60-61 relevant).

KLEMENT, K.W.
* 1957 Revision der Gattungzugehörigkeit einige in die Gattung Gymnodinium einge-
stufter Arten jurassischer Dinoflagellaten. Neu. Jb. Geol. Palaont., Mh.,
no. 9, pp. 408-10, text-fig. 1.

1960a Dinoflagellaten und Hystrichosphaerideen aus der Malm Südwestdeutschlands
unter besonderer Berücksichtigung stratigrafisch wichtiger Arten. Paläont.
Z., vol. 34, pt. 1, p. 11.

* 1960b Dinoflagellaten und Hystrichosphaerideen aus dem Unteren und Mittleren Malm
Sudwestdeutschlands. Palaeontographica, ser. A., Vol. 114, nos. 1-4,
pp. 1-104, pls. 1-10, text-figs. 1-37.

* 1961 Kritische Stellungnahme zur Gattung Bulbodinium O. Wetzel 1960 (Dinoflagellaten). Neu. Jb. Geol. Paläont., Mh., No. 9, pp. 489-92.

KLUMKO, S.A.,
See Maliavkina, V.S., Samoilovitch, S.R., Voitziel, Z.A., Klumko,
Rovuna, L.V., Ivanova, I.A., A. Markova, L.G. and Mtchedlishvili, N.D.

KLUMPP, B.,
* 1963 Beitrag zur Kenntnis der Mikrofossilien des Mittleren und Oberen Eozän.
Palaeontographica, ser. A., vol. 103, nos. 5-6, pp. 377-406, pls. 16-20,
text-figs. 1-5.

KONISHI, K.
See Johnson, J.H., and Konishi.

KORALLOVA, V.V.
1963 The Khadum spore and pollen complexes in the Oligocene deposits of the East
Black Sea coast (in Russian). Akad. Nauk. S.S.S.R., Dokl., vol. 148,
no. 5, pp. 1162-3.

KÖWING, K.
1956 Ausbildung und Gliederung des Miozans im Raum von Bremen. Naturwiss.
Verein, Bremen, Abh., vol. 34, pt. 2, pp. 69-171, text-figs. 1-17, tabs. A-C.
(pp. 97, 106, 127 relevant).

KRAFT, P.
1926 Ontogenetische Entwicklung und Biologie von Diplograptus und Monograptus.
Paläont. Z., vol. 7, pp. 208-47, pls. 1-15, text-figs. 1-4, (p. 247 relevant).

KRÄUSEL, R.
1939 Palaeobotanische Notizen XXI: Sind die Palaeozoischen Hystrichosphären
Einzellen oder Pflanzensporen? Senckenbergiana, vol. 21, nos. 5-6,
pp. 358-63, text-figs. 1-2.

1940 Palaeobotanische Notizen XXII n.s.w: Noch einmal devonische Sporen und
Hystrichosphaerideen. Senckenbergiana, vol. 22, nos. 1-2, pp. 1-2.

* 1941 Die Sporokarpien Dawsons, Eine neue Thallophyten-Klasse des Devons.
Palaeontographica. ser. B., vol. 86, pts. 4-6, pp. 113-33, pls. 28-34,
text-figs. 1-3 (Tasmanaceae).

1960 Spongiophyton nov. gen. (Thallophyta) e Haplostigma Seward (Pteridophyta) no
Devoniano Inferior do Parana. Brasil, Min. da Agricultura, Dep. Nac. da
Produçao Mineral, Div. de Geol. et Mineral. Monografia, no. 15, 41 pp.,
11 pls. (Tasmanaceae, pp. 8-10).

KRÄUSEL, R. and SCHAARSCHIMDT, F.
    1963   <u>Aufstieg der Mikropalaobotanik</u>. Natur u. Museum, vol. 93, no. 6, pp. 222-30,
          text-figs. 1-6, pp. 228-9, text-figs. 5-6 relevant.

KRIVÁN HUTTER, E.
    * 1963a   <u>Microplankton from the Palaeogene of the Dorog Basin 1</u>. Univ. Sci. Budapest.,
          Ann., Geol., vol. 6, pp. 71-9, pls. 1-6.

    1963b   <u>Szénhidrogéntermelo planktonalgák á Dorogi Paleogénböl</u>. Földt. Kozl., vol. 93
          no. 2, pp. 231-4, pl. 12, text-figs. 1-2 (p. 231 relevant).

KRUTZSCH, W.
    1962   <u>Die Mikroflora der Geisetalbraunkohle III.   Süsswasserdinoflagellaten aus
          subäquatorisch gebildeten Blatterkohlenlagen des mittleren Geiseltales</u>.
          Hallesches Jb. Mitteldeutsch. Erdgesch., vol. 4, pp. 40-45, pls. 10-11,
          text-fig. 1.

KUFFERATH, H.
    * 1950   <u>Recherches sur le plancton de la mer flamande (mer du Nord méridionale). 1.
          Quelques flagellés, protistes et "caetera"</u>. Inst. Roy. Sci. Nat. Belg., Bull.,
          vol. 26, No. 29, 43 pp, 40 text-figs.

KUYL, O.S., MULLER, J., and WATERBOLK, H.T.
    1955   <u>The application of palynology to oil geology, with special reference to western
          Venezuela</u>. Geol. Mijnb., new ser., vol. 17, no. 3, pp. 49-88, pls. 1-8.

LAIRD, H.C.
    1935   <u>The nature and origin of chert in the Lockport and Onondaga Formations</u>. Roy.
          Canad. Inst., Trans., vol. 20, pt. 2, no. 44, pp. 231-304, pls. 16-22, text-
          figs. 1-11b. (p. 256, text-fig. 7 relevant).

LANTZ, J.
    1958   <u>Étude palynologique de quelques échantillons mésozoiques de Dorset (Grande-
          Bretagne)</u>. Inst. Fr. Pétrôle, Rev., vol. 13, no. 6, pp. 917-40, pl. 1-7.

LEBEDEVA, A.E., and TIMOFEYEV, B.V.
    1958   <u>On organic remains from the Lower Cambrian "Blue Clay"</u>. (in Russian).
          Leningrad Univ., Vestnik, Geol. & Geogr. Ser., no. 12, pp. 42-8, text-
          figs. 1-7.

LEFÈVRE, M.
    1932   <u>Sur la présence de Péridiniens dans un dépôt fossils des Barbades</u>. Acad. Sci.
          Paris, C.R., vol. 197, pp. 2315-6.

    1933a   <u>Sur la structure de la thèque chez les Péridinites</u>. Acad. Sci. Paris, C.R.,
          vol. 198, pp. 81-3.

    * 1933b   <u>Recherches sur les Péridiniens fossiles des Barbades</u>. Mus. Hist. Nat. Paris,
          Bull., ser. 2, vol. 5, no. 5, pp. 415-8.

    * 1933c   <u>Les Péridinites des Barbades</u>. Ann. Crypt. Exot., vol. 6, pp. 215-29, text-
          figs. 1-30.

    1940   <u>Sur la nature de la thèque originelle des Péridinites</u>. Acad. Sci. Paris, vol. 211,
          no. 23, pp. 599-601.

LEJEUNE, M.
    1936a   <u>Sur un moyen d'isoler les microfossiles inclus dans les silex</u>. Acad. Sci. Paris,
          C.R., vol. 203, pp. 435-7.

1936b   L'étude microscopique des silex (1^{ière} Note).   Son enseignement dans les domaines paléontologie et géologie.   Soc. Géol. Belg., Ann., vol. 59, Bull. no. 7, pp. 190-7.

1937a   L'étude microscopique des silex (2ième Note).   Un fossile anciennement connu et pourtant méconnu, Hystrichosphaera ramosa Ehrbg.   Soc. Géol. Belg., Ann., vol. 60, bull. nos. 7, pp. B. 239-60, pl. 1-2.

1937b   A propos des Péridiniens fossiles des silex (Note préliminaire). Soc. Géol. Belg., Ann., vol. 60, bulls. nos. 8-9, pp. B296-8.

1937c   L'étude microscopique des silex (3ième Note).   Encore Hystrichosphaera ramosa Ehrbg.; les coques "dédoublées", le "flagelle".   Soc. Géol. Belg., Ann., vol. 60, bulls. nos. 8-9, pp. B321-33, pl. 1.

LEJEUNE - CARPENTIER, M.
1937   L'étude microscopique des silex (4ième Note).   Une interessante préparation d'Ehrenberg.   Soc. Géol. Belg., Ann., vol. 61, bull. nos. 2-3, pp. B59-71, pls. 1-2.

1938a   L'étude microscopique des silex (5ième Note).   Nouvelles remarques sur les Hystrichosphères à excroissance latérale.   Soc. Géol. Belg., Ann., vol. 61, bull. no. 6, pp. B179-86, text-figs. 1-4.

* 1938b   L'étude microscopique des silex (6ième Note).   Areoligera: nouveau genre d'Hystrichosphaeridée.   Soc. Géol. Belg., Ann., vol. 62, bull. no. 3, pp. B163-74, text-figs. 1-7.

* 1938c   Peridinium pyrophorum Ehrenberg.   Mus. Roy. Hist. Nat. Belg., Bull., vol. 14, no. 44, pp. 1-13, text-figs. 1-10.

* 1939   L'étude microscopique des silex (7ième Note).   Un nouveau Péridinien crétacique, Gonyaulax wetzeli.   Soc. Géol. Belg., Ann., vol. 62, bulls. nos. 10-11, pp. B525-9, text-figs. 1-2.

* 1940   L'étude microscopique des silex (8ième Note).   Systématique et morphologie des "Tubifères".   Soc. Géol. Belg., Ann., vol. 63, bull. no. 5, pp. B216-36, text-figs. 1-14.

* 1941   L'étude microscopique des silex (9ième Note).   Sur Hystrichosphaeridium hirsutum (Ehrenberg) et quelques formes voisines.   Soc. Géol. Belg., Ann., vol. 63, bull. no. 3, pp. B71-92, text-figs. 1-9.

* 1942   L'étude microscopique des silex (10ième Note).   Péridiniens nouveaux ou peu connus.   Soc. Géol. Belg., Ann., vol. 65, bull. no. 6, pp. B181-92, text-figs. 1-22.

* 1943   L'étude microscopique des silex (11ième Note).   Une Hystrichosphaeridée à classer parmi les Péridiniens. Soc. Géol. Belg., Ann., vol. 67, bull. no. 1, pp. B22-8, text-figs. 1-6.

* 1946   L'étude microscopique des silex (12ième Note).   Espèces nouvelles ou douteuses de Gonyaulax.   Soc. Géol. Belg., Ann., vol. 69, bull. no. 4, pp. B187-97, text-figs. 1-5.

* 1951   L'étude microscopique des silex (13ième Note).   Gymnodinium et Phanerodinium (Dinoflagellates) de Belgique.   Soc. Géol. Belg., Ann., vol. 74, bull. no. 4, pp. B307-13, text-figs. 1-7.

LEONARD, A. B.
1955   Rinvenimento di Hystrichosphaeridae in depositi fluviali del Quaternario.
        G. Geol.,vol. 26, p. 155-8.

LEOPOLD, E. B.
        See McKee, E. D., Chronic, J., and Leopold.

LETULLIER, A.
        See Jekhowsky, B. de , Sah, S. C. H., and Letullier.

LEWIS, H. P.
1940   The microfossils of the Upper Caradocian phosphate deposits in Montgomery-
        shire, North Wales. Ann. Mag. Nat. Hist., ser. 11, vol. 5, pp. 1-39,
        pls. 1-4, text-figs. 1-3.

LINNARSON, G.
1880   De äldre paleozoiska lagren: trakten kring Motala. Geol. Fören. Stockh.,
        Förh., vol. 5, pt. 1 no. 57, pp. 23-30, 1 map. (p. 30 relevant).

LOHMANN, H.
1904   Eier und sogenannte Cysten der Plankton - Expedition. Anhang: Cyphonautes.
        Kiel: Wissenschaft Ergebnisse der Plankton - Expedition Humboldt-Stiftung, new
        ser., vol. 4, pp. 1-62, pls. 1-7. (p. 25 relevant).

LOVE, L. G.
1962   Further studies of micro-organisms and the presence of syngenetic pyrite.
        Palaeontology, vol. 5, pt. 3, pp. 444-59, pls. 63-4, text-fig. 1. (pp.445
        and 456 relevant).

LUBER, A. A.
1962   Activities of the International Commission on the Palaeozoic microflora (in
        Russian). Akad. Nauk. S.S.S.R., Pal. Z., no. 1, pp. 171-3.

LUDBROOK, N. H.
1963   News reports: Australia. Micropaleontology, vol. 9, no. 3, pp. 341-3.

MACGREGOR, D. C.
        See Radforth, N. W., and Macgregor.

MACKÓ, S.
 * 1957   Lower Miocene pollen flora from the valley of Kłodnicka near Gliwice (Upper
           Silesia). Soc. Sci. Wroclaw, Trav., ser. 13, no. 88, pp. 1-313, pl. 1-80.
           (pp. 113, 214, pl. 71 relevant).

MADLER, K.
1958   Neue mikrobotanische Untersuchungen im Posidonienschiefer. Paläont. Z.,
        vol. 32, pp. 13-4. (Tasmanaceae).

MAIER, D.
1958   Zur Gliederung des Tertiärs mit Hystrichosphaerideen. Neu. Jb. Geol.
        Paläont., Mh., no. 10, p. 468-72.

 * 1959   Planktonuntersuchungen in tertiären und quatären marinen Sedimenten. Neu. Jb.
           Geol. Paläont., Abh., vol. 107, no. 3, pp. 278-340, pls. 27-33.

MAIER - KÖSTER, D.
1961   Zur Verbreitungen der Hystrichosphaerideen im Miozän und den benachbarten
        Stufen. Meyniana, vol. 10, pp. 10-12.

MALIAVKINA, V.S., SAMOILOVITCH, S.R., VOITZIEL, Z.A., KLUMKO, S.A.,
    ROVUNA, L.V., IVANOVA, I.A., MARKOVA, L.G., and
    MTCHEDLISHVILI, N.D. 1961
        Pollen and spores of Western Siberia: Jurassic – Paleocene. A symposium
        (in Russian). Vses. Neft. Nauchno-Iss. Geol. Inst., Trudy, no. 177.

MALLOY, R.E.
        See Hoffmeister, W.S., Staplin, F.L., and Malloy.

MANTELL, G.A.
  * 1844   The Medals of Creation: or,First lessons in Geology and the study of organic
        remains. London; Bohn. 2 vols., 1016 pp., 6 + 2 pls., 167 text-figs. (vol. 1,
        pp. 239–42, text-fig. 53 relevant).

    1845   Notes of a microscopical examination of the Chalk and Flint of Southeast England,
        with remarks on the Animalculites of certain Tertiary and modern deposits. Ann.
        Mag. Nat. Hist., vol. 16, no. 103, pp. 73–88.

    1848   The wonders of geology; or, a familiar exposition of geological phenomena.
        First Ed. London: Bohn, 2 vols., 938 pp., 6 pls., 198 text-figs. (pp. 305–6
        relevant).

  * 1849   Thoughts on a pebble; or, a first lesson in Geology. London: Reeve. 102 pp.,
        27 text-figs. (pp. 35–8, text-figs. 10–11 relevant).

  * 1850   A pictorial atlas of fossil remains, consisting of coloured illustrations selected from
        Parkinson's "Organic remains of a former World", and Artis's "Antediluvian
        Phytology". London: Bohn. 208 pp, 74 pls. (p. 191 relevant).

  * 1854   The Medals of Creation; or, first lessons in Geology and the study of organic
        remains. Second Ed. London: Bohn. 2 vols., 930 pp., 6 pls., 275 text-figs.
        (vol. 1, p. 91, 239–42 and text-figs. 77–9 relevant).

    1857   The wonders of geology; or, a familiar exposition of geological phenomena.
        Seventh Ed. London: Bohn. 2 vols., 1019 pp., 213 text-figs. (pp. 311–3, text-
        figs, 58–9 relevant),

MANUM, S.
  * 1960a   Some dinoflagellates and hystrichosphaerids from the Lower Tertiary of Spitzbergen.
        Nytt Mag. Bot., vol. 8, pp. 17–24, pl. 1, text-figs. 1–3.

    1960b   Some dinoflagellates and hystrichosphaerids from the Lower Tertiary of Spitzbergen.
        Meddelelser Norsk Polarinst., no. 85, 10 pp., 1 pl., 3 text-figs

  * 1963   Some new species of Deflandrea and their probable affinity with Peridinium,
        Norsk. Polarinst., Arbők 1962, pp. 55–67, pls. 1–3, text-figs. 1–4.
        See also Cookson, I.C., and Manum.

MARTIN, P.S., and GRAY, J.
    1962   Pollen analysis and the Cenozoic. Science, vol. 137, no. 3524, pp. 103–11,
        text-figs. 1–5. (text-fig. 2 relevant).

MARKOVA, L.G.
        See Maliavkina, V.S., Samoilovitch, S.A., Voitziel, Z.A., Klumko, S.A.,
        Rovuna, L.V., Ivanova, I.A., Markova and Mtchedlishvili, N.D.

MARTINSSON, A.
    1956   Neue Funde kambrischer Gänge und ordovizischer Geschiebe im südwestlichen
        Finnland. Geol. Inst. Univ. Uppsala, Bull., vol. 36, pt. 1, pp. 79–105.
        pls. 1–2, text-figs. 1–10.

MASLOV, V. P.
* 1956   Fossil calcareous algae of the U.S.S.R. (in Russian). Akad. Nauk. S.S.S.R.,
Inst. Geol. Trudy, no. 160, 301 pp., 86 pls., 135 text-figs., 9 tabs.
(pp. 258-64, pl. 86 relevant).

MATTHES, H. W.
1956   Einführung in die Mikropaläontologie. Leipzig: Hirzel, 348 pp., 1050 text-
figs, 53 tabs. (pp. 187-91, 216-19, text-figs. 119, 156 relevant).

McCLURE, K.
See Tasch, P., McClure and Oftedahl, O.

McKEE, E. D., CHRONIC, J., and LEOPOLD, E. B.
1959   Sedimentary belts in lagoon of Kapingamarangi atoll. Amer. Assoc. Petrol. Geol.
Bull., vol. 43, pt. 1, no. 3, pp. 501-62, pl. 1, text-figs. 1-21, tabs. 1-9.

MERCIER, J.
1938a   Microplancton du Crétacé superieur de l'Ouest du bassin de Paris. Note
préliminaire. Soc. Géol. Fr., C.R. Somm., no. 6, pp. 95-6.

1938b   Micro-organismes du Bajocien et du Bathonien. (Note préliminaire). Soc.
Géol. Fr., C.R. Somm., no. 7, pp. 114-5.

1938c   Nouvelles observations sur le microplancton du Dogger. Soc. Géol. Fr., C.R.
Somm., no. 17, pp. 334-5.

MEDVEDEVA, A. M. and CHEPILOVA, I. K.
1961   Protoleiosphaeridium sorediforme Tim. and Pr. conglutinatum Tim. from the
petroleum and rocks of the Volga-Ural region. (in Russian). Akad. Sci. S.S.S.R.
Dokl., vol. 139, no. 2, pp. 461-2 (Translation in Amer. Geol. Inst., Dokl.
Acad. Sci. U.S.S.R., Earth Sciences Sect., 1963, pp. 847-8).
See also Chepikov, K.R., and Medvedeva.

MERRILL, J. A.
* 1895   Fossil sponges of the flint nodules in the Lower Cretaceous of Texas. Mus. Comp.
Zool. Harv. Bull. (Geology Ser. III), vol. 28, no. 1, pp. 1-26, pl. 1.

MEUNIER, A.
1919   Microplancton de la mer Flamande IV. Les tintinnidés et caetera. Mus. Roy.
Hist. Nat. Belg., Mém., vol. 8, no. 2, pp. 1-55, pls. 22-3. (pp. 1-55, pls.
22-3 relevant).

MICHAELIS, A.
1962   Science and the citizen. Secrets of rock and ice. Daily Telegraph, no. 33265,
p. 15, 1 text-fig.

MILON, Y.
See Choux, J., Durand, S., and Milon.

MOORE, D. G.
See Shephard, F. P., and Moore.

MOORE, R. C.
1954   Kingdom of organisms named Protista. J. Paleont., vol. 28, no. 5, pp. 588-98.

MORRIS, J.
1854   A catalogue of British fossils; comprising the genera and species hitherto
described; with reference to their geological distribution and to the localities
in which they have been found. London: The Author. 372 pp. (p. 32
relevant).

MTCHEDLISHVILI, N.D.,
>See Maliavkina, V.S., Samoilovitch, S.A., Voitziel, Z.A., Klumko, S.A., Rovuna, L.V., Ivanova, I.A., Markova, L.G., and Mtchedlishvili.

MÜLLER, A.H.
>1958   Lehrbuch der Paläozoologie. vol. 2. Invertebrata. Pt. 1. Protozoa - Mollusca. Jena: VEB Gustav Fischer. 566 pp., 652 text-figs. (pp. 17-19, 96-9, text-figs. 8-9, 80-3 relevant).

MULLER, J.
>1959   Palynology of Recent Orinoco delta and shelf sediments. Micropaleontology, vol. 5, pp. 1-32, pl. 1, text-figs. 1-23, diagr. 1-2, table 1.
>See also Kuyl, O.S., Muller and Waterbolk, H.T.

MULLER, K.J.
>1956   Taxonomy, nomenclature, orientation and stratigraphic evaluation of conodonts. J. Paleont., vol. 30, no. 6, pp. 1324-40, pl. 145. (p. 1337 relevant).

NATHORST, A.G.
>1879a   Enegendomlig strukturvarietet al lerhaltig kalksten från Grennatrakten. Geol. Fören. Stockh., Förh., vol. 4, pt. 8, no. 50, pp. 213-17. (p. 216 relevant).

>1879b   Om de äldre sandstens - och skiffelbildningarne vid Vettern. Geol. Fören. Stockh., Förh., vol. 4, pt. 14, no. 56, pp. 421-36, 1 text-fig., 1 map. (p. 435 relevant).

>1879c   Om de äldre sandstens - och skiffelbildningarne vid Vettern. Sverig. Geol. Unters., Afh., ser. C, no. 39 18 pp., 1 text-fig., 1 map. (p. 17 relevant).

>1884   Upplysningar till Geologisk Ofversigtskarte öfver Sverige Södra bladet. Sverig. Geol. Unters., Afh., ser. Ba, no. 4, pp. 1-35. (p. 14 relevant).

>1886a   Några ord om Visingsöserien. Geol. Fören. Stockh.. Förh., vol. 8, pt. 1, no. 99, pp. 5-23, 15 text-figs. (p. 18 relevant).

>1886b   Några ord om Visingsöserien. Sverig. Geol. Unters., Afh., ser. C, no. 79, 21 pp., 15 text-figs. (p. 17 relevant).

>1894   Jordens historia. Stockholm: Beijers Bokforlagsaktiebolag. 2 vols., 1128 pp., c. 1000 text-figs. (p. 595 relevant).

NAUMOVA, S.N.
>1949   Lower Cambrian spores (in Russian). Akad Nauk. S.S.S.R., Isv., Ser. Geol., pp. 49-56, text-figs. 1-3.

>1950   Spores from the Lower Silurian (in Russian). Trudy Vsesoj. Konf. po Spor. - pylz Analys., Izd. Mosc. Univ. Moscow. pp. 165-190, pl. 1-5.

>1953   Spore - pollen complexes of the Upper Devonian of the Russian Platform and their stratigraphic value (in Russian). Inst. Geol. Sci., Trav., vol. 143, no. 60,, 154 pp., 19 pl.

>* 1961   Spore-pollen complexes of the Riphean and Lower Cambrian in U.S.S.R. (in Russian). Geol. Kong., XXI. Sess., Mezhd., 1960. Doklad. Soviet. Geol., pp. 109-17, text-fig. 1.

>1962   Lower Paleozoic and Precambrian flora. Abstr., International Conference on Palynology, Tucson, Arizona, 1962. Pollen et Spores, vol. 4, no. 2, pp. 366-7.

NAUMOVA, S. N. , and PAVLOVSKY, E. V.
    * 1961   The discovery of plant remains (spores) in the Torridonian Shales of Scotland
            (in Russian). Doklad.. Akad. Nauk. S.S.S.R. , vol. 141, No. 1, pp. 181-2,
            pl. 1.

NEALE, J.W. , and SARJEANT, W.A.S.
    * 1962   Microplankton from the Speeton Clay of Yorkshire. Geol. Mag. , vol. 99,
            no. 5 , pp. 439-58, pls. 19-20, text-figs. 1-9.

NEVES, R. , and DALE, B.
    1963   A modified filtration system for palynological preparations. Nature, vol. 198,
            no. 4882, pp. 775-6, text-figs. 1-2.

NEWTON, E. T.
    * 1875   On "Tasmanite" and Australian "White Coal". Geol. Mag. , ser. 2, vol. 2,
            no. 8, pp. 337-42, pl. 10. (Tasmanaceae).

NOREM, W. L.
    1955a   Pollen, spores and other organic microfossils from the Eocene of Venezuela.
            Micropaleontology, vol. 1, no. 3, pp. 261-7, pls. 1-2, text-fig. 1.

    * 1955b   Tytthodiscus, a new microfossil genus from the California Tertiary. J. Paleont. ,
             vol. 29, no. 4, pp. 694-5, pl. 68. (Tasmanaceae).
             See also Waloweek, W. , and Norem .

NORRIS, G.
    1962   Some glacial deposits and their relation to the Hippotamus-bearing beds at
            Barrington, Cambridgeshire. Geol. Mag. , vol. 99, no. 2, pp. 97-118, text-
            figs. 1-6. (p. 113 relevant).

OFTEDAHL, O.
    See Tasch, P. , McClure, K. , and Oftedahl.

ORTON, E.
    1883   A source of the bituminous matter of the black shales of Ohio. Amer. Assoc.
            Adv. Sci. , Proc. , 31st Meeting, Montreal, pp. 373-84. (Tasmanaceae).

OYEN, F.H. van.
    * 1963   Compte rendu de la réunion du Groupe 9 Acritarcha (ex.; hystrichosphères) de la
            Commission Internationale de Microflore du Paléozique, à Paris, les 20 et 21 Juin
            1963. Pau, France; Société Nationale des Pétrôles d'Aquitaine. 24 pp.

PAGE, D.
    1859   Handbook of geological terms and geology. Edinburgh. Blackwood. 416 pp.

PASTIELS, A.
    1945   Étude histochimique des coques d'Hystrichosphères. Mus. Roy. Hist. Nat. Belg. ,
            Bull. , vol. 21, no. 17, pp. 1-20.

    * 1948   Contributions à l'étude des microfossiles de l'Eocene belge. Mus. Roy. Hist. Nat.
            Belg. , Mém. , No. 109, pp. 1-77, pls. 1-6, text-figs. 1-3.

PAVLOVSKY, E.V.
    See Naumova, S.N. , and Pavlovsky.

PEACH, B.N. , HORNE, J. , GUNN, W. , CLOUGH, C.T. and HINXMAN, L.W.
    1907   The geological structure of the North-west Highlands of Scotland. Geol.
            Survey. , Mem. , 668 pp. , pl. 36-52, 66 text-figs. (p.288, pl. 52 relevant).

PHILIPOTT, A.
  * 1949   Contributions à la paléontologie des silex crétacés. Trois nouveaux micro-
            fossiles. Soc. Scient. Bretagne, Bull., vol. 24, pp. 55-8, text-figs. 1-3.

PICTET, F. J.
    1846   Traité élémentaire de paléontologie, ou histoire naturelle des animaux fossiles,
            considérés dans leurs rapports zoologiques et géologiques. Paris: Langlois &
            Leclerq. 4 vols., 1710 pp., 72 pls. (vol. 4, p. 342 relevant).

PIERCE, R. L.
    1961   Lower Upper Cretaceous plant microfossils from Minnesota. Minn. Geol. Surv.,
            Bull., no. 42, 86 pp., pls. 1-3, tabs. 1-3, 1 un-numbered text-fig.
            (p. 66 relevant).
            See also Brown, C.W., and Pierce.

POCOCK, S. A. J.
  * 1962   Microfloral analysis and age determination of strata at the Jurassic-Cretaceous
            boundary in the Western Canada plains. Palaeontographica, ser. B, vol. 111,
            pp. 1-95, pls. 1-15, text-figs. 1-20.

POKORNY, V.
    1954   Zaklady Zoologické Mikropaleontologie. Prague: Nakladatelstvi Sesko-
            slovenska Akad. Ved. (not seen).

    1958   Grundzüge der zoologischen Mikropaläontologie. vol. 1. Berlin: VEB Deutscher
            Verlag der Wissenschaften. 582 pp., 549 text-figs. (pp. 454-68, text-figs. 527-
            49 relevant).

    1963   Principles of zoological micropalaeontology. vol. 1. Oxford; Pergamon Press.
            652 pp., 548 text-figs. (pp. 499-515, text-figs, 527-49 relevant).

POTTER, D. E.
    1962   Devonian Chitinozoa and Hystrichospherids from Paraguay. Abstr., International
            Conference on Palynology, Tucson, Arizona, 1962. Pollen et Spores, vol. 4,
            no. 2, pp. 373.

POZARYSKA, K.
    1960   News reports: Poland. Micropaleontology, vol. 6, no. 3, pp. 338-40.

    1962   News reports: Poland. Micropaleontology, vol. 8, no. 2, pp. 279-81.

PRITCHARD, A.
    1841   A history of Infusoria, living and fossil: arranged according to "Die Infusoriens-
            thierchen" of C. G. Ehrenberg. London: Whittaker. 439 pp., 12 pls.
            (pp. 186-9, pl. 12 relevant).

    1852   A history of infusorial animalcules, living and fossil. London: Whittaker.
            704 pp., 24 pls. (pp. 256-9 relevant).

PRYOR, W.A., and GLASS, H.D.
    1961   Cretaceous-Tertiary clay mineralogy of the Upper Mississippi embayment.
            J. Sed. Pet., vol. 31, no. 1, pp. 38-57, text-figs. 1-7. (pp. 40-6 relevant).

RADFORTH, N.W., and MACGREGOR, D.C.
    1954   Some plant microfossils important to pre-Carboniferous stratigraphy and contributing
            to our knowledge of the early floras. Canad. J. Bot., vol. 32, no. 5,
            pp. 601-21, pls. 1-2, tab. 1.

    1956   Antiquity of form in Canadian plant microfossils. Roy. Soc. Canada, Trans.,
            ser. 3, vol. 50, sect. 5, pp. 27-31, pls. 1-3.

RADFORTH, N.W., and ROUSE, G.E.
    1956   Floral transgressions of major geological time zones. Roy. Soc. Canada, Trans.,
               ser. 3, sect. 5, vol. 1, pp. 17-26, pl. 1, charts 1-2. (pp. 20-24, pl. 1,
               chart 1 relevant).

RALFS, J.
    1848   The British Desmidieae. London: Reeve. 226 pp., 35 pls. (pp. 12-13 relev-
               ant).

READE, Rev. J.B.
  * 1839   On some new organic remains in the Flint of Chalk. Ann. Nat. Hist. vol. 2,
               pp. 191-8, pls. 8-9.

REGNÉLL, G.
    1955   Leiosphaera (Hystrichosph.) aus unterordovizischem Kalkstein in SO-Schonen,
               Schweden. Geol. Fören., Stockh., Förh., vol. 77, No. 4, pp. 545-56, text-
               figs. 1-5.

REINSCH, P.F.
    1884   Micro-Palaeophytologia formationis carboniferae. Erlangen: Krische. 2 vols.,
               vii + 80 + 55 pp., 95 pls. (Tasmanaceae, vol. 2, pp. 1-13, pls. 67-72).

    1905   Die Palinosphärien, ein mikroskopischer vegetabile Organismus in der Mukronat-
               enkreide. Cbl. Min. Geol. Palaeont., pp. 402-7, text-figs. 1-2.

REISS, Z.
    1962   News reports: Israel. Micropaleontology, vol. 8, no. 4, pp. 532-3.

    1963   News reports: Israel. Micropaleontology, vol. 9, no. 4, pp. 482-3.

REISSINGER, A.
    1948   Die "Pollenanalyse" ausgedehnt auf all Sedimentgesteine der geologischen Vergan-
               genheit I. Palaeontographica, ser. B., vol. 84, pp. 1-20.

    1950   Die "Pollenanalyse" ausgedehnt auf alle Sedimentgesteine der geologischen
               Vergangenheit II. Palaeontographica, ser. B., vol. 90, pp. 90-126, pls. 11-19.

RIVEIRO, F. - Ch. de, and BERMUDEZ, P.J.
    1963   Micropaleontologia general. Caracas: Univ. Central de Venezuela. 808 pp.,
               147 text-figs. (not seen).

ROBLOT, M. -M.
    1963   Découverte de sporomorphes dans des sédiments antérieurs à 550 M.A. (Briovérien).
               Acad. Sci. Paris, C.R., vol. 256, pp. 1557-9, 1 pl.

RODIC, I.
    1931   Radiolarien in Kieselschiefern Mittelböhmens. Lotos, Prague, vol. 79, pp. 118-
               36, pls. 8-10.

ROSSIGNOL, M.
  * 1961   Analyse pollinique de sédiments marins Quaternaires en Israël. I. Sediments
               récents. Pollen et Spores, vol. 3, no. 2, pp. 301-24, pls. 1-2, 5 text-figs.,
               tabs. 1-4.

  * 1962   Analyse pollinique de sédiments marins Quaternaires en Israël II. Sediments
               Pleistocènes. Pollen et Spores, vol. 4, no. 1, pp. 121-48, pls. 1-2, tabs. 1-2,
               map. 1.

    1963   Aperçus sur le developpement des Hystrichosphères. Mus. Nat. Hist. Nat., Bull.,
               ser. 2, vol. 35, no. 2, pp. 207-12, pls. 1-2, 1 text-fig.

ROTHPLETZ, A.
    1880   Radiolarien, Diatomaceen und Sphaerosomatiten im silurischer Kieselschiefer von Langenstriegis in Sachsen. Deutsch. Geol. Ges., Z., vol. 32, pp. 447-67, pl. 21.

ROVUNA, L.V.
    See Maliavkina, V.S., Samoilovitch, S.A., Voitziel, Z.A., Klumko, S.A.,.., Rovuna, Ivanova, I.A., Markova, L.C., and Mtchedlishvili, N.D.

ROUSE, G.E.
    See Radforth, N.W., and Rouse.

RUEDEMANN, R., and WILSON, T.Y.
    1936   Eastern New York Ordovician cherts. Geol. Soc. Amer., Bull., vol. 47, no. 10, pp. 1535-86, pls. 1-7, text-figs. 1-2 (? Tasmanaceae, pp. 1579-80, pl. 6, fig. 19).

SAH, S.C.H.
    1953   Spores and other micro-remains from a carbonaceous shale (Jurassic) in Andigama, Ceylon. Spolia Zelandia, vol. 27, pt. 1, pp. 1-12.
            See also Jekhowsky, B. de, Sah and Letullier, A.

SALTER, J.W.
    1873   A catalogue of the collection of Cambrian and Silurian fossils contained in the Geological Museum of the University of Cambridge. Cambridge Univ. Press. 204 pp. (Tasmanaceae, p. 188).

SAMOILOVITCH, S.R.,
    See Maliavkina, V.S., Samoilovitch, Voitziel, Z.A., Klumko, S.A., Rovuna, L.V., Ivanova, I.A., Markova, L.G., and Mtchedlishvili, N.D.

SANDERS, J. McCONNELL
    1937   The microscopical examination of crude petroleum. Inst. Petrol. Techn., J., vol. 23, pp. 525-73, pls. 1-17, text-figs. 1-13. (pls. 6, 12 relevant).

SANNEMANN, D.
    * 1955   Hystrichosphaerideen aus dem Gothlandium und Mittel-Devon des Frankenwaldes und ihr Feinbau. Senck. Leth., vol. 36, nos. 5-6, pp. 321-46, pls. 1-6, text-figs. 1-18.

SARJEANT, W.A.S.
    * 1959   Microplankton from the Cornbrash of Yorkshire. Geol. Mag., vol. 96, no. 5, pp. 329-46, pl. 13, text-figs. 1-8.

    * 1960a   New hystrichospheres from the Upper Jurassic of Dorset. Geol. Mag., vol. 97, no. 2, pp. 137-44, pl. 6, text-figs. 1-4.

    1960b   The mystery of the Hystrichospheres. Univ. Sheffield Geol. Soc., J., vol. 3, no. 6, pp. 161-7, text-fig. 1.

    * 1960c   Microplankton from the Corallian rocks of Yorkshire. Yorks. Geol. Soc., Proc., vol. 32, pt. 4, no. 18, pp. 389-408, pls. 12-14, text-figs. 1-3, tabs. 1-2.

    * 1961a   Microplankton from the Kellaways Rock and Oxford Clay of Yorkshire. Palaeontology, vol. 4, pt. 1, pp. 90-118, pls. 13-15, text-figs. 1-15.

    1961b   The Hystrichospheres; a review and discussion. Grana Palynologica, vol. 2, pt. 3, pp. 102-11.

* 1961c   <u>Systemataphora Klement and Polystephanosphaera Sarjeant.</u>   J. Paleont.,
vol. 35, no. 5, pp. 1095-6.

* 1962a   <u>Upper Jurassic microplankton from Dorset, England.</u>   Micropaleontology, vol. 8,
no. 2, pp. 255-68, pls. 1-2, text-figs. 1-8, tabs. 1-4.

* 1962b   <u>Microplankton from the Ampthill Clay of Melton, South Yorkshire.</u>   Palaeontology, vol. 5, pt. 3, pp. 478-97, pls. 69-70, text-figs. 1-13, tabs. 1-3.

* 1963a   <u>Favilamax, new genus of Mesozoic hystrichospheres.</u>   J. Paleont., vol. 37,
no. 3, pp. 719-21.

   1963b   <u>Fossil algae and modern rock-dating.</u>   New Scientist, vol. 18, no. 344, pp. 668-
70, text-figs. 1-2.

* 1963c   <u>Fossil dinoflagellates from Upper Triassic sediments.</u>   Nature, vol. 199, no. 4891,
pp. 353-4, text-figs. 1-3.

* 1963d   <u>Two new Jurassic species of Gonyaulax(Dinophyceae).</u>   Rev. Micropaléont.,
vol. 6, No. 2, pp. 85-8, pl. 1.
See also Churchill, D.M., and Sarjeant; Downie, C., Evitt, W.R. and
Sarjeant; Downie, C., and Sarjeant; Downie, C., Williams, G.L., and
Sarjeant; Eagar, S.H., and Sarjeant; Neale, J.W., and Sarjeant.

SARMIENTO, R.
   1957   <u>Microfossil zonation of Mancos Group.</u>   Amer. Assoc. Petrol. Geol., Bull.,
vol. 41, no. 8, pp. 1683-93, pl. 1, text-figs. 1-4.

SCHAARSCHMIDT, F.
* 1963   <u>Sporen und Hystrichosphaerideen aus dem Zechstein von Büdingen in der Wetterau.</u>
Palaeontographica, ser. B, vol. 113, pp. 39-91, pls. 11-20, text-figs. 1-29.
See Kräusel, R., and Schaarschmidt.

SCHARER, G.
       See Zetsche, F., Vicari, H., and Scharer.

SCHERER, F.
   1961   <u>Hystrichosphaerideen und Dinoflagellaten aus der oligozänen, subalpinen
Molasse der Entlebuchs und des Thunerseegebiets.</u>   Ver. Schweizer. Petrol. Geol.
u. - Ing., Bull., vol. 27, No. 73, pp. 15-16.

SCHOPF, J.M.
   1957a   <u>Spores and related plant microfossils - Palaeozoic: annotated bibliography.</u>   in
Ladd, H.S. (ed.): <u>Treatise on Marine Ecology and Paleoecology.II. Paleoecology.</u>   Geol. Soc. Amer., Mem. no. 67, pp. 703-8. (Tasmanaceae, p. 704).

* 1957b   <u>"Spores" and problematic plants commonly regarded as marine: Annotated bibliography.</u> in Ladd, H.S. (ed.): <u>Treatise on Marine Ecology and Paleoecology. II:
Paleoccology.</u>   Geol. Soc. Amer., Mem. no. 67, pp. 709-18.(Tasmanaceae).

SCHOPF, J.M., WILSON, L.R., and BENTALL, R.
   1944   <u>An annotated synopsis of Paleozoic fossil spores and the definition of generic
groups.</u>   Illinois Geol. Surv., Report of Investigations, no. 91, 73 pp., 3 pls.,
5 text-figs. (Tasmanaceae).

SCHUH, F.
   1932   <u>Die Ergebnisse einiger Tiefbohrungen insbesondere in Bezug auf Verbreitung und
Stratigraphie von Kreide und Alttertiär sowie in Bezug die magnetische Vermessung
Mecklenburgs.</u>   Deutsch. Geol. Ges., Z., vol. 84, pp. 677-91, text-figs. 1-3.

(pp. 680, 685 relevant).

SCOTT, A. J.
        See Collinson, C. , and Scott.

SHCHIGURYAYEVA, A. A.
    1956   Atlas of the microspores from Tertiary beds of the U.S.S.R. (in Russian).
            Kharkhov. 118 pp. , 128 pls.,2 tabs. (not seen).

SHEPARD, F. P. , and MOORE, D. G.
    1955   Central Texas coast sedimentation: Characteristics of sedimentary environment,
            recent history and diagenesis. Amer. Assoc. Petrol. Geol. Bull. , vol. 39,
            no. 8, pp. 1463-1593, text-figs. 1-75. (p. 1518 relevant).

SHEPELEVA, E. D. , and TIMOFEYEV, B. V.
    1963   A contribution to the micropaleophytological description of the Pachelm Series
            and its stratigraphic analogues (in Russian). Akad. Nauk. S.S.S.R. , Dokl. ,
            vol. 153, no. 5, pp. 1158-9, pl. 1 (facing p. 1121).

SIMONCSICS, P. and KEDVES, M.
    1961   Palaeobotanical examinations on Manganese Series in Urkut (Hungary, Transyl-
            vania). Acta Miner. Petr. Szeged. , vol. 14, pp. 27-57, pls. 1-10, text-fig. 1.
            (pp. 29-30, pls. 1-2 relevant).

SINGH, T. C. N.
    1932   Notes on the fossil spores in an oil shale from Tasmania. Roy. Soc. Tasmania,
            Proc. for 1931, pp. 32-6, pl. 9. (Tasmanaceae).
SOLÉ DE PORTA, N.
 * 1959   Presencia de Tyttodiscus Norem en Colombia. Univ. Ind. Santander, Bol.
            Geol. , no. 3, pp. 63-5, text-fig. 1. (Tasmanaceae).

    1961   Contribucion al estudio palinológico del terciario de Colombia, Univ. Ind.
            Santander, Bol. Geol., no. 7., pp. 55-81, pls. 1-5. (pp. 72-3 relevant).

SOMMER, F. W.
    1951   O problema de Protosalvina braziliensis Dawson. Acad. Brasilieira, Cienc.
            Anais, vol. 23, no. 4, pp. 415-9 (Tasmanaceae).

 * 1953   Os esporomorfos do folhelho de Barreirinha. Div. Geol. Miner. , Bol. , no.
            140, pp. 1-49, text-figs. 1-8 (Tasmanaceae).

 * 1955a   Contribução a Paleofitografia do Parana. in F. W. Lange: Paleontologia do
            Parana. Vol. Comemor. do 1º Cent do Estado do Parana, pp. 176-94, pls. 15-
            20 (Tasmanaceae, pp. 179-82, pls. 15-16).

    1955b   Contribuição ao conhecimento dos esporomorfos do Oriente da Bolívia. Acad.
            Brasiliera, Ciênc. Anais, vol. 27, no. 2, pp. 183-7, text-figs. 1-2.
            (Tasmanaceae).

 * 1956   South American Paleozoic Sporomorphae without haptotypic structures. Micro-
            paleontology, vol. 2, no. 2, pp. 175-81, pl. 1-2, (Tasmanaceae).

 * 1956b   Novas espécies de Tasmanites do Devoniano do Pará. Acad. Brasiliera Ciênc.
            Anais, vol. 28, no. 4, pp. 455-63, pls. 1-2, 1 text-fig.

    1960a   Controvérsias sistematicas acérea do genero Tasmanites. Acad. Brasiliera, Ciênc.
            Anais, vol. 32, nos. 3-4, pp. 151-16. (Tasmanaceae).

    1960b   Nota prévia sobre microfosseis infra devonianos da bacia amazônica. Acad.
            Brasiliera, Ciênc. Anais, vol. 32, nos. 3-4, pp. 27-8. (Tasmanaceae).

SOMMER, F.W., and BOEKEL, N.M. van.
    1961   Os Tasmanites do furo 56, Bon Jardim Itaibre, Rio Tapajos, Para; résumé. Acad.
             Brasiliera, Cienc. Anais, vol. 33,

SPANDEL, E.
    1909   Der Rupelton des Mainzer Beckens: seine Abteilungen und deren Foraminiferen-
             fauna, sowie einige weitere geologisch-paläontologisch Mitteilungen über das
             Mainzer Becken. Offenbacher Ver. Naturk., 43-50 Ber. (1901-9), pp. 57-
             247, pls. 1-3, (pp. 221-2 relevant).

SPEDEN, I.G.
             See Cranwell, L.M., Harrington, H.J., and Speden.

SPRUMONT, G.
             See Delcourt, A., and Sprumont.

SRIVASTAVA, S.K.
    1962   Palynology - a gift of flowers. Science and Culture, vol. 28, pp. 265-9.

    1963   Application of palynology to problems of stratigraphy in India. Oil & Natural
             Gas Comm. Reporter, vol. 1 (1962-3), pp. 10-16. (pp. 12, 14, pl. 1 relevant).

STAESCHE, K.
    1937   Die Gliederung des nordwestdeutschen Tertiärs auf Grund von Mikrofossilien.
             Preuss. Geol. Landesanst., Jb., vol. 58, pp. 730-45. (p. 741 relevant).

STAPLIN, F.L.
    1960   News reports: Canada. Micropaleontology, vol. 6, no. 4, pp. 433-5.

    1961a News reports: Canada. Micropaleontology, vol. 7, no. 4, pp. 500-2.

  * 1961b Reef-controlled distribution of Devonian microplankton in Alberta. Palaeont-
             ology, vol. 4, no. 3, pp. 392-424, pls. 48-51, text-figs. 1-9.

    1962   News reports: Canada. Micropaleontology, vol. 8, no. 4, pp. 526-8.
             See also Hoffmeister, W.S., Staplin and Malloy, R.E.

STEIN, F. von.
    1883   Der Organismus der Infusionsthiere, 3. Abth., 2 Halfte: Die Naturgeschichte
             der arthrodelen Flagellaten. Leipzig: Engelmann. 30 pp., 25 pl. (pp. 18-19
             relevant).

STOCKMANS, F.
    1960   Initiation à la Paléobotanique stratigraphique. Les Naturalistes Belges, vols.
             41-43, pts. 3, 4, 5, pp. 11-30, 163-93, 213-29. (pp. 179-81, 219-23,
             text-figs. 43, 60 relevant).

    1962   Géologie de la brique. Les Naturalistes Belges, vol. 43, pp. 333-58, text-
             figs. 1-19. (p. 356, text-fig. 19 relevant).

STOCKMANS, F., and WILLIERE, Y.
  * 1960   Hystrichosphères du Dévonien belge (Sondage de l'Asile d'aliénés à Tournai).
             Senck. Leth., vol. 4, no. 1-6, pp. 1-11, pls. 1-2.

  * 1962a Hystrichosphères de Dévonien belge (Sondage de l'Asile d'aliénés à Tournai).
             Soc. Belg. Géol., Bull., vol. 71, no. 1, pp. 41-77, pls. 1-2, text-figs. 1-34.

  * 1962b Hystrichosphères du Dévonien belge (Sondage de Wépion). Soc. Belg., Géol.,
             Bull., vol. 71, no. 1, pp. 83-99, pls. 1-2, text-figs. 1-16.

* 1962c   Description de trois Hystrichosphères. In W. P. van Leckwijk and C. H. Chesaux, Étude de l'horizon marin de Petit Buisson dans la partie occidentale du Massif du Borinage. Centre Nat. de Géol. Huillière, Publ., no. 5. Observations sur la Paléontologie, la Lithologie et la Stratigraphie du Westphalien B et C dans la partie occidentale du Massif du Borinage (District du Couchant de Mons). pp. 11–30, pl. 1, text-figs. A–C, 1–3, a–c, tabs. 1–111.

* 1963   Les hystrichosphères ou mieux les Acritarches du Silurien belge. Sondage de la Brasserie Lust à Courtrai (Kortrijk). Soc. Belg. Géol., Bull., vol. 71, pt. 3, pp. 450–481, pls. 1–3, text-figs. 1–37.

STOVER, L. E.
    1962   New Cretaceous palynomorphs from West Africa. Abstr., International Conference on Palynology, Tucson, 1962. Pollen et Spores, vol. 4, no. 2, p. 380.

    * 1963   Some Middle Cretaceous palynomorphs from West Africa. Micropaleontology, vol. 9, no. 1, pp. 85–94, pls. 1–2.

SUJKOWSKI, Zb.
    1933   Radiolaryty dolno – karbónskie gor Swiętokrzyskich. Spraw. Polsk. Inst. Geol., vol. 7, no. 4, pp. 637–700, pls. 29–31, 3 text-figs. (text-fig. 1 relevant).

SUTTON, J.
    1962   Torridonian microfossils. Geol. Mag., vol. 99, no. 4, p. 379.

TASCH, P.
    1962   Paleoecologic significance of newly discovered Hystrichosphaerids from the Kansas Permian (Artinskian). Abstr., International Conference on Palynology, Tucson, 1962. Pollen et Spores, vol. 4, no. 2, p. 382.

    * 1963a   Hystrichosphaerids and dinoflagellates from the Permian of Kansas. Micropaleontology, vol. 9, no. 3, pp. 332–6, pl. 1.

    1963b   Fossil content of salt and association evaporites. Ohio Geol. Soc. Symposium on Salt, 1963, pp. 96–102. (p. 98 relevant).

TASCH, P., McCLURE, K., and OFTEDAHL, O.
    1962   Biostratigraphy of a Hystrichosphaerid-Dinoflagellate assemblage from the Kansas Cretaceous (Albian). Abstr., International Conference on Palynology, Tucson, 1962. Pollen et Spores, vol. 4, no. 2, p. 381.

TAUGOURDEAU-LANTZ, J.
    1960   Sur la microflore du Frasnien inférieur de Beaulieu (Boulonnais). Rev. Micropaléont., vol. 3, no. 3, pp. 144–54, pls. 1–2. (pl. 1, figure 28? relevant).

TAUGOURDEAU, P.
    1962   Le problème des Leiosphaeridia: un detail morphologique nouveau. Soc. Géol. Fr., C. R. Somm., no. 2, p. 59, text-fig. 1.

THALMANN, H. E.
    1954   Status of invertebrate paleontology, 1953: II Protozoa. Mus. Comp. Zool. Harv., Bull., vol. 112, no. 3, pp. 99–108, (p. 100 relevant).

    1955   Practical value of some microfossils. Amer. Assoc. Petrol. Geol., Bull., vol. 39, no. 7, pp. 1196–1201. (pp. 1198–9 relevant).

THIERGART, F.
    1942   Mikropaläobotanische Mitteilungen 3: Uber ein Austreten von Hystrichosphaerideen in der unter miozänen Braunkohle von Finkenheerd bei Frankfurt a. O. Reichsst. Bodenforsch., Jb., (1941), vol. 62, pp. 113–16, text-fig. 3.

1944   Die Pflanzenreste der Posidonienschiefer . In B. Brockamp: Zur Palaeogeographie und Bitumenführung des Posidonienschiefers im Deutschen Lias. Arch. Lager-stättenforsch. , vol. 77, pp. 1-59, pl. 1-4, text-figs. 1-20. (Tasmanaceae, pp. 45-8, pl. 3).

THIESSEN, R.
1921   Origin and composition of certain oil shales. Econ. Geol. , vol. 16, pp. 289-300, pls. 9-10. (Tasmanaceae).

1925   Microscopic examination of Kentucky oil shales. in R. Thiessen, D. White and C.S. Crouse; Oil Shales of Kentucky. Kentucky Geol. Surv. ser. 6, vol. 21, 242 pp. (pp. 1-47, pls. 1-37). (Tasmanaceae).

THOMAS, B.W.
        See Johnson, H.A. , and Thomas.

TIMOFEYEV, B.V.
1952   Lower Paleozoic sediments in Moldavia (in Russian). Akad. Nauk. S.S.S.R. , Dokl. , vol. 86, no. 6, pp. 1207-9.

1955a   Discovery of spores in Cambrian and Precambrian formations of Eastern Siberia (in Russian). Akad. Nauk. S.S.S.R. , Dokl. , vol. 105, no. 3, pp. 547-50.

1955b   On the micropalaeontological characteristics of the Lower Cambrian "Blue Clay" (in Russian). V.N.I.G.R.I. , Geol. Sbornik, vol. 3, pt. 4. (not seen).

* 1956a Hystrichosphaeridae from the Cambrian. (in Russian). Akad. Nauk. S.S.S.R. , Dokl. , vol. 106, no. 1, pp. 130-2, text-fig. 1.

1956b   Early Palaeozoic flora of the Baltic Provinces and the main stages of its develop-ment. 20th Int. Geol. Cong. , Mexico 1956, Resumenos de los Trabajos Presentados, pp. 187-8.

* 1956c On the age of the Ostrog beds in Volhynia and their position in the Paleozoic (in Russian). Akad. Nauk. S.S.S.R. , Dokl. , vol. 107, no. 6 , pp. 871-4, text-figs. 1-2.

* 1957a On a new group of fossil spores (in Russian). Ezhegodnik. Vses. Pal. ab-na. , vol. 16, pp. 280-4, pl. 1.

1957b   Spores of the Onega Beds of Karelia (in Russian). V.N.I.G.R.I. , Trudy, Geol. & Geochim. , vol. 1, no. 7, p. 153, pl. 1.

1958a   Proterozoic spores and Lower Palaezoic deposits of Eastern Siberia and their strati-graphical significance (in Russian). Sob. Razrab. Strat. Skhem. Sibiri 1956, Trudy. , Dokl. Strat. Dokemb. Ottozh., Moscow. pp. 226-30, pl. 1-2.

1958b   Uber das Alter sächsischer Grauwacken. Mikropaläophytologische Untersuch-ungen von Proben aus der Weesensteiner und Lausitzer Grauwacke. Geologie, vol. 7, pts. 3-6, pp. 826-45, pls. 1-3.

* 1959 The ancient flora of the Baltic Regions and its stratigraphic significance (in Russian). V.N.I.G.R.I. , Leningrad, Mem., no. 129, 350 pp, 25 pls.

* 1960a Sur la caractéristique micropaléontologique de la Formation de Visingsö. Geol. Fören. , Stokh. , Förh. , vol. 82, no. 1, pp. 28-42, pl. 2.

1960b   Methods of micropalaeontological analysis (in Russian). V.N.I.G.R.I. , Leningrad. Izv. Trudy V.N.I.G.R.I. , vol. 163, Geol.Sb. , no.5, pp.473-85, text-figs. 1-6.

1961a   Pre-Cambrian spores (in Russian). Geol. Kongr., XXI. Sess., 1960, Mezhd., Dokl. Soviet Geol., pp. 128-47, pl. 1.

1961b   Spores and phytoplankton from the Proterozoic and early Palaeozoic of Eurasia (in Russian). Geol. Kongr., XXI Sess., 1960, Mezhd., Soviet Geol. Spores & Pollen, pp. 177-88, pls. 1-2.

* 1962   A small palaeontological theodolite table (a new method of research into fossil microplankton). (in Russian). Trudy V.N.I.G.R.I., no. 196, Palaeont. Act. 3, pp. 601-47, pls. 1-20, text-fig. 1.

1962b   Sur l'âge des couches sédimentaire-métamorphiques de l'Antarctic oriental et de l'"Australie méridionale (Données de l'analyse micropaléontologique). Abst., International Conference on Palynology, Tucson, Arizona, 1962, Pollen et Spores, vol. 4, no. 2, pp. 382-3.

1962c   La méthode du théodolithe dans la Palynologie (Recherches sur la morphologie du microplancton fossile et des Sporae dispersae). Abstr., International Conference on Palynology, Tucson, Arizona, 1962, Pollen et Spores, vol. 4, no. 2, pp. 383-4.

1963   On organic remains in the Eocambrian of Norway. Norsk Geol. Tidsskr., vol. 43, no. 4, pp. 473-6, 1 un-numbered pl.
See also Alyushinskiy, Y.A., Kirichenko, G.I., and Timofeyev; Lebedeva, A.E., and Timofeyev; Shepeleva, E.D, and Timofeyev; Vialov, O.S., and Timofeyev; Vladimirskaya, I.V., Timofeyev, and Chachia, N.G.

TRAVERSE, A.
* 1955   Pollen analysis of the Brandon Lignite of Vermont. U.S. Dept. Interior, Bureau of Mines, Rept., no. 5151, 107 pp., 150 text-figs.

TSCHUDY, R.H.
1957   Pollen and spore formulae - a suggestion. Micropaleontology, vol. 3, no. 3, pp. 277-80, tabs. 1-3. (p. 278 relevant).

1961   Palynomorphs as indicators of facies environments in Upper Cretaceous and Lower Tertiary strata, Colorado and Wyoming. Wyoming Geol. Assoc. Symposium on Late Cretaceous Rocks Guidebook, pp. 53-9, text-fig. 1.

TSYRINA, T.S.
1952   On the question of the descent of fossil spine-bearing organisms (in Russian). Akad. Nauk. S.S.R., Dokl., vol. 83, no. 1, pp. 145-7, text-fig. 1.

TURPIN, C.R.
1837   Analyse ou étude microscopique des différents corps organises et autres corps de natur diverse qui peuve, accidentellement, se trouver envelopper dans le pâte translucide des silex. Acad. Sc. Paris, C.R., vol. 4, pp. 304-14 and 351-62.

TYLER, S.A., and BARGHOORN, E.S.
1954   Occurrence of structurally preserved plants in Pre-Cambrian rocks of the Canadian Shield. Science, vol. 119, pp. 606-8, text-figs. 1-4.
See also Barghoorn, E.S., and Tyler.

UMBGROVE, J.H.F.
1925   Bijdrage tot de kennis der stratigrafie, tektoniek en petrografie van het Sennon in Zuid Limburg. Leidsche Geol. Medd., vol. 1, pp. 255-332, pls. 18-23, 33 text-figs, 28 tabs, (pp. 301-4, text-fig. 20 relevant).

URBAN, J.B.
1960   Microfossils of the Woodford Shale (Devonian) of Oklahoma. Univ. of Oklahoma, Abstr. no. 202, 1 p., 9 pls., 1 text-fig.
See also Wilson, L.R., and Urban.

UTECH, K.
* 1962   Uber eine Tasmanites – Art aus dem Mittleren Buntsandstein des Hildesheimer
Waldes.   N. Jb. Geol. Paläont. , Mh. , no. 2, pp. 90-1, text-fig. 1.

VACHEY, G. and JARDINÉ, S.
1962   Aperçu sur la microflore des séries "albiennes" de Côte d'Ivoire.   Soc. Géol.
Fr. , C.R. Somm. , no. 4, pp. 102-3.

VALENSI, L.
1947   Note préliminaire à une étude des microfossiles des silex jurassiques de la région
de Poitiers.   Acad. Sci. Paris. , C.R. , vol. 225, pp. 816-8, text-figs. 1-8.

* 1948   Sur quelques micro-organismes planctoniques des silex du Jurassique moyen du
Poitou et de Normandie.   Soc. Géol. Fr. , Bull. , ser. 5, vol. 18, pp. 537-50,
text-figs. 1-6.

* 1953   Microfossiles des silex du Jurassique moyen.   Remarques pétrographiques.   Soc.
Géol. Fr. , Mem. , no. 68, 100 pp. , 16 pls. , 7 text-figs.

1954   Confirmation de l'âge jurassique moyen des silex de la région de Bressuire (D.S.).
Poitiers, Ann. Univ. , Ser. 5, no. 5, Actes 73e Congr. A.F.A.S. , p. 295.

1955a   Sur quelques micro-organismes des silex crétacés du Magdalénien de Saint-Amand
(Cher).   Soc. Géol. Fr. , Bull. , ser. 6, vol. 5, pp. 35-40, text-figs. 1-2.

* 1955b   Étude micropaléontologique des silex du Magdalénien de Saint-Amand (Cher).
Soc. Préhist. Fr. , Bull. , vol. 52, nos. 9-10, pp. 584-96, pls. 1-5.

1957   Micropaléontologie des silex du Grand Pressigny.   Soc. Géol. Fr. , Bull. , ser. 6,
vol. 7, pp. 1083-90, pl. 48, text-figs. 1 and I-II .

1960   De l'origine des silex Protomagdaléniens de l'Abri Pataud, les Eyzies.   Soc. Préhist. Fr. , Bull. , vol. 57, nos. 1-2, pp. 80-4, pl. 1.

VARMA, C.P. , and DANGWAL, A.K.
1962   Tertiary hystrichosphaerids from India.   Abstr. International Conference on Palynology, Tucson, Arizona, 1962.   Pollen et Spores, vol. 4, no. 2, p. 387.

VENKATACHALA, B.S. , and BALTES, N.
1962a   Studii palinologice asupra depozitelor tertiare din Depresiunea precarpatică romînă
– Depresiunea getică.   Petrol si Gaze, vol. 13, no. 6, pp. 244-58, pls. 1-4,
text-figs. 1-4, tabs. 1.

1962b   Studii palinologice aspura depozitelor tertiare din Depresiunea precarpatică romînă
– Depresiunea getică.   Consideratii stratigrafice.   Petrol si Gaze, vol. 13, no. 6,
pp. 295-7, pls. 1-6.

VENKATACHALA, B.S. , and BEJU, D.
1961   Asupra prezentii devonianului in fundamentul zonei Călărasi.   Petrol si Gaze,
vol. 12, no. 11, pp. 494-5. (Tasmanaceae).

VIALOV, O.S. , and TIMOFEYEV, B.V.
1959   The first find of ancient spores in Antarctica.   (in Russian).   Akad. Nauk Ukrain.
S.S.R. , Dopovidi, no. 10, pp. 1134-5.

VICARI, H.   See Zetsche, F. , Vicari and Scharer, G.

VLADIMIRSKAYA, I.V., TIMOFEYEV, B.V., and CHACHIA, N.G.
    1956   New facts about the age of the "Basement Beds" west of the Southern Urals (in Russian). Akad. Nauk. S.S.S.R., Dokl., vol. 3, no. 3, pp. 667-9.

VOITZIEL, Z.A.,
    See Maliavkina, V.S., Samoilovitch, S.R., Voitziel, Klumko, S.A., Rovuna, L.V., Ivanova, I.A., Markova, L.G., and Mtchedlishvili, N.D.

VOORTHUYSEN, J.H. van.
    1950   News: Belgium. The Micropaleontologist, vol. 4, no. 2, pp. 5-8.

    1951a   News: Benelux. The Micropaleontologist, vol. 5, no. 1, pp. 11-13.

    1951b   News: Benelux. The Micropaleontologist, vol. 5, no. 4, pp. 13-17.

    1952   News: Benelux. The Micropaleontologist, vol. 6, no. 4, pp. 19-21.

VOZZHENNIKOVA, T.F.
    * 1960   Palaeoalgological characteristics of the Mesozoic and Cainozoic beds of the Western Siberian Lowland (in Russian). Akad. Nauk. S.S.S.R., Sibirskoy Otdelinni, Trud. Inst. Geol. Geogr. vol. 1, pp. 7-64, pl. 3, (pp. 24, 27-8, relevant).

    * 1961   A contribution to the problem of the taxonomy of fossil Peridinae (in Russian). Akad. Nauk. S.S.S.R., Dokl., vol. 139, no. 6, pp. 1461-2. (Translation in Amer. Geol. Inst., Dokl. Acad. Sci. U.S.S.R., Earth Sciences Sect., 1963, pp. 852-3).

WALL, D.
    * 1962   Evidence from recent plankton regarding the biological affinities of Tasmanites Newton 1875 and Leiosphaeridia Eisenack 1958. Geol. Mag., vol. 99, no. 4, pp. 353-62, pl. 17, text-figs. 1-2.

WALL, D., and DOWNIE, C.
    * 1963   Permian hystrichospheres from Britain. Palaeontology, vol. 5, no. 4, pp. 770-84, pls. 112-14, text-figs. 1-4.

WALOWEEK, W., and NOREM, W.L.
    1957   Geographic range of Tyttodiscus extended to Alaska. J. Paleont., vol. 31, no. 3, pp. 674-5. (Tasmanaceae).

WALTON, H.S.
    1962   Cambrian Hystrichospheres from Western Canada. Abstr., International Conference on Palynology, Tucson, Arizona, 1962. Pollen et Spores, vol. 4, no. 2, p. 387.

WATTS, W.A.
    1959   Pollen spectra from the interglacial deposits at Kirmington, Lincolnshire. Yorks. Geol. Soc., Proc., vol. 32, pt. 2, no. 7, pp. 145-52. (p. 148 relevant).

WEIDMANN, M.
    1963   Un nouveau lambeau de la nappe de la Simme les Prealpes du Chablais. Univ. Lausanne, Bull. Labs. Geol. Min. Geophys., no. 140, pp. 1-22, text-figs. 1-6 (pp. 6, 12-13 relevant).

WEIGELT, I.
    1930   Onchus windti n.sp., eine neue Fischrest aus einem obersilurischen Geschiebe. Z. Geschiebeforsch., vol. 6, pt. 1, pp. 6-10, text-fig. 1. (pp. 7-8 relevant).

WEILER, H.
* 1956   Uber einem Fund von Dinoflagellaten, Coccolithophoriden und Hystrichosphaerideen im Tertiär des Rheintales.   N. Jb. Geol. Paläont., Abh., vol. 104,
no. 2, pp. 129–47, pls. 11–13.

WEST, R. G.
1961   Vegetational history of the Early Pleistocene of the Royal Society borehole at
Ludham, Norfolk.   Roy. Soc., Proc., ser. B., vol. 155, pp. 437–53, text-
figs. 1–3.   (pp. 452–3 relevant).

WETHERED, E.
1886   On the occurrence of spores of plants in the Lower Limestone Shales of the Forest
of Dean Coalfield and in the Black Shales of Ohio, United States.   Cotteswold
Nat. Fld. Cl., Proc., vol. 8, pp. 167–73, pl. 1.   (Tasmanaceae).

WETZEL, O.
1926a   Die paläontologischen Befund im Feuerstein unter dem Mikroskop.   Mikrokosmos,
vol. 19, pp. 114–17, text-figs. 1–12.

1926b   Die farbenden und mineralischen Einschlüsse des Feuersteins.   Mikrokosmos,
vol. 20, pp. 42–4.

* 1932   Die Typen der baltischen Geschiebefeuersteine beurteilt nach ihrem Gehalt an
Mikrofossilien.   Z. Geschiebeforsch., vol. 8, pp. 129–46, pls. 1–3.

* 1933   Die in organischer Substanz erhaltenen Mikrofossilien des Baltischen Kreide-
Feuersteins.   Palaeontographica, vol. 77, pp. 141–88, text-figs. 1–10, and
vol. 78, pp. 1–110, pls. 1–7, text-figs. 11–14.

* 1935   Die Mikropaläontologie des Heiligenhafner Kieseltones (Unter–Eozän).   Nieders-
achs. Geol. Verein., Jb., no. 27, pp. 41–76, pls. 8–10, text-fig. 1.

1936   Geschichtliche Umschau über die Mikropaläontologie.   Z. Geschiebeforsch.,
vol. 13, pp. 143–76, text-figs. 1–6.   (pp. 59–66 relevant).

1940   Mikropaläontologische Untersuchungen an der obersenonen Kreide von Stevns
Klint–Kridtbrud auf der dänischen Insel Seeland und an ihrem Feuerstein in
geschiebekundlicher Hinsicht.   Z. Geschiebeforsch., vol. 16, pt. 2, pp. 118–56,
pls. 1–5, text-fig. 1.

1943   Die Mikropaläontologie des norddeutschen Kreide-Feuersteins.   Natur u. Volk,
vol. 73, nos. 11–12, pp. 309–31, pls. 1–4, text-figs. 1–3.

1944   Reste von Kieselorganismen und kleine "Problematische" in Kreide – Feuerstein.
Z. Geschiebeforsch., vol. 19, pt. 2, pp. 132–40, pls. 1–2.

1948a   Mikropaläontologische Funde in Gesteinsproben einer holsteinischen Bohrung,
besonders in Kreide – und Keuperschichten.   N. Jb. Mineral. ,u.s.w., Abh.,
vol. 89, pp. 315–43, pl. 33–8, 5 tabs.

1948b   Micro-organisms in chert.   The Micropaleontologist, vol. 2, no. 2, pp. 32–3.

1950   Deutungsversuche an ausgewahlten Grippen vorn Mikrofossilien und Mikrostructuren
im baltischen Geschiebefeuerstein und in einigen andere Gesteine der Kreidezeit.
N. Jb. Mineral., Abh., vol. 91, no. 2, pp. 161–92, pls. 11–13.

1951a   Die Mikropaläontologie des baltischen Kreide-Feuersteins, auch eine Angelegenhei
der modernen Paläobotanik.   Svensk Botan. Tidskr., vol. 45, no. 1, pp. 249–53.

1951b   Mikroskopische Reste von vermutlichen Algen im Feuerstein der Kreide Norddeutschlands. N. Jb. Geol. Paläont, Abh., vol. 94, no. 1, pp. 101-11, pl. 13.

1951c   Mikroskopische Reste von Kalkorganismen als Feuersteinfossilien besonderen Aussehens. N. Jb. Geol. Paläont., Abh., vol. 94, no. 1, pp. 112-20, pl. 14. (pp. 114, 116 relevant).

1953a   Resumé of microfossils from Upper Cretaceous flints and chalks of Europe. J. Paleont., vol. 27, no. 6, pp. 800-4.

1953b   Ubersichte über die im Feuerstein erhaltene Protisten der baltischen Kreide. Paläont. Z., vol. 27, nos. 1-2, pp. 37-46, pls. 1-2.

1956   Massen produktion, Sedimentation und Fossilisation von Mikro-Organismen im Gebiet der Nord - und Ostsee, Ein Beitrag zur Paläo-Planktologie Europas. XIV Int. Cong. Zool., Copenhagen, 1953, Proc., Sect. 11, Paleozoology, pp. 102-3.

1957   Fossil "microforaminifera" in various sediments and their reaction to acid treatment. Micropaleontology, vol. 3, no. 1, pp. 61-4, pl. 1.

1958a   Reste von Blutenpflanzen im Feuerstein. Meyniana, vol. 6, pp. 56-9, pls. 1-2.

1958b   Neue Mikrofossilien aus dem Lias, in besondere aus dem Posidonienschiefer. Paläont. Z., vol. 32, p. 15 (Tasmanaceae).

1959   New problematic microfossils from the German Upper Lias. XVII Int. Cong. Zool. Paper Read in Title, no. 50, p. 1060.

* 1960   Ein neue Dinoflagellaten - Gruppe aus dem baltischen Geschiebefeuerstein. Naturwiss. Vereins Schlesw. - Holstein. Schr., vol. 31, pp. 81-6, pl. 1.

* 1961   New microfossils from Baltic Cretaceous flintstones. Micropaleontology, vol. 7, no. 3, pp. 337-50, pls. 1-3.
     See also Wetzel, W., Wetzel and Deflandre, G.

WETZEL, W.
1922   Sediment - petrographischen Studien. 1. Feuerstein. N. Jb. Mineral., u.s.w., Beil., vol. 47, pp. 39-92, pl. 1, text-fig. 3. (pp. 58-63 relevant).

* 1952   Beitrag zur Kenntnis des dan-zeitlichen Meeresplanktons. Geol. Jahrb. for 1950, vol. 66, pp. 391-419, pl. A, text-figs. 1-35, tabs. 1-2.

* 1955   Die Dan - Scholle vom Katharinenhof (Fehmarn) und ihr Gehalt an Planktonen. N. Jb., Geol. Paläont., Mh., no. 1, pp. 30-46, text-figs. 1-26, tab. 1.

WETZEL, W., WETZEL, O., and DEFLANDRE, G.
1941   Die Feuersteine der Kreidezeit: Kieselsaüre als Versteinerungsmittel. Die Umschau, vol. 45, no. 18, pp. 275-9, text-figs. 1-9.

WHITE, D., and STADNICHENKO, T.
1923   Some motherplants of petroleum in the Devonian black shales. Econ. Geol., vol. 18, pp. 238-52, pls. 5-9. (Tasmanaceae).

WHITE, H.H.
* 1842   On fossil Xanthidia. Microsc. J., vol. 11, pp. 35-40, pl. 4.

1844a   On fossil Xanthidia. Microsc. Soc. Lond., Trans., vol. 1, pp. 77-86, pl. 8, text-figs. 1-11.

    * 1844b   On a new species of fossil Xanthidium.   Microsc. Soc. Lond., Trans., vol. 1, p. 87, pl. 9 (pars).

WHITE, M.C.
    * 1862   Discovery of microscopic organisms in the siliceous nodules of the Palaeozoic rocks of New York.   Amer. J. Sci., ser. 2, vol. 33, pp. 385-6, text-figs. 1-30.

WIESNER, H.
    * 1936   Sur la découverte de Diatomées et autres microfossiles peu connus dans le Crétacé supérieur de la Bohême.   Ann. Protist., vol. 5, pp. 151-5, pls. 6-7.

WILKINSON, S.J.
    1849   Observations on Xanthidium, both fossil and recent.   Microsc. Soc. Lond., Trans., vol. 2, pp. 89-92, pl. 13.

WILLIAMS, G.L.
    See Downie, C., Williams and Sarjeant, W.A.S.

WILLIAMSON, W.C.
    1848   On some of the microscopical objects found in the mud of the Levant, and other deposits: with remarks on the mode of formation of calcareous and infusorial silicious rocks.   Manchester Lit. & Phil. Soc., Mem., ser. 2, vol. 8, pp. 1-128, pl. 1-2. (pp. 11-12 relevant).

WILLIÈRE, Y.
    See Stockmans, F., and Willière.

WILSON, L.R.
    1956   Composite micropaleontology and its application to Tertiary and near-recent stratigraphy.   Micropaleontology, vol. 2, no. 1, pp. 1-6, tab. 1.

    1958   A Chitinozoan faunule from the Sylvan Shale of Oklahoma.   Oklahoma Geol. Notes, vol. 18, no. 4, pp. 67-71, pl. 1. (p. 67 relevant).

    1960   A Permian Hystrichosphaerid from Oklahoma.   Oklahoma Geol. Notes, vol. 20, no. 7, p. 170, text-fig. 1.

    1963   A geological history of Oklahoma's vegetation.   Shale Shaker, vol. 13, no. 9, pp. 4-20, pls. 1-6, text-fig. 1. (Tasmanaceae, p. 8).
        See also Schopf, J.M., Wilson and Bentall, R.

WILSON, L.R., and HEDLUND, R.W.
    1960   Two techniques for staining Hystrichosphaerids.   Oklahoma Geol. Notes, vol. 20, no. 4, pp. 101-2.

    1962   Acid-resistant microfossils of the Sylvan Shale (Ordovician) of Oklahoma.   Abst. International Conference on Palynology, Tucson, Arizona, 1962. Pollen et Spores, vol. 4, no. 2, p. 388.

WILSON, L.R., and HOFFMEISTER, W.S.
    1955a   Morphology and geology of the Hystrichosphaerida.   Soc. Econ. Pal. & Min., 29th Ann. Meeting, Program, pp. 122-3.

    1955b   Morphology and geology of the Hystrichosphaerida: abstract.   J. Sed. Pet., vol. 25, no. 2, p. 137.

    1955c   Morphology and geology of the Hystrichosphaerida: abstract.   J. Paleont., vol. 29, no. 4, p. 735.

WILSON, L.R., and URBAN, J.B.
   * 1963   An incertae sedis palynomorph from the Devonian of Oklahoma.   Oklahoma Geol.
            Notes, vol. 23, no. 1, pp. 16-9, pl. 1.

WILSON, T.Y.
            See Ruedemann, R., and Wilson.

WIMAN, C.
     1895   Paläontologische Notizen 1: ein Präkambrisches Fossil.   Geol. Inst. Uppsala,
            Bull., vol. 2, pp. 109-13, pl. 5.

WINSLOW, M.R.
   * 1962   Plant spores and other microfossils from the Upper Devonian and Lower Mississippian
            rocks of Ohio.   U.S. Geol. Survey.   Professional Paper no. 364, 93 pp.,
            27 pls., 12 text-figs.

WIT, R. de
   * 1943   Hystrichosphaeridae in Limburgsche Vuursten.   Verh. u. Geol. Mijrib. Gen.,
            vol. 13, pp. 363-92, text-figs. 1-15.

     1944   Micro-organismen in Limburgsche Vuursten.   Natuurh. Maandbl., nos. 7-8,
            pp. 52-4, text-figs.

WOLF, M.
     1961   Sporenstratigrafische Untersuchung in der Gefalteten Molasse der Murnauer Mülde
            (Oberbayern).   Geol. Bavarica, vol. 46, pp. 53-92, pls. 1-8, text-figs. 1-5.

WOODS, R.D.
     1955   Spores and pollen: a new stratigraphic tool for the oil industry.   Micropaleon-
            tology, vol. 1, no. 4, pp. 368-75, pl. 1, text-figs. 1-2.

WRAY, J.L.
     1962   Palynology of Paleozoic rocks of Libya: resumé.   Amer. Assoc. Petrol. Geol.,
            Bull., vol. 46, no. 1, p. 284.

ZAKLINSKAYA, E.D.
     1963   Angiosperm pollen and their significance for substantiation of the stratigraphy of
            the Upper Chalk and Palaeogene (in Russian).   Akad. Nauk. S.S.S.R., Trudi
            Geol. Inst., no. 74, pp. 1-258, pls. 1-44, text-figs. 1-32.   (p. 139, text-fig.
            24 relevant).

ZETSCHE, F., VICARI, H., and SCHARER, G.
     1931   Untersuchung über die Membran der Sporen und Pollen.   IV, 3.   Fossiles Sporo-
            pollenin aus dem Tasmanit und der Moskauer Braunkohle.   Helv. Chim. Acta,
            vol. 14, pt. 1, pp. 67-78.

ZINDEREN BAKKER, E.M. Van
     1962   Palynology in Africa.   7th Report, Blomfontein.

(------)
     1960   500 million years ago today.   Esso Mag. vol. 9, no. 2, pp. 12-14, cover pl.

SECTION II: INDEX TO FORMATIONS CONTAINING DINOFLAGELLATES,
ACRITARCHS, ETC.

INDEX OF FORMATIONS CONTAINING DINOFLAGELLATES AND ACRITARCHS.

The following is a listing of the names of formations and faunal zones from which assemblages have been described or recorded.   The formations are listed alphabetically under the appropriate geological system: the names of the authors of articles referred to and the date of publication are quoted.   An asterisk (*) precedes the publication date of articles which contain faunal lists for the indicated formation or zone.   Where pebbles or rock fragments of an older deposit are contained in a more recent sediment, the article quoted is listed under both relevant systems.

PROTEROZOIC

Applecross Beds (Torridonian):   Scotland - Downie, 1962.

Aultbea Beds (Torridonian):   Scotland - Downie, 1962;   Peach, Horne, and others, 1907.

Birrimian: Ivory Coast - Hovasse, 1956.

Bothnian Formation: Finland - Timofeyev, 1960.

Brioverian: France - Cayeux, 1894;   Deflandre, 1894;   Deflandre, 1948c, 1955, 1957a, 1960;   Graindor, 1956, 1957:   Roblot, 1963.

Diabaig Beds (Torridonian):   Scotland - Downie, 1962;   Naumova and Pavlovsky, 1961;   Sutton, 1962.

Eocombrian: Norway - Timofeyev, 1963.

Gunflint Formation: Canada - Eocambrian: Barghoorn and Tyler, 1962;   Tyler and Barghoorn, 1954.

Jotnian Series: Baltic U.S.S.R. - Timofeyev, * 1959.

Karelian Series: Baltic U.S.S.R. - Timofeyev, * 1959.

Ladoga Series: Baltic U.S.S.R. - Timofeyev, * 1959.

Mogilev Series: Moldavia, U.S.S.R. - Timofeyev, 1952.

Onega Series: Karelia, U.S.S.R. - Timofeyev, 1957, 1961a, 1961b.

Onguren Series: Baikal, U.S.S.R. - Timofeyev, 1958, 1960, 1961b.

Ostrog Beds: Ukraine, U.S.S.R. - Timofeyev, 1956c.

Pachelm Series (Sinian):   Northern U.S.S.R. - Shepeleva and Timofeyev, 1963.

Riphean: U.S.S.R. - Naumova, 1961.

Serdobsk Series: Baltic U.S.S.R. - Timofeyev, * 1959.

Serdobsk Series (Sinian):   Northern U.S.S.R. - Shepeleva and Timofeyev, 1963.

Sinian: Siberia, U.S.S.R. - Timofeyev, 1958:   Yenisei Ridge, U.S.S.R. - Alyushinskiy, Kirichenko and Timofeyev, 1957;   Timofeyev, 1958.

Sparagmite Formation: Norway - Timofeyev, 1958;   Shepeleva and Timofeyev, 1963.

Taply-Hill Schists: South Australia - Timofeyev, 1962b.

Upper Proterozoic: Russia, U.S.S.R. - Andreyeva, 1961.
        Urals, U.S.S.R. - Vladimirskaya, Timofeyev and Chachia, 1956.

Valdai Series: Baltic U.S.S.R. - Naumova, 1961: Shepeleva and Timofeyev, 1963.

Vendy Series: Baltic U.S.S.R. - Timofeyev, * 1959.

Visingsö Formation: Sweden - Brotzen, 1941; Holm, 1885; Linnarsson, 1880; Nathorst, 1879a,
    1879b, 1884, 1886, 1894; Timofeyev, 1960; Wiman, 1895.
    (See also POST-PLEISTOCENE. Proterozoic? pebble in moraine: Antarctica - Vialov
    and Timofeyev, 1959).

CAMBRIAN (UNDIVIDED)

Unnamed formation: Czechoslovakia - Timofeyev, 1961b: Ingrid Kristensen Coast, Antarctica -
    Timofeyev, 1962b: Kirghiz, U.S.S.R. - Timofeyev, 1961b: Libya - Wray, 1962:
    Queen Mary's Land, Antarctica - Timofeyev, 1962b: Russia, U.S.S.R. -
    Andreyeva, 1961.

LOWER CAMBRIAN

Blue clay: Baltic U.S.S.R. - Lebedeva and Timofeyev, 1958; Naumova, 1949; Reissinger, 1938;
    Timofeyev, 1955b, 1956a, 1957, *1959, 1961b.

Dyemnia Series: Urals, U.S.S.R. - Vladimirskaya, Timofeyev and Chachia, 1956.

Eophyton Beds: Baltic U.S.S.R. - Timofeyev, 1956a, * 1959.

Lausitzer Greywacke: Germany - Timofeyev, 1958, 1961b.

Unnamed formation: Prebaltic, U.S.S.R. - Naumova, 1950.

Weesensteiner Greywacke: Germany - Timofeyev, 1958.
    (See also POST-PLEISTOCENE. L. Cambrian pebble in moraine: Antarctica - Timofeyev,
    1962).

MIDDLE CAMBRIAN

Izhorski Beds: Baltic U.S.S.R. - Timofeyev, 1956a, 1957, * 1959: Vologda, U.S.S.R. -
    Timofeyev, 1961b.

Nizhniv Avzyan Series: Urals, U.S.S.R. - Vladimirskaya, Timofeyev and Chachia, 1956.

Paradoxides Beds: Sweden - Timofeyev, 1962.

Unnamed formation: Canada - Walton, 1962.

UPPER CAMBRIAN

Kolm Oil Shale: Sweden - Darrah, 1937, 1939.

Obolus Beds: Baltic U.S.S.R. - Naumova, 1950; Timofeyev, 1956a, 1957, * 1959, 1960, 1961a.
    (see also PLEISTOCENE. Upper Cambrian pebbles in drift; Baltic - Eisenack, 1951).

ORDOVICIAN (UNDIVIDED)

Chert nodules, Rheinischer Schiefergebirges - Eisenack, 1939b.

Unnamed formation: Bohemia - Eisenack, 1951: Libya - Wray,1962: Pre-Baltic, U.S.S.R. -

Naumova, 1950: Russia, U.S.S.R. - Andreyeva, 1961: Sahara - **Bureau du Recherche** du Pétrôle, 1959.
(See also PLEISTOCENE. Ordovician pebbles in drift: Baltic - Eisenack, 1931, 1934, 1938a, 1938b, 1951, 1963 c, d: Finland - Martinsson, 1956).

LOWER ORDOVICIAN

Ceratopyge - Stufe: Baltic - Eisenack, 1959a, 1962a: Sweden - Regnéll, 1955.

Churochnaya Series: Urals, U.S.S.R. - Vladimirskaya, Timofeyev and Chachia, 1956.

Deepkill Cherts (Beekmantown Series): New York, U.S.A. - Ruedemann and Wilson, 1956.

Dictyonema Beds: Novgorod, U.S.S.R. - Timofeyev, 1961b.

Dictyonema - Schiefer: Baltic - Eisenack, 1951, 1958b; Timofeyev, 1956a, * 1959.

Expansus - Kalk: Baltic - Eisenack, 1959a, 1962a, 1963d.

Glauconite - Kalk: Baltic - Eisenack, 1951, 1958b, 1959a, 1963d.

Glauconite - Sand: Baltic - Eisenack, 1951, 1958b, 1959a, 1962a; Naumova, 1950; Timofeyev, 1959, 1961b.

Grès Armoricain: France - Deunff, 1958.

Shineton Shales (Tremadocian): England - Downie, 1958.

Tremadocian: Sahara - Deunff, 1961.

Unnamed formation: Vologda, U.S.S.R. - Timofeyev, 1961b.

Vaginaten - Kalk: Baltic - Eisenack, 1951, 1959a, 1963e.

MIDDLE ORDOVICIAN

Äseri - Stufe: Baltic - Eisenack, 1962c.

Echinosphaeriten - Kalk: Baltic - Eisenack, 1959a.

Edinburg Limestone (Cyrtonella Zone); Virginia, U.S.A. - Eisenack, 1962d.

Jewe 'sche Stufe: Baltic - Eisenack, 1962c, 1963d, 1963e.

Kegel'sche - Stufe: Baltic - Eisenack, 1962c, 1963d.

Kuckers'sche Stufe: Baltic - Eisenack, 1962c Timofeyev, 1962a.

Lasnamägi - Stufe: Baltic - Eisenack, 1962c.

Llandeilian: France - Deunff, 1955b.

Molodov horizon: Podolia, U.S.S.R. - Timofeyev, 1962.

Normanskill Cherts: New York, U.S.A. - Ruedemann and Wilson, 1936.

Revaler - Stufe: Baltic - Eisenack, 1962c, 1963e.

Sarka Shales: Czechoslovakia - Eisenack, 1948.

Schistes à Calymènes: France – Deunff, 1951, 1958.

Schistes du Veryhac'h: France – Deunff, 1955, 1958.

Schroeteri Kalk: Baltic – Eisenack, 1959a.

Uhaku – Stufe: Baltic – Eisenack, 1962c.

Wasalemm' sche – Stufe: Baltic – Eisenack, 1962c.

UPPER ORDOVICIAN

Borkholmer – Stufe: Germany – Eisenack, 1963d.

Calcschiste de la Grange–du–Pin (Ashgillian):   France – Deflandre, 1942b, 1945a.

Chasmops – Kalk: Baltic – Eisenack, 1959a.

Grés de Kermeur: France – Deunff, 1958.

Lyckholmer – Stufe: Baltic – Eisenack, 1951, 1959a, 1962c, 1962d.

Ostsee Kalk: Baltic – Eisenack, 1958a, 1959a, 1963d, e.

Pirgu – Stufe: Baltic – Eisenack, 1962c.

Schistes de Raguenez: France – Deunff, 1958.

Sylvan Shale: Oklahoma, U.S.A. – Hedlund, 1960;   Wilson, 1958;   Wilson and Hedlund, 1962.

Unnamed formation: Vologda, U.S.S.R. – Timofeyev, 1961b.

Wesenberger – Stufe: Baltic – Eisenack, 1962c.

SILURIAN (UNDIVIDED)

Calcaire de la Combe d'Yzarne: France – Deflandre, 1945a.

Calcareous nodules, Gothlandien Armoricain: France – Deunff, 1954a.

Unnamed formations: Bohemia – Eisenack, 1951, 1958a: Brazil – Sommer and Boekel, 1961;
        Canada – Radforth and MacGregor, 1954:   Libya – Combaz, 1962.
        (See also PLEISTOCENE.   Silurian pebbles in Baltic drift – Eisenack, 1931, 1934,
        1938a, 1938b, 1963d;   O. Wetzel, 1933).

LOWER SILURIAN

Estonus – Kalk: Baltic – Eisenack, 1959a.

Llandovery: Sahara – Taugourdeau, 1962.

Visby Mergel: Baltic – Eisenack, 1954a.

MIDDLE SILURIAN

Buildwas Shales: England – Downie, 1959.

Calcaire de la Roquemaillère (Wenlockian):   France – Deflandre, 1942, 1945a.

Calcaire, Ruisseau du Ribouyrel (Wenlockian):   France – Deflandre, 1945a.

Coalbrookdale Beds: England – Downie, 1959.

Corniferous Limestone (Lockport Formation):   New York, U.S.A. – Dawson, 1886; M.C. White, 1962.

Dlouha Lora Limestone: Bohemia – Eisenack, 1934.

Dudley Limestone: England – Deunff, 1959.

Eurypterus Dolomit: Baltic – Eisenack, 1958a.

Högklint – Kalk: Baltic – Eisenack, 1959a.

"Kieselschiefer":   Czechoslovakia – Rodic, 1931.

Kieselschiefer with Monograptus priodon: Germany – Rothpletz, 1880.

Lockport Formation: Canada – Laird, 1935.

Maplewood Shale: New York, U.S.A. – Fisher, 1953; Evitt, 1961c.

Neahga Shale: New York, U.S.A. – Fisher, 1953.

Slite Mergel: Baltic – Eisenack, 1959a.

Unnamed formations: Kaliningrad, U.S.S.R. – Timofeyev, 1961b; New York, U.S.A. – (–), 1960.

Wenlock: White Russia, U.S.S.R. – Timofeyev, 1960.

Wenlockian: Poland – Timofeyev, 1962.

Wenlock   Limestone: England – Eisenack, 1951.

Wenlock Shale: England – Downie, 1959, * 1963.

UPPER SILURIAN

Beyrichia – Kalk (U. Ludlow):   Baltic – Eisenack, 1954a, 1955.

Herschieder Schiefer: Germany – Eisenack, 1939b.

Ludlow Bone Bed: England – Hooker, 1852; Salter, 1873.

Orthoceratenkalk: Germany – Sannemann, 1955.

Saalfelder Feengrotten (phosphate nodules):   Germany – Eisenack, 1939b.

South Kaliningrad Quartzite: Baltic U.S.S.R. – Timofeyev, 1962.

Unnamed formations: Brazil – Sommer, 1956; Canada – Dawson, 1871c.

DEVONIAN (UNDIVIDED)

Oil Shales: Kentucky, U.S.A. – Thiessen, 1925.

Petroleum: Volga–Ural region, U.S.S.R. – Medvedeva and Chepilova, 1961.

Unnamed formations: Bohemia – Eisenack, 1958a; Bolivia – Sommer, 1955b, 1956:

Brazil - Barbosa, 1949; Dawson, 1884a, 1884b; Sommer, 1951, 1954, 1956a, 1956b;
Sommer and Boekel, 1961.: Canada - Dawson, 1871a, 1871b, 1871c; Deunff, 1959;
Wilson and Urban, 1963: North America (undivided) - Hoffmeister, Staplin and Malloy,
1955; Reinsch, 1884: Paraguay-Potter, 1962: Peru - Wilson and Urban, 1963:
Roumania - Venkatachala and Beju, 1961.

LOWER DEVONIAN

Downton Sandstone: England - Salter, 1873.

Schistes de St. Cénéré: France - Deunff, 1954.

Siegenian: Germany - Sannemann, 1955.

Unnamed formation: Brazil - Sommer, 1960b.

MIDDLE DEVONIAN

Barreirinha Shale: Brazil - Dawson, 1886; Sommer, 1953, 1956.

Calcaire gris à lamellibranchs (Couvinien Sup.): France - Deunff, 1954b.

Cedar Valley Formation: Illinois, U.S.A. - Collinson and Scott, 1958.

Columbus Limestone: Ohio, U.S.A. - Winslow, 1962.

Delaware Limestone: Ohio, U.S.A. - Winslow, 1962.

Fleringer Schichten: Germany - Eisenack, 1963d.

Hamilton Shales: New York, U.S.A. - Dawson, 1866; Hough, 1934.

Marcellus Shales: Canada - Clarke, 1885.

Onondaga Chert: New York, U.S.A. - Baschnagel, 1942.

Onondaga Limestone: Canada - Deunff, 1954d, 1955a, 1957.

Ostiolatus - Horizont: Germany - Eisenack, 1963c.

Winnipegosis Formation (Elk Point Group): Canada - Jodry and Campau, 1961; Kent, 1963.

UPPER DEVONIAN

Birdbear Formation: Canada - Jodry and Campau, 1961; Kent, 1963.

Budesheimer Schiefer: Germany - Eisenack, 1963d.

Chagrin Shale: Ohio, U.S.A. - Winslow, 1962.

Chattanooga Shale: Kentucky, U.S.A. - Thiessen, 1921; Tennessee, U.S.A. - Thiessen, 1921.

Dolomie de Beaulieu (L. Frasnian): France - Tougourdeau - Lantz, 1960.

Duperow Formation (Saskatchewan Group): Canada - Jodry and Campau, 1961; Kent, 1963.

Frasnian: Belgium - Stockmans and Willière, 1960, 1962a, 1962b.

Genesee Shales: Canada - Clarke, 1885; New York, U.S.A. - Dawson, 1886.

New Albany Shale: Indiana, U.S.A. - Thiessen, 1921.

54.

Nisku Formation (Saskatchewan Group):   Canada - Jodry and Campau, 1961.

Ohio Shale: Kentucky, U.S.A. - Thiessen, 1921: Ohio, U.S.A. - Dawson, 1886, 1888a;
        Guise, 1886; Reinsch, 1884; Orton, 1882; Wethered, 1886; White and Stadnichenko,
        1923; Winslow, 1962.

Olentaugy Shale: Ohio, U.S.A. - Winslow, 1962.

Schistes de l'Île Longue: France - Deunff, 1954.

Unnamed formation: Canada - Radforth and MacGregor, 1954.

Woodbend Formation: Canada - Staplin, * 1961.

Woodford Formation: Oklahoma, U.S.A. - Eisenack, 1962a, 1963d; Urban, 1960; Wilson and
        Urban, 1963; Wilson, 1963.

CARBONIFEROUS (UNDIVIDED)

Coals: Central Russia - Reinsch, 1884: Czechoslovakia - Reinsch, 1884: Germany - Peinsch, 1884.

Petroleum: Volga-Ural region, U.S.S.R:- Medvedeva and Chepilova, 1962.

LOWER CARBONIFEROUS

Avonian (undivided):   England - Deunff, 1959: France - Deunff, 1959.

Bakken Formation (Madison Group):   Canada - Jodry and Campau, 1961.

Bedford Shale: Ohio, U.S.A. - Winslow, 1962.

Berea Sandstone: Ohio, U.S.A. - Winslow, 1962.

Charles Formation (Madison Group):   Canada - Jodry and Campau, 1961.

Couches de Lydiennes de la Montagne Noire (Viséan Inf.):   France - Deflandre, 1946d.

Dinantian Shales: Poland - Sujkowski, 1933.

Goodard Shale: Oklahoma, U.S.A. - Wilson and Urban, 1963.

Joggins Coal: Canada - Dawson, 1865.

Leaf Coal: Central Russia, U.S.S.R. - Reinsch, 1884.

Lower Limestone Shales: England - Guise, 1886; Wethered, 1886.

Mississippian (undivided):   North America - Hoffmeister, Staplin and   Malloy, 1955.

Stanley Shale: Oklahoma, U.S.A. - Wilson and Urban, 1963.

UPPER CARBONIFEROUS

Desmoinesian Shale;   Texas, U.S.A. - Wilson and Urban, 1963.

Laminated Coal of Saxony, Bavaria and Saar; Germany - Reinsch, 1884.

Petit Buisson marine band: Belgium - Stockmans and Willière, 1963.

Stephanian Chert: France - Carpentier, A. , 1932.

"Steinkohle von Potschappel":   Germany – Ehrenberg, 1854.

PERMIAN (UNDIVIDED)

Petroleum: Volga–Ural region, U.S.S.R. – Medvedeva and Chepilova, 1961.

LOWER PERMIAN

Lower Permian Marl: England – Wall and Downie,*1963.

Wellington Formation: Kansas, U.S.A. – Tasch, 1962, * 1963a.

MIDDLE PERMIAN

Belloy Formation: Canada – Jansonius, 1962.

Flowerpot Formation: Oklahoma, U.S.A. – Wilson, 1960.

Mersey Coals (Tasmanite): Tasmania – David, 1950; Dulhunty, 1949a, 1949b; Eisenack, 1963d;
        Newton, 1875; Reinsch, 1884; Singh, 1932.

UPPER PERMIAN

Unnamed Formations: Libya – Jekhowsky, 1961: Madagascar – Jekhowsky, 1961: Tunis –
        Jekhowsky, 1961.

Zechstein: Germany – Schaarschmidt, * 1963.

TRIASSIC (UNDIVIDED)

Unnamed Formation: U.S.A. – Deflandre, 1963.

LOWER TRIASSIC

Indian: Siberia, U.S.S.R. – Kara-Murza, 1961.

Kockatea Shale: Western Australia – Balme, 1963.

Mittleren Buntsandstein: Germany – Utech, 1962; Eisenack, 1963d.

Toad/Grayling Formations: Canada – Jansonius, 1962.

Unnamed Formations: Libya – Jekhowsky, 1961: Madagascar – Jekhowsky, 1961: Tunisia –
        Jekhowsky, 1961: Yugoslavia – Jekhowsky, 1961.

MIDDLE TRIASSIC

Anisian: Siberia, U.S.S.R. – Kara-Murza, 1961.

Dolomit–Zone (Mittlerer Muschelkalk):   Switzerland – Brosius and Bitterli, * 1961.

Hauptmuschelkalk (Oberer Muschelkalk):   Switzerland – Brosius and Bitterli, * 1961.

Ipswich Coal Measures (lower):   Queensland, Australia – Jersey, 1961.

Muschelkalk: Germany – Eisenack, 1962d.

Nodosuskalk (Plattenkalk) (Oberer Muschelkalk):   Switzerland – Brosius and Bitterli, * 1961.

Obere Sulfat–Zone (Mittlerer Muschelkalk):   Switzerland – Brosius and Bitterli, * 1961.

Trigonodusdolomit (Oberer Muschelkalk);   Switzerland - Brosius and Bitterli, * 1961.

Trochitenkalk (Oberer Muschelkalk):   Switzerland - Brosius and Bitterli, * 1961.

Wellenkalk (Unterer Muschelkalk):   Switzerland - Brosius and Bitterli, * 1961.

Wellenmergel (Unterer Muschelkalk):   Switzerland - Brosius and Bitterli, * 1961.

UPPER TRIASSIC

Cotham Beds (Rhaetic):   England - Sarjeant, 1963b.

Ipswich Coal Measures (upper):   Queensland, Australia - Jersey, 1962.

Karnian: Siberia, U.S.S.R. - Kara-Murza, 1961.

? Norian (Rhaetic):   Siberia, U.S.S.R. - Kara-Murza, 1961.

JURASSIC (UNDIVIDED)

Andigama Shale: Ceylon - Sah, 1953.

Unnamed Formations: Lvov-Volyu Region, U.S.S.R. - Isagulova, 1963.
        (See also PLEISTOCENE.   Flints worked by Magdalenians - Valensi, 1955a, 1955b.)

LOWER JURASSIC

Aalenian (undivided):   France - Valensi, 1947, * 1953.

Lias (undivided):   England - Love, 1962; Wall, 1962; Germany - Alberti, * 1961; Reinsch, 1884.

Lias Epsilon: Germany - Eisenack, 1957.

Manganese Series: Hungary - Simoncscis and Kedves, 1962.

Marnes à Pseudogrammoceras pedicum: France - Choux and Durand, 1961.

Pleuroceras spinatum and Amaltheus margaritatus Zone (Lias Delta):   Denmark - Evitt, 1961b.

Posidonienschiefer (Lias Epsilon):   Germany - Madler, 1958; Switzerland - Bitterli, 1961.

Rosewood Coals: Queensland, Australia - Balme, 1957.

Schlotheimia angulata Zone (Lias Alpha):   Denmark - Evitt, 1961a.

Upper Lias: Germany - O. Wetzel, 1959.

MIDDLE JURASSIC

Bajocian (undivided):   France - Mercier, 1938b; Valensi, 1947, 1948, * 1953.

Basal Oil Shale (Great Estuarine Series):   Scotland - Hudson, 1963.

Bathonian (undivided):   France - Mercier, 1938b, 1938c; Valensi, 1947, 1948, * 1953.

Callovian: Siberia, U.S.S.R. - Maliavkina et al., 1961.

Cornbrash (Callovian):   England - Sarjeant, 1959.

Dingo Siltstone (middle portion):   Western Australia – Cookson and Eisenack,   * 1958.

Dogger: Germany – Alberti,   * 1961.

? Dogger: West Pakistan – Evitt, 1961c.

Dogger – Malm: Madagascar – Jekhowsky, Sah and Letullier, 1960.

Garantiana Clay: Scotland – Hudson, 1963.

Kellaways Rock: England – Sarjeant,   * 1961a.

Oolithe blanche à Parkinsonia parkinsoni: France – Deflandre, 1947d.

Ostrea hebridica var. elongata Bed, Upper Fullers Earth (Bathonian):   Lantz, 1958.

Oxford Clay (K. jason Zone):   England – Sarjeant, 1960a,   * 1962a.

Staffin Bay Beds: Scotland – Hudson, 1963.
(See also PLEISTOCENE.   Callovian pebbles in drift: Baltic – Deflandre, 1947d; Eisenack, 1935, 1936a, 1936b; Evitt, 1961c.)

UPPER JURASSIC

Alexander Formation: Western Australia – Cookson and Eisenack,   * 1960b.

Ampthill Clay (C. cordatum – P. plicatilis Zone) – Sarjeant,   * 1962b.

Corallian (undivided):   England – Lantz, 1958.

Corallrag: Poland – Ehrenberg, 1843.

Dingo Claystone (upper portion):   Western Australia – Cookson and Eisenack,   * 1960b.

Dingo Siltstone (upper portion):   Western Australia – Cookson and Eisenack,   * 1958.

Fernie Group: Canada – Pocock,   * 1962.

Hambleton Oolite: England – Sarjeant,   * 1960c, 1962b.

Jarlemai Siltstone: Western Australia – Balme, 1957; Cookson and Eisenack,   * 1960b.

Jordan Cliff Clays (Oxfordian):   England – Sarjeant, 1963d.

Kimeridge Clay (A. pseudomutabilis Zone):   England – Lantz, 1958.

Kimeridge Clay (Subplanites Zone to Pectinatus Zone):   England – Downie, 1957; Sarjeant, 1960a.

Learmouth Formation: Western Australia – Cookson and Eisenack,   * 1958; Evitt, 1961c.

Lower Calcareous Grit: England – Sarjeant,   * 1960c,   * 1962a, 1962b.

Malm Alpha: Germany – Klement,   * 1960b.

Malm Beta: Germany – Klement,   * 1960b.

Malm Delta: Germany – Evitt, 1961c; Klement,   * 1960b.

Malm Gamma: Germany – Klement,   * 1960b.

Malm (undivided): Germany - Klement, 1957, 1960a.

Marly horizon with Cardioceras cf. cordatum: Switzerland - Sarjeant, 1963d.

Nothe Clay: England - Sarjeant, * 1962a.

Oolithe ferrugineuse à Cardioceras cordatum: France - Deflandre, 1938e, 1938f.

Osmington Oolite: England - Sarjeant, 1960a, * 1960c, * 1962a, 1962b.

Oxford Clay (C. cordatum Zone): England - Lantz, 1958; Sarjeant, * 1960a, 1962b.

Oxford Clay (Q. mariae Zone): England - Lantz, 1958; Sarjeant, * 1961a, 1962b.

Oxfordian: Siberia, U.S.S.R. - Maliavkina et al., 1961.

Portlandian (undivided): Germany - Doring, 1961.

Purbeck: England - Lantz, 1958.

Ringstead Waxy Clay: England - Sarjeant, 1960a, * 1962a.

Sandsfoot Clay: England - Sarjeant, * 1962a.

Schistes calcaires bitumineux d'Orbagnoux: France - Deflandre, 1938d, 1939b, 1941b.

Unnamed Formations: Denmark - Evitt, 1961c:(---------), 1960: Papua - Cookson and
        Eisenack, * 1958: Western Australia - Cookson and Eisenack, * 1958; Evitt, 1961c.

Upper Calcareous Grit: England - Sarjeant, * 1960c.

Vanguard Formation: Canada - Pocock, * 1962.

Villers Marls (Oxfordian): France - Deflandre, 1938b, 1938e, 1938f, 1948d.

Volgian (Upper): Siberia, U.S.S.R. - Maliavkina et al., 1961.

CRETACEOUS (UNDIVIDED)

Petroleum: Mexico - Sanders, 1937.

Unnamed Formation: Antarctica - Cranwell, Harrington and Speden, 1960: Graham Island,
        Arctic Canada - Manum, 1963.
        (See also PLEISTOCENE.   Flints worked by Protomagdalenians and Magdalenians -
        Valensi, 1955a, 1955b, 1960).

LOWER CRETACEOUS

Albian (undivided): Germany - Alberti, * 1961: Venezuela - Evitt, 1961c.

"Albian": Ivory Coast - Vachey and Jardiné, 1962.

Albian - Turonian (undivided): Portuguese Guinea - Stover, 1963: Senegal - Stover, 1963.

Aptian (undivided): Germany - Alberti, 1959b, * 1961; Eisenack, * 1958c, 1962d;
        Evitt, 1961c.

Argile à Cladophlebis, Ginkgoites, etc. (Wealden): Belgium - Delcourt and Sprumont, 1957.

Barremian (undivided): Germany - Alberti, 1959b, * 1961.

Bivirgaten – Schichten (U. Hauterivian):   Germany – Gocht,   * 1959.

Dichotomitensandstein (U. Valanginian):   Germany – Gocht, 1957,   * 1959.

Dichotomitenschichten (U. Valanginian):   Germany – Gocht, 1957,   * 1959.

Dilkuna Formation: West Pakistan – Evitt, 1961c.

Flysch à lentilles de Couches Rouges: Switzerland – Weidmann, 1963.

Gearle Siltstone (Lower):   Western Australia – Cookson and Eisenack,   * 1958, 1962b;   Eisenack and Cookson, 1960.

Goru Formation (Lower):   West Pakistan – Evitt, 1961c.

"Grierson Member", Birdrong Formation: Western Australia – Cookson and Eisenack, 1958.

Grey sandstone, Onepah: New South Wales, Australia – Cookson and Eisenack,   * 1958: Deflandre and Cookson, 1955; Evitt, 1961c.

Grey siltstone, Cootabarlow: South Australia – Cookson, 1956; Cookson and Eisenack,   * 1958.

Hauterivian (undivided):   Germany – Alberti,   * 1961:   Poland – Alberti,   * 1961.

Kootenay Formation (Upper Part):   Canada – Pocock,   * 1962.

Mannville Group: Canada – Pocock,   * 1962.

Molecap Greensand: Western Australia – Cookson and Eisenack, 1962b; Deflandre and Cookson, 1955.

Muderong Shale: Western Australia – Cookson and Eisenack,   * 1958.

Neocomian (undivided):   Germany – Evitt, 1961c.

"Neokom-Ton" (Barremian):   Germany – Gocht, 1957,   * 1959.

Noricus – Schichten (L. Hauterivian):   Gocht, 1957,   * 1959.

Platylenticeratenschichten (Wealden):   Germany – Gocht, 1957,   * 1959.

Polyptychitenschichten: Germany – Gocht, 1957,   * 1959.

Roma Formation: Queensland, Australia – Cookson and Eisenack,   * 1958, 1962b; Eisenack and Cookson, 1960.

Speeton Clay: England – Neale and Sarjeant, 1962.

Styx River Series: Queensland, Australia – Cookson and Eisenack,   * 1958.

Tonmergelsandstein (U. Hauterivian):   Germany – Gocht, 1957,   * 1959.

Unnamed Formations: Papua – Cookson and Eisenack,   * 1958,   * 1960b; Cookson and Manum, 1960; Deflandre and Cookson, 1955: New South Wales, Australia – Deflandre and Cookson, 1954: Queensland, Australia – Cookson and Eisenack,   * 1960b, 1962b; Eisenack and Cookson, 1960: Pakistan – Evitt, 1963: Texas, U.S.A. – Merrill, 1895: Western Australia – Cookson and Eisenack, 1958 (?), 1962a, 1962b; Eisenack, 1962d; Eisenack and Cookson, 1960.

Valanginian (undivided): Bulgaria - Alberti, * 1961: Siberia, U.S.S.R. - Maliavkina et al., 1961.

Wealden (undivided): Belgium - Delcourt and Sprumont, 1955, 1959: England - Hughes, 1960; Germany - Alberti, * 1961; Doring, 1961.

Windalia Radiolarite: Western Australia - Cookson and Eisenack, * 1958; Eisenack and Cookson, 1960.

UPPER CRETACEOUS

Albian to Turonian (undivided): Portuguese Guinea - Stover, 1963; Senegal - Stover, 1962, 1963.

Assise de Nouvelles (Senonian): Belgium - Lejeune - Carpenter, 1951.

Assise de Spiennes (Senonian): Belgium - Evitt, 1961c; Lejeune, 1937a, 1937b; Lejeune-Carpentier, 1937, 1938a, 1938b, 1940, 1941, 1942, 1944, 1946, 1951.

Austin Chalk: Texas, U.S.A. - Brown and Pierce, 1962.

Blair Formation: Wyoming, U.S.A. - Tschudy, 1961.

Brazeau Formation: Canada - Radforth and Rouse, 1956.

Bryozoenkreide: Germany - W. Wetzel, 1955: Kazakhstan, U.S.S.R. - Zaklinskaya, 1963

Campanian (undivided): Kazakhstan, U.S.S.R. - Zaklinskaya, 1963: Poland - Gorka, * 1963: Siberia, U.S.S.R. - Maliavkina et al., 1961.

Campanian to Santonian (undivided): Germany - Alberti, 1959b, * 1961.

Chalk and chalk flints. (These are treated within a large group of papers, in which distinction is rarely made on whether the fossil was derived from a flint or the chalk itself, or if the former, whether the flint was in situ or loose in surface drift. In some cases, the flints are considered to belong to a particular stage (Senonian, Turonian, etc.). For simplicity's sake, all such papers are here grouped together unless a precise formation name is quoted. See also PLEISTOCENE): Belgium - Conrad, 1941: Czechoslovakia - Wiesner, 1936: Denmark - Ehrenberg, 1854: England - Bowerbank, 1841a, 1841b, 1841c; Deane, 1845, 1849; Ehrenberg, 1838b; Griffith and Henfrey, 1860; Mantell, 1845, 1849, 1850, 1853, 1857; Morris, 1854; Pritchard, 1841, 1852; Ralfs, 1848; Reade, 1839; O. Wetzel, 1960; H.H. White, 1842, 1844a, 1844b; Wilkinson, 1849: France - Deflandre, 1934, 1935a, 1935b, 1935c, 1936a, 1936b, 1936c, 1937a, 1937b, 1937c, 1939a, 1940a, 1943a, 1948a; Deflandre and Courteville, 1939; Deflandre - Rigaud, 1954, 1955; Firtion, 1952; Mercier, 1938a; Philippot, 1949: Germany - Ehrenberg, 1838a, 1854; Hucke, 1932, 1954; Lejeune, 1937a, 1937c; Lejeune - Carpentier, 1937, 1938a, 1939, 1940, 1942, 1946; Turpin, 1837; O. Wetzel, 1926a, 1926b, 1932, 1933, 1940, 1943, 1944, 1948a, 1948b, 1950, 1951a, 1951b, 1951c, 1953a, 1953b, 1960, 1961; W. Wetzel, 1922, 1952, 1955: Poland - O. Wetzel, 1960.

Cenomanian (Lower): France - Firtion, 1952.

Cenomian (undivided): Germany - Alberti, * 1961: Poland - Gorka, * 1963. (See also under "Chalk and chalk flints".)

Cody Shale: Wyoming, U.S.A. - Tschudy, 1961.

Colon Formation (Upper Cretaceous to Paleocene): Venezuela - Kuyl, Muller and Waterbolk, 1955.

Coniacian (undivided): Germany - Alberti, 1959b: Siberia, U.S.S.R. - Maliavkina et al., 1961.

Craie blanche de Vendôme: France - Deflandre, 1940a.

Craie de Meudon (Maestrichtian):   France - Deflandre - Rigaud, 1954;   Ehrenberg, 1938b.

Craie d'Obourg (Senonian):   Belgium - Lejeune - Carpentier, 1941.

Danian (undivided):   Germany - W. Wetzel, 1952, 1955:   Kazakhstan, U.S.S.R. - Zaklinskaya, 1963.

Eagle Ford Group: Texas, U.S.A. - Brown and Pierce, 1962.

Emschérian (undivided):   Poland - Gorka,   * 1963.

Gearle Siltstone (Upper):   Western Australia - Cookson and Eisenack, 1960a, 1960b.

Goru Formation (Upper):   West Pakistan - Evitt, 1961c.

Gulpensch-Krijt: Netherlands - Umbgrove, 1925; Wit, 1943.

"Hornstein":   Germany - Ehrenberg, 1854.

Kiowa Shale: Kansas, U.S.A. - Tasch, McClure and Oftedahl, 1962.

Korojon Calcarenite: Western Australia - Cookson and Eisenack,   * 1958.

Kunrader Kalk: Netherlands - Wit, 1944.

Labiatusplaner (Turonian):   Germany - Alberti,   * 1961.

Lewis Formation: Wyoming, U.S.A. - Tschudy, 1961.

Lohmgrundmergel (Turonian):   Germany - Alberti,   * 1961.

Maestrichtian (undivided):   Belgium - Conrad, 1941:   Kazakhstan, U.S.S.R. - Zaklinskaya, 1963:   Poland - Alberti, 1959b;   Gorka,   * 1963:   Siberia, U.S.S.R. - Maliavkina et al., 1961.

Maestrichtsch Krijt;   Netherlands - Wit, 1944.

Mancos Group: Utah, U.S.A. - Sarmiento, 1957:   Wyoming, U.S.A. - Tschudy, 1961.

Mesaverde Formation: Wyoming, U.S.A. - Tschudy, 1961.

"Meteorpapier of Rauden, Curland":   Latvia, U.S.S.R. - Ehrenberg, 1854.

Moeraki Formation (Teurian):   New Zealand - Couper, 1960.

Mukronatenkreide: Germany - Reinsch, 1905.

Navesink Formation: New Jersey, U.S.A. - Evitt, 1961c, 1963.

Oberplaner (Turonian):   Germany - Alberti,   * 1961.

Osbourne Formation: Western Australia - Cookson and Eisenack, 1960a, 1962b.

Plenus-Zone: Germany - Alberti,   * 1961.

Red Bank Formation: New Jersey, U.S.A. - Evitt, 1961c, 1963.

Rock Springs Formation: Wyoming, U.S.A. - Tschudy, 1961.

Santonian (undivided):   Poland - Gorka,   * 1963:   Siberia, U.S.S.R. - Maliavkina et al., 1961.

Saurian Sands (Haumurian):   New Zealand – Couper, 1960.

"Schreibkreide":   Denmark – Ehrenberg, 1854.

Schistes des Follys: Switzerland – Weidmann, 1963.

Senonian (undivided):   France – Deflandre, 1947a; Deflandre-Rigaud, 1955; Germany – Alberti,
        1959b, * 1961; O. Wetzel, 1948a, 1953a: Graham Land, Antarctica – Cranwell, 1962.
        (See also under "Chalk and chalk flints)."

Senonian (Upper):   Denmark – O. Wetzel, 1940.

"Sulphur Mudstone"(Teurian):   New Zealand – Couper, 1960.

Third Coal (Orocué) Formation: Venezuela – Kuyl, Muller and Waterbolk, 1955.

Tonbank von Zeichen (Turonian):   Germany – Alberti, 1959b.

Ton von Zatschke (Turonian):   Germany – Alberti, 1959b.

Toolonga Calcilutite: Western Australia – Cookson and Eisenack, 1960a.

Turonian (undivided):   France – Valensi, 1957: Germany – Alberti, 1959b: Poland – Gorka, 1963:
        Siberia, U.S.S.R. – Maliavkina et al., 1961.   (See also under "Chalk and Chalk Flints)".

Unnamed Formations: California, U.S.A. – Evitt, 1963: Victoria, Australia – Cookson and
        Eisenack, 1961a, 1962b; Deflandre and Cookson, 1954, * 1955; Douglas, * 1960a:
        Western Australia – Cookson, 1956; Cookson and Eisenack, 1960a, 1962a; Deflandre and
        Cookson, 1954.

Unterer Grünsandstein (Turonian):   Germany – Alberti, * 1961.

Unterer Mergel (Turonian):   Germany – Alberti, * 1961.

Waipawa Black Shale (Teurian):   New Zealand – Couper, 1960.

Waipawa Greensand (Teurian):   New Zealand – Couper, 1960.

LOWER TERTIARY (UNDIVIDED)

"Coffee Rock":   Western Australia – Deflandre and Cookson, * 1955.

Radiolarian Earth: Barbados – Lefèvre, 1932, 1933a, 1933b, 1933c.

Unnamed Formations: Colombia – Solé de Porta, 1961: Germany – O. Wetzel, 1948a: Irtysch
        District, U.S.S.R. – Alberti, 1959b: Spitzbergen – Cookson and Manum, * 1960;
        Douglas, * 1960a, 1960b: Volga-Ural watershed, U.S.S.R. – Shchiguryayeva, 1956:
        Western Australia – Cookson and Eisenack, * 1961b, 1962a; Cookson and Manum, 1960.

PALEOCENE

Brightseat Formation: Maryland, U.S.A. – Groot, 1962.

Clayton Formation, Midway Group: Mississippi, U.S.A. – Pryor and Glass, 1961.

Colon Formation (U. Cretaceous to Paleocene):   Venezuela – Kuyl, Muller and Waterbolk, 1955.

Diatomites of Kusnetzsk: U.S.S.R. – Deflandre, 1940b.

Fort Union Formation: Wyoming, U.S.A. – Tschudy, 1961.

Onakanawa Formation: Canada - Radforth and Rouse, 1956.

Pebble Point Formation (lower):   Victoria, Australia - Deflandre and Cookson, 1954 * 1955.

Porters Creek Formation: Mississippi, U.S.A. - Pryor and Glass, 1961.

Radiolariengestein: Germany - Schuh, 1932.

Sparnacian: Hungary - Kedves, 1961.

Unnamed Formations: Germany - Alberti, * 1961; Schuh, 1932: Kazakhstan, U.S.S.R. -
     Zaklinskaya, 1963: Poland - Gorka, * 1963: Siberia, U.S.S.R. - Maliavkina et al.,
     1961; Vozzhennikova, 1960: Stalingrad, U.S.S.R. - Alberti, 1959b.

EOCENE

Agua Fresca Formation: Chile - Katz, 1961.

Arnold Series: New Zealand - Couper, 1960.

Argile d'Asse (Ypresian):   Belgium - Stockmans, 1962.

Argiles de Campbon: France - Durand, 1960.

Argile des Flandres (Ypresian):   Belgium - Pastiels, * 1948.

Argile d'Orp-le-Grand (Landenian):   Belgium - Stockmans, 1962.

Argile de Toulven: France - Choux, Durand and Milon, 1961a, 1961b.

Baikhozinsk Suite, M. Eocene: Kazakhstan, U.S.S.R. - Abuzyarova, 1962.

Basal clay of Castle Cove Section: Victoria, Australia - Deflandre and Cookson, * 1955.

Calcaire de Chaussy (Lutetian):   France - Deflandre, 1948d.

Dannevirke Series: New Zealand - Couper, 1960.

Dilwyn Clay (upper):   Victoria, Australia - Deflandre and Cookson, * 1955.

Geiseltalbraunkohle: Germany - Krutzsch, 1962.

Gosport Sand, Claibourne Group: Alabama, U.S.A. - Gray, 1960.

Green River Formation: Wyoming, U.S.A. - Tshudy, 1961.

Grès á Sabals: France - Durand, 1960.

Kanev Beds: U.S.S.R. - Shchiguryayeva, 1956.

"Kieselton" (L. Eocene):   Germany - Staesche, 1937; O. Wetzel, 1935.

Kopili Formation, Jaintia Series: Assam, India - Baksi, 1962.

Kreyenhagen Formation: California, U.S.A. - Norem, 1955b.

London Clay: England - Eagar and Sarjeant, 1963.

Lower Eocene (undivided):   Belgium - Alberti, 1959b; Stalingrad, U.S.S.R. - Alberti, 1959b, * 196

Lutetian (undivided):   France - Jekhowsky and Jacob, 1961.

Middle Eocene (undivided):   Germany - Klumpp,   * 1953.

Pebble Point Formation (upper):   Victoria, Australia - Deflandre and Cookson,   * 1955.

Princetown Member, Dilwyn Clay: Victoria, Australia - Deflandre and Cookson,   * 1955.

Pukemira Sandstone (Arnold):   New Zealand - Couper, 1960.

Sables de Campbon (Lutetian):   France - Durand, 1958.

Sparnacian (undivided):   France - Jekhowsky and Jacob, 1961.

Sylhet Formation, Jaintia Series: Assam, India - Baksi, 1962.

Unnamed Formations: Germany - Gripp, 1925; Schuh, 1932: Hungary - Kriván Hutter, 1963a, b:
      India - Varma and Dangwal, 1962: Kara-Tau, Turgai, U.S.S.R. - Alberti, 1959b, * 1961:
      Kazakhstan, U.S.S.R. - Zaklinskaya, 1963: South Australia - Cookson, 1956;   Deflandre
      and Cookson, * 1955: Siberia, U.S.S.R. - Vozzhennikova, 1961: Victoria, Australia -
      Douglas, 1960b: Western Australia - Deflandre and Cookson, 1954.

Upper Eocene (undivided):   Aral Sea area, U.S.S.R. - Alberti, 1959b, * 1961: Germany -
      Alberti, 1959b; Klumpp, * 1953: India - Srivastava, 1963: Ob district, U.S.S.R. -
      Alberti, 1959b, * 1961.

Vincentown Formation: New Jersey, U.S.A. - Evitt, 1961c, 1963.

Wind River Formation: Wyoming, U.S.A. - Tschudy, 1961.

Ypresian (undivided):   Belgium - Pastiels, * 1948: France - Jekhowsky and Jacob, 1961:
      Germany - Reissinger, 1950.

OLIGOCENE

Anglesea Formation: Victoria, Australia - Cookson, 1953.

Barail Series: Assam, India - Baksi, 1962.

Baustein - Schichten (Gefalteten Molasse):   Germany - Wolf, 1961.

Bernsteinformation: East Prussia, U.S.S.R. - Eisenack, 1938c, * 1954b;   Eisenack and Gocht,
      1960.

Blaue Erde: East Prussia, U.S.S.R. - Eisenack, * 1954b;   Eisenack and Gocht, 1960;   Evitt,
      1961c.

Brandon Lignite: Vermont, U.S.A. - Traverse, 1955.

Carbonaceous sandy shale, Gellibrand River: Victoria, Australia - Cookson, 1953.

Fischschiefer: Germany - Weiler, 1956.

Flöz Frimmersdorf: Germany - Averdieck, 1958.

Glaukenitischer Mehlsand: Germany - Maier, 1958, * 1959.

Grünsand (facies equivalent of Rupelton):   Germany - Brosius and Gramann, 1959.

Kasseler Meeressand: Germany - Brosius, * 1963.

71

Khadum Stage: Black Sea region, U.S.S.R. - Korallova, 1963.

Lower Oligocene (undivided):   North Irtysch district, U.S.S.R. - Alberti, * 1961.

Melanienton: Germany - Brosius and Gramann, 1959.

Molasse: Switzerland - Scherer, 1961.

Rupelton: Germany - Brelie, 1958; Brosius and Gramann, 1959; Gocht, 1952, 1960; Spandel, 1909.

Sannoisian (undivided):   France - Jekhowsky and Jacob, 1961.

Septarienton: Germany - Alberti, 1959a, * 1961; Brelie, 1958; Deflandre and Cookson, 1955; Gocht, 1952, 1955, 1960; Maier, * 1959.

Stampian (undivided):   France - Jekhowsky and Jacob, 1961.

Tonmergel - Schichten (Gefalteten Molasse):   Germany - Wolf, 1961.

Unnamed Formations: California, U.S.A. - Norem, 1955b: Germany - Alberti, 1959b, * 1961; Gerlach, * 1961; Gocht, 1955 (?): Hungary - Kriván Hutter, 1963a, 1963b: India - Scrivastava, 1963; Varma and Dangwal, 1962: Roumania-Venkatachala and Baltes, 1962a, 1962b: Victoria, Australia - Douglas, 1960b.

Upper Oligocene (undivided):   Colombia - Solé de Porta, 1959: Germany - Brelie and Wolters, 1958.

MIOCENE

Aquitanian: Roumania - Venkatachala and Baltes, 1962a, 1962b.

Balcombian Series: Victoria, Australia - Cookson, 1953; Deflandre and Cookson, * 1955.

Braunkohle: Germany - Thiergart, 1942.

Burdigalian: Roumania - Venkatachala and Baltes, 1962a, 1962b.

Cerithien - Schichten (Steinsalzlager):   Germany - Kirchheimer, 1950.

"Faulschlamm":   Germany - Hiebenthal, 1930.

Freeman - Jewett Member,   Temblor Formation: California, U.S.A. - Norem, 1955b.

Gellibrand Clay, Heytesbury Group: Victoria, Australia - Deflandre and Cookson, * 1955.

Gram Formation: Denmark - Maier, 1958, * 1959.

Gramer Stufe: Germany - Maier, 1958, * 1959.

Helvetian: Roumania - Venkatachala and Baltes, 1962a, 1962b.

Hemmoorer Stufe: Germany - Brelie, 1958; Maier, 1958, * 1959.

Langenfelder Stufe: Germany - Köwing, 1956.

Las Flores Formation: Venezuela - Norem, 1955a.

Lower Miocene (undivided):   Poland - Mackó, 1957.

Petroleum (unlocated):   Mexico – Sanders, 1937.

Potreritos Formation: Venezuela – Norem, 1955a.

Puffy Member, Katalla Formation: Alaska, U.S.A. – Waloweek and Norem, 1957.

Reinbek – Dingdener Stufe: Germany – Köwing, 1956; Maier, 1958, * 1959.

Sahelian: Algeria – Deflandre, 1947b, 1948d.

Sarmatian: Roumania – Venkatachala and Baltes, 1962a, 1962b.

Salt Formation (petroleum):   Roumania – Sanders, 1937.

Steinsalzlager: Poland – Kirchheimer, 1950.

Surma Series: Assam, India – Baksi, 1962.

Tortonian: Roumania – Venkatachala and Baltes, 1962a, 1962b.

Tripoli: Virginia, U.S.A. – Ehrenberg, 1854.

Unnamed Formations: California, U.S.A. – Norem, 1955b: Germany – Gerlach, * 1961:
    Victoria, Australia – Douglas, 1960b: Virginia, U.S.A. – Ehrenberg, 1854.

Upper Miocene (undivided):   off California coast, U.S.A. – Martin and Gray, 1962: Victoria,
    Australia – Deflandre and Cookson, 1954.

Vedder Member, Temblor Formation: California, U.S.A. – Norem, 1955b.

Vierlander Stufe: Germany – Maier, 1958, * 1959.

Waitemata Series: New Zealand – Couper, 1960.

Yakataga Formation: Alaska, U.S.A. – Waloweek and Norem, 1957.

PLIOCENE

Etchegoin Formation: California, U.S.A. – Norem, 1955b.

Lower Pliocene: off California coast, U.S.A. – Martin and Gray, 1962.

Unnamed Formations: Algeria – Ehrenberg, 1854: Greece – Ehrenberg, 1854: Roumania –
    Venkatachala and Baltes, 1962a, 1962b: Victoria, Australia – Deflandre and
    Cookson, * 1955 (?).

QUATERNARY (UNDIVIDED)

Clays, Moyne River: Victoria, Australia – Cookson, 1953.

PLEISTOCENE

Argiles de Campine: Belgium – Dricot, 1962.

Barrington Beds: England – Norris, 1962.

Calabrian (undivided):   Israel – Rossignol, 1962.

Boulder clay: Germany – Reinsch, 1884: Illinois, U.S.A. – Johnson and Thomas, 1884.

Crag deposits (early Pleistocene):   England – West, 1961.

Glacial deposits: Denmark – Iversen, 1942.

Hoxnian silt and peat: England – Watts, 1959.

Lake sediments: Minnesota, U.S.A. – Fries, 1962.

Late glacial marine clay: Sweden – Fries, 1951.

Magdalenian worked flints (Jurassic and Cretaceous):   France – Valensi, 1955a, 1955b.

Mergelton (Mindel-Riss Interglacial):   Germany – Maier, * 1959.

Pebbles and flints in drift (Cretaceous) (see "UPPER CRETACEOUS.   Chalk and chalk flints" for
    comments and list of papers among which descriptions are to be found.)

Pebbles in drift (Lower Paleozoic):   Germany – Eisenack, 1931, 1934, 1938a, 1938b, 1944, 1951;
    Weigelt, 1930:   Finland – Martinsson, 1956.

Pebbles in drift (Middle Jurassic):   Germany – Deflandre, 1947d; Eisenack, 1935, 1936a, 1936b,
    1944.

Post-Tyrrhenian (undivided):   Israel – Rossignol, 1962.

Protomagdalenian worked flints (Cretaceous):   France – Valensi, 1950.

Sicilian (undivided):   Israel – Rossignol, 1962.

Tyrrhenian (undivided):   Israel – Rossignol, 1962.

POST-PLEISTOCENE

Brackish waters, Lake Maràcaibo: Venezuela – Tschudy, 1961.

Calcite sand and mud, Kapingamarangi Atoll, Caroline Islands – McKee, Chronic and
    Leopold, 1959.

Chicago water supply: Illinois, U.S.A. – Johnson and Thomas, 1884.

Fluvial clays;   Italy – Leonard, 1955.

Freshwater peats (Atlantic to Sub-Atlantic):   Western Australia – Churchill and Sarjeant,
    1962, 1963.

Marine muds: Israel – Rossignol, 1961, 1963.

Marine sediments: Belgium – Kufferath, 1950; Meunier, 1919: Sweden – Erdtman, 1950, 1954,
    1955; Fries, 1951: Texas, U.S.A. – Shepard and Moore, 1955.

Morainic pebbles (Proterozoic ?):   Antarctica – Vialov and Timofeyev, 1959.

Residue from melted sea-ice: Arctic – Ehrenberg, 1854.

Sediment from sea bottom at 12,000 feet: Atlantic – Ehrenberg, 1854.

Silts of Lake Michigan: Hough, 1934.

SECTION III: INDEX TO DINOFLAGELLATE AND ACRITARCH
GENERA AND SPECIES

INDEX TO DINOFLAGELLATE AND ACRITARCH TAXA

The index which follows contains reference to all taxa of generic or infrageneric status. Taxa of suprageneric status are not included, since the classification of the microplankton is at present under review.   The two alternative systems of classification at present used are summarised in Eisenack, 1961b and 1963a, and Downie, Evitt and Sarjeant, 1963, to which readers are referred.

VALID TAXA

The type species of each genus is indicated by an asterisk*.   The symbol ° indicates uncertainty that the references quoted (in all cases Russian) are in fact the original descriptions.

ACANTHODIACRODIUM Timofeyev, 1958b, p. 831, emend.   Deflandre and Deflandre-Rigaud, 1961, p.9.

A. abortivum Timofeyev, 1959, p. 73, pl. 6, fig. 22, M. Cambrian, U.S.S.R.

A. aciferum (Naumova, 1950), p. 184, pl. 3, fig. 6.   (as Azonomonoletes), L. Ordovician, Baltic U.S.S.R.   ---, comb. nov.

A. aciferum (Timofeyev, 1959, non Naumova, 1950), p. 86, pl. 7 fig. 26 (as Acanthorytidodiacrodium). M.-U.   Cambrian, U.S.S.R.   ---, Deflandre and Deflandre-Rigaud, 1961, p. 9 (by implication).

A. acre (Timofeyev, 1959), pp. 82-3, pl. 7 fig. 10 (as Acanthorytidodiacrodium). U. Cambrian-L. Ordovician, U.S.S.R. ---, Deflandre and Deflandre-Rigaud, 1961, p. 9(by implication).

A. adelphicum Timofeyev, 1959, p. 70, pl. 6 fig. 3.   M. Cambrian, U.S.S.R.

A. anceps Timofeyev, 1959, p. 73, pl. 6 fig. 20. M. Cambrian, U.S.S.R.

A. apertum (Timofeyev, 1959), p. 83, pl. 7 fig. 11 (as Acanthorytidiacrodum). M. Cambrian, U.S.S.R. ---, Deflandre and Deflandre-Rigaud, 1961, p.9 (by implication).

A. barbullatum Timofeyev, 1959, p. 74, pl. 6 fig. 27. M. Cambrian, U.S.S.R.

A. biplicatum (Timofeyev, 1959), pp. 79 and 81, pl. 7 fig. 3 (as Acanthorytidodiacrodium). M.-U. Cambrian, U.S.S.R. --- Deflandre and Deflandre-Rigaud, 1961, p. 9 (by implication).

A. brevispinum (Naumova, 1950), p. 185, pl. 3 fig. 15 (as Azonomonoletes). L. Ordovician, Baltic U.S.S.R. --- , comb. nov.

A. capsulare Timofeyev, 1959, p. 70, pl. 6 fig. 6. M. Cambrian, U.S.S.R.

A. commune Timofeyev, 1959, p. 75, pl. 6 fig. 31. U. Cambrian, U.S.S.R.

A. conforme Timofeyev, 1959, p. 75, pl. 6 fig. 30. U. Cambrian, U.S.S.R.

A. constrictum (Deunff, 1961a), pp. 43-4, pl. 3 fig. 8 (as Diornatosphaera). L. Ordovician, Sahara.   --- , Deflandre and Deflandre-Rigaud, 1959, p. 10.

A. convexum Timofeyev, 1959, p. 79, pl. 6 fig. 50. L. Ordovician, U.S.S.R.

A. cornutum Timofeyev, 1959, p. 73, pl. 6 fig. 23.   M. Cambrian, U.S.S.R.

A. crenatum Timofeyev, 1959, p. 70, pl. 6 fig. 5. M. Cambrian, U.S.S.R.

A. curvispinum (Naumova, 1950), p. 184, pl. 3 fig. 7   (as Azonomonoletes). L. Ordovician, Baltic U.S.S.R. --- , comb. nov.

A. decipiens(Timofeyev, 1959), p. 87, pl. 7 fig. 29 (as Acanthorytidodiacrodium).U. Cambrian-L. Ordovician, U.S.S.R. --- , Deflandre and Deflandre-Rigaud, 1961, p. 9 (by implication).

A. denticulatum (Naumova, 1950), p. 184, pl. 3 fig. 8, (as Azonomonoletes).L. Ordovician, Baltic U.S.S.R. --- , comb. nov.

* A. dentiferum Timofeyev, 1958b, p. 831, pls. 1 fig. 2, 3 fig. 2.   L. Cambrian, Germany.

A. dichotomum(Timofeyev, 1959),pp. 86-7, pl. 7 fig. 28 (as Acanthorytidodiacrodium). M. Cambrian, U.S.S.R. --- ,Deflandre and Deflandre-Rigaud 1961, p. 9 (by implication).

A. diffusum(Timofeyev, 1959),p. 86, pl. 7 fig. 27 (as Acanthorytidodiacrodium).M. Cambrian-L. Ordovician, U.S.S.R. --- , Deflandre and Deflandre-Rigaud 1961, p. 9 (by implication).

A. divaricatum Timofeyev, 1959, p. 77, pl. 6 fig. 41. U. Cambrian, U.S.S.R.

A. divisum (Deunff, 1961a) p. 44, pl. 3 fig. 12 (as Diornatosphaera),L. Ordovician,Sahara. --- Deflandre and Deflandre-Rigaud, 1961, p. 10.

A. duplex(Timofeyev, 1959), p. 88, pl. 7 fig. 34 (as Acanthozonodiacrodium).U. Cambrian, U.S.S.R. --- , Deflandre and Deflandre-Rigaud, 1961, p. 9 (by implication).

A. duplicativum Timofeyev, 1959, p. 74, pl. 6 fig. 26. M. Cambrian, U.S.S.R.

A. echinatum (Naumova, 1950), p. 184, pl. 3 fig. 9 (as Azonomonoletes).L. Ordovician, Baltic U.S.S.R. --- ,comb. nov.   (see also p. 186).

A. echinatum (Timofeyev, 1959, non Naumova, 1950), p. 87, pl. 7 fig. 31   (as Acanthorytidodi-acrodium). L. Ordovician, U.S.S.R. --- , Deflandre and Deflandre-Rigaud, 1961, p. 9 (by implication).

A. endemicum Timofeyev, 1959, p. 69, pl. 6 fig. 1. M. Cambrian, U.S.S.R.

A. enodum Timofeyev, 1959, p. 71, pl. 6 fig. 13. M. Cambrian, U.S.S.R.

A. erinaceum (Timofeyev, 1959), p. 82, pl. 7 fig. 7 (as Acanthorytidodiacrodium).U. Cambrian, U.S.S.R. --- , Deflandre and Deflandre-Rigaud, 1961, p. 9 (by implication).

A. fibulaeforme Timofeyev, 1959, p. 76,pl. 6 fig. 35. U. Cambrian, U.S.S.R.

A. filamentare Timofeyev, 1959, p. 72, pl. 6 fig. 16. M-U. Cambrian, U.S.S.R.

A. flabellatum (Timofeyev, 1959), p. 87, pl. 7 fig. 30 (as Acanthorytidodiacrodium). U. Cambrian, U.S.S.R. --- , Deflandre and Deflandre-Rigaud, 1961, p. 9 (by implication).

A. hebetatum Timofeyev, 1959, p. 75, pl. 6 fig. 32, U. Cambrian, U.S.S.R.

A. hipocrateriforme (Timofeyev, 1959), p. 88, pl. 7 fig. 33 (as Acanthorytidodiacrodium). U. Cambrian, U.S.S.R. ---, Deflandre and Deflandre-Rigaud, 1961, p. 9 (by implication).

A. hippocrepiforme (Timofeyev, 1959), p. 84, pl. 7 fig. 18 (as Acanthorytidodiacrodium). M. Cambrian, U.S.S.R. ---, Deflandre and Deflandre-Rigaud, 1961, p. 9 (by implication).

A. hirtum (Naumova, 1950), p. 186, pl. 4 fig. 3.   (as Azonomonoletes). L. Ordovician, Baltic, U.S.S.R. --- , comb. nov.

A. ignoratum (Deunff, 1961a),p. 44, pl. 3 fig. 16 (as Diornatosphaera) . L. Ordovician, Sahara. --- , Deflandre and Deflandre-Rigaud, 1961, p. 10.

A. immarginatum Timofeyev, 1959, p. 70, pl. 6 fig. 7. M. Cambrian, U.S.S.R.

A. involutum Timofeyev, 1959, p. 74, pl. 6 fig. 28. M. Cambrian, U.S.S.R.

A. lanatum (Timofeyev, 1959), p. 87, pl. 7 fig. 32 (as Acanthorytidodiacrodium).L. Ordovician,
U.S.S.R. ---, Deflandre and Deflandre-Rigaud, 1961, p. 9 (by implication).

A. lasianthum Timofeyev, 1959, p. 78, pl. 6 fig. 47. L. Ordovician, U.S.S.R.

A. lazarewi Timofeyev,1962,pl.8 fig. 1. L.Camb.,Antarctica(from moraines). No desc.val.doubtful)

A. lentiforme (Timofeyev, 1959), pp. 84-5, pl. 7 fig. 20 (as Acanthorytidodiacrodium). M-U.
Cambrian, U.S.S.R. ---, Deflandre and Deflandre-Rigaud, 1961, p. 9 (by implication).

A. lineatum (Deunff, 1961a), p. 44, pl. 3 fig. 11 (as Diornatosphaera). L. Ordovician, Sahara,
--- , Deflandre and Deflandre-Rigaud, 1961, p. 10.

A. longum Timofeyev, 1959, p. 75, pl. 6 fig. 33. U. Cambrian, U.S.S.R.

A. mediale Timofeyev, 1959, p. 71, pl. 6 fig. 10. M. Cambrian, U.S.S.R.

A. meonanthum (Naumova, 1950) pp. 183-4, pl. 3 fig. 5,   (as Azonomonoletes). L. Ordovician,
Baltic, U.S.S.R.   ---, comb. nov.

A. micronatum Timofeyev, 1959, p. 77, pl. 6 fig. 44. L. Ordovician, U.S.S.R.

A. micronulatum (Timofeyev, 1959), pp. 83-4, pl. 7 fig. 15 (as Acanthorytidodiacrodium).U.
Cambrian, U.S.S.R. ---, Deflandre and Deflandre-Rigaud, 1961, p. 9 (by implication).

A. mitraeforme Timofeyev, 1959, pp. 72-3, pl. 6 fig. 19. M. Cambrian, U.S.S.R.

A. nidiusculum (Timofeyev, 1959), p. 79, pl. 7 fig. 2 (as Acanthorytidodiacrodium). U. Cambrian,
U.S.S.R.   --- , Deflandre and Deflandre-Rigaud, 1961, p. 9 (by implication).

A. novum Timofeyev, 1959, p. 74, pl. 6 fig. 29. U. Cambrian, U.S.S.R.

A. numerosum Timofeyev, 1959, p. 71, pl. 6 fig. 12.M. -U.Cambrian, U.S.S.R.

A. oblongatum (Timofeyev, 1959), p. 82, pl. 7 fig. 8 (as Acanthorytidodiacrodium).U. Cambrian,
U.S.S.R. --- , Deflandre and Deflandre-Rigaud, 1961, p. 9 (by implication).

A. obolense Timofeyev, 1962, pl. 8 fig. 2. U. Cambrian, U.S.S.R.

A. ordinarium Timofeyev, 1959, p. 72, pl. 6 fig. 18. M. Cambrian, U.S.S.R.

A. orthoploceum (Timofeyev, 1959), p. 83, pl. 7 fig. 12 (as Acanthorytidodiacrodium). U. Cambrian,
U.S.S.R. --- , Deflandre and Deflandre-Rigaud, 1961, p. 9 (by implication).

A. papillare Timofeyev, 1959, p. 74, pl. 6 fig. 25, L. Ordovician, U.S.S.R.

A. papilliforme (Timofeyev, 1959), p. 83, pl. 7 fig. 14 (as Acanthorytidodiacrodium).
U. Cambrian-L. Ordovician, U.S.S.R. ---, Deflandre and Deflandre-Rigaud, 1961,
p. 9 (by implication).

A. partiale Timofeyev, 1959, p. 78, pl. 6 fig. 46. L. Ordovician, U.S.S.R.

A. patulum (Timofeyev, 1959), p. 85, pl. 7 fig. 22 (as Acanthorytidodiacrodium).M. Cambrian-
L. Ordovician, U.S.S.R. ---, Deflandre and Deflandre-Rigaud, 1961, p. 9
(by implication).

A. perspicuum Timofeyev, 1959, p. 78, pl. 6 fig. 48. L. Ordovician, U.S.S.R.

A. petrovi Timofeyev, 1959, p. 77, pl. 6 fig. 43. U. Cambrian-L. Ordovician, U.S.S.R.

A. phaseolus (Deunff, 1961), p. 44, pl 3 fig. 14. (as Diornatosphaera), L. Ordovician, Sahara.
    --- , Deflandre and Deflandre-Rigaud, 1961, p. 10.

A. plenum Timofeyev, 1959, p. 72, pl. 6 fig. 17. M. Cambrian, U.S.S.R.

A. polimorphum Timofeyev, 1959, p. 71, pl. 6 fig. 9. M.-U. Cambrian, U.S.S.R.

A. prolatum (Timofeyev, 1959), p. 79, pl. 7 fig. 1 (as Acanthorytidodiacrodium) M. Cambrian,
    U.S.S.R. --- , Deflandre and Deflandre-Rigaud, 1961, p. 9 (by implication).

A. prolongatum (Timofeyev, 1959), p. 82, pl. 7 fig. 6 (as Acanthorytidodiacrodium). M. Cambrian-
    L. Ordovician, U.S.S.R. ---- , Deflandre and Deflandre-Rigaud, 1961, p. 9
    (by implication).

A. proximum Timofeyev, 1959, p. 70, pl. 6 fig. 4. M. Cambrian, U.S.S.R.

A. punctulatum Timofeyev, 1959, p. 77, pl. 6 fig. 42. U. Cambrian, U.S.S.R.

A. quadrandularis (Naumova, 1950), p. 187, pl. 4 figs. 11-12 (as Azonomonoletes) L. Ordovician,
    Baltic U.S.S.R. --- , comb. nov.

A. quadrangulum Timofeyev, 1959, p. 78, pl. 6 fig. 49. L. Ordovician, U.S.S.R.

A. reclinatum Timofeyev, 1959, p. 77, pl. 6 fig. 40. U. Cambrian, U.S.S.R.

A. rigidulum (Timofeyev, 1959), p. 83, pl. 7 fig. 13 (as Acanthorytidodiacrodium).U. Cambrian,
    U.S.S.R. --- , Deflandre and Deflandre-Rigaud, 1961, p. 9 (by implication).

A. rigidiusculum Timofeyev, 1959 , p. 76, pl. 6 fig. 39, U. Cambrian, U.S.S.R.

A. scaberrimum (Timofeyev, 1959), p. 85, pl. 7 fig. 23 (as Acanthorytidodiacrodium) U. Cambrian,
    U.S.S.R. --- , Deflandre and Deflandre-Rigaud, 1961, p. 9 (by implication).

A. schmidti Timofeyev, 1959, pp. 71-2, pl. 6 fig. 14. M. Cambrian, U.S.S.R.

A. secundarium Timofeyev, 1959, p. 70, pl. 6 fig. 8. M. Cambrian, U.S.S.R.

A. selectum Timofeyev, 1959, p. 75, pl. 6 fig. 34. U. Cambrian, U.S.S.R.

A. seronitum (Timofeyev, 1959), p. 82, pl. 7 fig. 9 (as Acanthorytidodiacrodium) L. Ordovician,
    U.S.S.R. --- , Deflandre and Deflandre-Rigaud, 1961, p. 9 (by implication).

A. sexcuspidatum Timofeyev, 1959, p. 76, pl. 6 fig. 37. U. Cambrian, U.S.S.R.

A. sexdentatum Timofeyev, 1959, p. 78, pl. 6 fig. 45. L. Ordovician, U.S.S.R.

A. simplissimum (Naumova, 1950), p. 187, pl. 4 fig. 10 (as Azonomonoletes).L. Ordovician,
    Baltic, U.S.S.R. --- , comb. nov.

A. spathulatum Timofeyev, 1959, p. 73,pl. 6 fig. 21. U. Cambrian-L. Ordovician, U.S.S.R.

A. spinellosum (Naumova, 1950), p. 183, pl. 3 fig. 3 (as Azonomonoletes). L. Ordovician,
    Baltic U.S.S.R. --- , comb. nov.

A. spinutisum Timofeyev, 1959, p. 76, pl. 6 fig. 38. U. Cambrian, U.S.S.R.

A. squarrosum Timofeyev, 1959, p. 72, pl. 6 fig. 15. M. Cambrian, U.S.S.R.

A. subbarbatum Timofeyev, 1959, p. 79, pl. 6 fig. 51. L. Ordovician, U.S.S.R.

A. subrotundum (Naumova, 1950), p. 183, pl. 3 fig. 4, (as Azonomonoletes). L. Ordovician,
    Baltic U.S.S.R. --- , comb. nov.

A. subscabrum (Naumova, 1950), p. 185, pl. 3 figs. 13-4 (as Azonomonoletes). L. Ordovician,
    U.S.S.R. --- , comb. nov.

A. sukatschevi Timofeyev, 1959, p. 76, pl. 6 fig. 36, U. Cambrian, U.S.S.R.

A. tectum (Timofeyev, 1959), pp. 81-2, pl. 7 fig. 5 (as Acanthorytidodiacrodium). M. Cambrian,
    U.S.S.R. --- , Deflandre and Deflandre-Rigaud, 1961, p. 9 (by implication).

A. trinatum (Timofeyev, 1959), p. 81, pl. 7 fig. 4 (as Acanthorytidodiacrodium). L. Ordovician,
    U.S.S.R. --- , Deflandre and Deflandre-Rigaud, 1961, p. 9 (by implication).

A. typicum (Timofeyev, 1959), p. 85, pl. 7 fig. 21 (as Acanthorytidodiacrodium). U. Cambrian,
    U.S.S.R. --- , Deflandre and Deflandre-Rigaud, 1961, p. 9 (by implication).

A. uniforme Timofeyev, 1959, p. 69, pl. 6 fig. 2. M. Cambrian - L. Ordovician, U.S.S.R.

A. unigeminum (Timofeyev, 1959), pp. 85-6, pl. 7 fig. 24 (as Acanthorytidodiacrodium).
    M. Cambrian, U.S.S.R. --- , Deflandre and Deflandre-Rigaud, 1961, p. 9
    (by implication).

A. varium (Naumova, 1950), p. 187, pl. 4 fig. 13 (as Azonomonoletes). L. Ordovician,
    Baltic U.S.S.R. --- , comb. nov.

A. varium (Timofeyev, 1959, non Naumova, 1950), p. 84, pl. 7 fig. 19 (as Acanthorytidodia-
    crodium).--- Deflandre and Deflandre-Rigaud, 1961, p. 9 (by implication).

A. vestitum (Timofeyev, 1959), p. 84, pl. 7 fig. 16 (as Acanthorytidodiacrodium) M. Cambrian,
    U.S.S.R. ---, Deflandre and Deflandre-Rigaud, 1961, p. 9 (by implication).

A. villosiusculum Timofeyev, 1959, pp. 73-4, pl. 6 fig. 24, M.-U.Cambrian, U.S.S.R.

A. vulgare (Timofeyev, 1959), p. 86, pl. 7 fig. 25 (as Acanthorytidodiacrodium). U. Cambrian-
    L. Ordovician, U.S.S.R. --- , Deflandre and Deflandre-Rigaud, 1961, p. 9
    (by implication).

A. zonatum (Timofeyev, 1959), p. 84, pl. 7 fig. 17 (as Acanthorytidodiacrodium). U. Cambrian,
    U.S.S.R. ---, Deflandre and Deflandre-Rigaud, 1961, p. 9 (by implication).

ACHOMOSPHAERA Evitt, 1963, p. 163.

* A. ramulifera (Deflandre, 1937c), pp. 74-5, pls. 15 figs. 5-6, 17, fig. 10. U. Cretaceous,
    France (as Hystrichosphaeridium). Baltisphaeridium ramuliferum Downie and Sarjeant, 1963,
    p.92. ---, Evitt, 1963, p. 163.

ACTINISCUS Ehrenberg,1854. No description. Description by Frenguelli, 1940, pp. 106-9.

A. ?discus Ehrenberg, 1854, pl. 21 fig. 49, Pliocene, Algeria (no text description).

A. elegans Ehrenberg, 1844 (reference not located) (as Dictyocha). Pliocene, Sicily. ---,
    Ehrenberg, 1854, pl. 22 fig. 31.

A. heptagonus Ehrenberg, 1841 (reference not located) (as Mesocena). Pliocene, Greece. ---,
    Ehrenberg, 1854, pl. 20 sect. 1 fig. 49.

* A. pentasterias Ehrenberg, 1841 (reference not located) Pliocene, Greece.   --- ,
         Ehrenberg, 1854, pls. 18 fig. 61, 19 fig. 45, 20 sect. 1 fig. 48, 33 sect. 17 fig. 1,
         35 pt. A. sect. 23 fig. 1.

A. ?rota Ehrenberg, 1854, pl. 21 fig. 50, Pliocene, Algeria (no text description).

A. sexfurcatus Ehrenberg, 1854, pl. 35 sect. 4 fig. 15, Recent,Atlantic (no text description).

A. sirius Ehrenberg, 1854, pl. 33 sect. 15 fig. 1,   Miocene, Virginia, U.S.A. (no text
         description).

A. ?stella Ehrenberg, 1838, (reference not located) (as Dictyocha).   Miocene, Virginia, U.S.A.,
         Pliocene, Sicily and Greece.   ---, Ehrenberg, 1854, pl. 22 fig. 52.

A. tetrasterias Ehrenberg, 1854, pl. 28 fig. 62, Miocene, Virginia, U.S.A. (no text description).

ACTINOTHECA Cookson and Eisenack, 1960a, pp. 9-10. (Generic description omitted).   Generic
         description in Cookson and Eisenack, 1961a, p. 75.

* A. aphroditae Cookson and Eisenack, 1960a, pp. 9-10, pl. 2 figs. 19-20, U. Cretaceous,
         Australia.

AIORA Cookson and Eisenack, 1960a, p. 9.

* A. fenestrata (Deflandre and Cookson, 1955), p. 283, pl. 3 fig. 2, (as Cannosphaeropsis).
         U. Cretaceous, Australia. --- , Cookson and Eisenack, 1960a, p.9.

AMPHIDIADEMA Cookson and Eisenack, 1960a, p. 4.

* A. denticulata Cookson and Eisenack, 1960a, p. 4, pl. 1 fig. 11. U. Cretaceous, Australia.

ANGULARIA Samoilovitch in Maliavkina et al., 1961, p. 255.

* A. viridula Samoilovitch in Maliavkina et al., 1961, p. 256, pl. 83 figs. 5a-d.
         U. Cretaceous, Siberia, U.S.S.R.

ANTHATRACTUS Deunff, 1954d, p. 1065.

* A. insolitus Deunff, 1954d, p. 1065, text-fig. 12,   Devonian, Canada. (Description in Deunff,
         1961b, p. 217).

ANTROSPHAERA Sarjeant, 1961a, pp. 111-12.

* A. calloviensis Sarjeant, 1961a, p. 112, pl. 13 fig. 7, text-fig. 12.   M. Jurassic, England.

APTEA Eisenack, 1958c, p. 393.

*A. polymorpha Eisenack, 1958c, p. 394-5, pl. 22 figs. 5-12.   L. Cretaceous, Germany.

APTEODINIUM Eisenack, 1958c, p. 385.

A. ciliatum Gocht, 1959, p. 65, pl. 8 figs. 5-6.   L. Cretaceous, Germany.

A. conjunctum Eisenack and Cookson, 1960, p. 5, pl. 1 figs. 7-8.   L. Cretaceous, Australia.

* A. granulatum Eisenack, 1958c, p. 386-7, pl. 23 figs. 8-14, text-fig. 1.   L. Cretaceous,
         Germany.

A. maculatum Eisenack and Cookson, 1960, pp. 4-5, pl. 2 figs. 1-3 .   L.-U. Creatceous,
         Australia.

APPLANOPSIS Döring, 1961, p. 112.

A. dampieri (Balme, 1957), p. 32, pl. 8 figs. 88-90 (as Zonalapollenites).
   L. Jurassic, Australia.   ---, Döring, 1961, p. 113.

* A. lenticularis Döring, 1961, p. 113, pl. 16 figs. 9-10.   U. Jurassic, Germany.

ARCHAEODISCINA° Naumova, 1961, p. 113.

 * A. granulata Naumova, 1961, p. 115, pl. 3 fig. 14.   L. Cambrian, U.S.S.R.

A. formosa ° Naumova and Pavlovski, 1961, p. 182, fig. 1. Pre-Cambrian, Scotland.

ARCHAEOFAVOSINA ° Naumova, 1961, p. 113.

* A. simplex Naumova, 1961, p. 113, pl. 3 fig. 11. Pre-Cambrian, U.S.S.R.

ARCHAEOHYSTRICHOSPHAERIDIUM Timofeyev, 1959, p. 32.   Type species not specified.
   (See comments in Downie and Sarjeant, 1963, p. 91.).

A. acanthaceum Timofeyev, 1959, p. 36, pl. 3 fig. 19.   M.-U. Cambrian, U.S.S.R.

A. accommodatum Timofeyev, 1959, p. 38, pl. 3 fig. 26.   M. Cambrian, U.S.S.R.

A. acer Timofeyev, 1959, p. 38, pl. 3 fig. 27.   M. Cambrian, U.S.S.R.

A. aculeatum Isagulova, 1963, pl. 1 fig. 25 (no text description).   Jurassic, Lvov-Volyu
   Region U.S.S.R.

A. acutangulatum Timofeyev, 1959, p. 48, pl. 3 fig. 78.   L. Ordovician, U.S.S.R.

A. acerosum Timofeyev, 1959, p. 34, pl. 3 fig. 9. U. Cambrian, U.S.S.R.

A. adligans Timofeyev, 1959, pp. 41-2, pl. 3 fig. 45.   U. Cambrian, U.S.S.R.

A. angulosum Timofeyev, 1959, p. 46, pl. 3 fig. 66.   M. Cambrian, U.S.S.R.

A. arenigum Timofeyev, 1959, p. 33, pl. 3 fig. 5.   L. Ordovician, U.S.S.R.

A. bifurcatum Timofeyev, 1959, p. 34, pl. 3 fig. 6.   M.-U. Cambrian, U.S.S.R.

A. capillatum Timofeyev, 1959, p. 40, pl. 3 fig. 36.   M.-U. Cambrian, U.S.S.R.

A. cellulare Timofeyev, 1959, p. 33, pl. 3 fig. 4.   M. Cambrian, U.S.S.R.

A. cinctum Timofeyev, 1959, p. 48, pl. 3 fig. 79.   L. Ordovician, U.S.S.R.

A. complicatum Timofeyev, 1959, p. 48, pl. 3 fig. 76.   L. Ordovician, U.S.S.R.

A. contortuplicatum Timofeyev, 1959, p. 48, pl. 3 fig. 75.   L. Ordovician, U.S.S.R.

A. coroniforme Timofeyev, 1959, p. 40, pl. 3 fig. 38.   M.-U. Cambrian, U.S.S.R.

A. crispatum Timofeyev, 1959, p.38, pl. 3 fig. 29.   M. Cambrian, U.S.S.R.

A. cuneidentatum Timofeyev, 1959, p. 42, pl. 3 fig. 47.   M. Cambrian, U.S.S.R.

A. curvativum Timofeyev, 1959, p. 37, pl. 3 fig. 21.   M. Cambrian, U.S.S.R.

A. cuspidatum Timofeyev, 1959, p. 41, pl. 3 fig. 43.   M. Cambrian, U.S.S.R.

A. dasyacanthum Timofeyev, 1959, p. 43, pl. 3 fig. 52.   M.-U. Cambrian, U.S.S.R.

A. dentatum Timofeyev, 1959, p. 41, pl. 3 fig. 44.   U. Cambrian-L. Ordovician, U.S.S.R.

A. denticulatum Timofeyev, 1959, p. 43, pl. 3 fig. 51.   U. Cambrian, U.S.S.R.

A. diadromum Timofeyev, 1959, p. 36, pl. 3 fig. 16.   L. Ordovician, U.S.S.R.

A. diploporum Timofeyev, 1959, p. 35, pl. 3 fig. 11.   M. Cambrian, U.S.S.R.

A. dorofeevi Timofeyev, 1959, p. 37, pl. 3 fig. 23.   L.-M. Cambrian, U.S.S.R.

A. duplicativum Timofeyev, 1959, p. 37, pl. 3 fig. 25.   M.-U. Cambrian, U.S.S.R.

A. ellipsoideum Timofeyev, 1959, pp. 34-5, pl. 3 fig. 10.   L. Ordovician, U.S.S.R.

A. extremum Timofeyev, 1959, p. 41, pl. 3 fig. 42.   L. Ordovician, U.S.S.R.

A. flexile Timofeyev, 1959, p. 39, pl. 3 fig. 31.   M. Cambrian, U.S.S.R.

A. genuinum Timofeyev, 1959, p. 46, pl. 3 fig. 68.   U. Cambrian, U.S.S.R.

A. girofleum Timofeyev, 1959, p. 39, pl. 3 fig. 35.   M.-U. Cambrian, U.S.S.R.

A. gladkovae Timofeyev, 1959, p. 44, pl. 3 fig. 56.   M. Cambrian, U.S.S.R.

A. ianischewskyi Timofeyev, 1959, p. 33, pl. 3 fig. 2.   L.-M. Cambrian, U.S.S.R.

A. impalpabile Timofeyev, 1959, p. 38, pl. 3 fig. 30.   M. Cambrian, U.S.S.R.

A. imperfectum Timofeyev, 1959, p. 47, pl. 3 fig. 73.   L. Ordovician, U.S.S.R.

A. innominatum Timofeyev, 1959, p. 36, pl. 3 fig. 20.   L. Cambrian, U.S.S.R.

A. kudrjawzevi Timofeyev, 1959, p. 48, pl. 3 fig. 77.   U. Cambrian, U.S.S.R.

A. laxum Timofeyev, 1959, p. 35, pl. 3 fig. 13.   L. Ordovician, U.S.S.R.

A. luber Timofeyev, 1959, p. 44-5, pl. 3 fig. 60.   U. Cambrian, U.S.S.R.

A. mickwitzi Timofeyev, 1959, p. 46, pl. 3 fig. 67.   L. Ordovician, U.S.S.R.

A. minimum Timofeyev, 1959, p. 44, pl. 3 fig. 58.   L. Ordovician, U.S.S.R.

A. minimum Isagulova, 1963 (non Timofeyev, 1959), pl. 1 fig. 24 (no text description). Jurassic, Lvov-Volyu Region, U.S.S.R.

A. minor Timofeyev, 1959, p. 33, pl. 3 fig. 3.   M. Cambrian, U.S.S.R.

A. nalivkini Timofeyev, 1959, p. 45, pl. 3 fig. 61.   U. Cambrian, U.S.S.R.

A. oblongum Timofeyev, 1959, p. 36, pl. 3 fig. 18.   L. Cambrian, U.S.S.R.

A. operculatum Timofeyev, 1959, p. 34, pl. 3 fig. 7. M. -U. Cambrian, U.S.S.R.

A. ovale Timofeyev, 1959, p. 35, pl. 3 fig. 14.   M. Cambrian, U.S.S.R.

A. panderi Timofeyev, 1959, pp. 42-3, pl. 3 fig. 50.   M. Cambrian, U.S.S.R.

A. papillatum Timofeyev, 1959, p. 43, pl. 3 fig. 54.   L. Ordovician, U.S.S.R.

A. papillosum Timofeyev, 1959, p. 37, pl. 3 fig. 22.   U. Cambrian-L. Ordovician, U.S.S.R.

A. parvum Timofeyev, 1959, p. 42, pl. 3 fig. 46.   M. Cambrian, U.S.S.R.

A. patentissimum Timofeyev, 1959, p. 43, pl. 3 fig. 53.   M. Cambrian, U.S.S.R.

A. pellucidum Timofeyev, 1959, p. 40, pl. 3 fig. 37.   L. Ordovician, U.S.S.R.

A. pentagonum Timofeyev, 1959, pp. 46-7, pl. 3 fig. 70.   L. Ordovician, U.S.S.R.

A. porrectum Timofeyev, 1959, p. 44, pl. 3 fig. 57.   M.-U. Cambrian, U.S.S.R.

A. protensum Timofeyev, 1959, p. 45, pl. 3 fig. 63.   U. Cambrian, U.S.S.R.

A. pungens Timofeyev, 1959, p. 39, pl. 3 fig. 33.   M. Cambrian, U.S.S.R.

A. quadricorne Timofeyev, 1959, p. 47, pl. 3 fig. 72.   M. Cambrian, U.S.S.R.

A. quadridentatum Timofeyev, 1959, p. 42, pl. 3 fig. 49.   U. Cambrian, U.S.S.R.

A. quadrinatum Timofeyev, 1959, p. 47, pl. 3 fig. 74.   U. Cambrian, U.S.S.R.

A. recticornum Timofeyev, 1959, p. 41, pl. 3 fig. 41.   M. Cambrian, U.S.S.R.

A. resistens Timofeyev, 1959, p. 37, pl. 3 fig. 24.   M. Cambrian, U.S.S.R.

A. scandeum Timofeyev, 1959, p. 46, pl. 3 fig. 69.   U. Cambrian, U.S.S.R.

A. scariosum Timofeyev, 1959, p. 47, pl. 3 fig. 71.   U. Cambrian, U.S.S.R.

A. scrotiforme Timofeyev, 1959, p. 44, pl. 3 fig. 59.   U. Cambrian, U.S.S.R.

A. semiclausum Timofeyev, 1959, pp. 43-4, pl. 3 fig. 55.   M. Cambrian, U.S.S.R.

A. semireticulatum Timofeyev, 1959, pp. 45-6, pl. 3 fig. 65.   M. Cambrian, U.S.S.R.

A. septangulum Timofeyev, 1959, p. 45, pl. 3 fig. 64.   U. Cambrian, U.S.S.R.

A. simplex Timofeyev, 1959, p. 39, pl. 3 fig. 32.   U. Cambrian, U.S.S.R.

A. singulare Timofeyev, 1959, p. 35, pl. 3 fig. 15.   L. Ordovician, U.S.S.R.

A. solitare Timofeyev, 1959, p. 34, pl. 3 fig. 8.   L. Ordovician, U.S.S.R.

A. stipiforme Timofeyev, 1959, p. 35, pl. 3 fig. 12.   L. Cambrian, U.S.S.R.

A. strictum Timofeyev, 1959, p. 38, pl. 3 fig. 28.   M. Cambrian, U.S.S.R.

A. tener Timofeyev, 1959, p. 40, pl. 3 fig. 39.   L. Ordovician, U.S.S.R.

A. triplicatum Timofeyev, 1959, p. 40, pl. 3 fig. 40.   U. Cambrian-L. Ordovician, U.S.S.R.

A. triviale Timofeyev, 1959, p. 36, pl. 3 fig. 17.   M.-U. Cambrian, U.S.S.R.

A. unguisum Timofeyev, 1959, p. 42, pl. 3 fig. 48.   U. Cambrian, U.S.S.R.

A. vologdense Timofeyev, 1959, pp. 32-3, pl. 3 fig. 1.   L. Cambrian, U.S.S.R.

A. waltz Timofeyev, 1959, p. 45, pl. 3 fig. 62.   U. Cambrian, U.S.S.R.

<u>A. zaleskyi</u> Timofeyev, 1959, p. 39, pl. 3 fig. 34.   L. Ordovician, U.S.S.R.

ARCHAEOPERISACCUS ° Naumova, 1961, p. 115.

* <u>A. balticus</u> Naumova, 1961, p. 115, pl. 3 fig. 17.   L. Cambrian, U.S.S.R.

ARCHAEOPERTUSINA ° Naumova, 1961, p. 113.

* <u>A. atava</u>° Naumova, 1961, p. 113, pl. 3 fig. 12.   Pre-Cambrian, U.S.S.R.

ARCHAEOSACCULINA ° Naumova ?   (in Naumova and Pavlovski 1961, p. 182).

<u>A. atava</u> ° Naumova ?   (in Naumova and Pavlovski 1961, p. 182, fig. 1.)   Pre-Cambrian,
      Scotland .

AREMORICANIUM Deunff, 1955b, p. 228.

* <u>A. rigaudae</u> Deunff, 1955b, pp. 228-9, text-figs. 1-3.   M. Ordovician, France.

AREOLIGERA Lejeune-Carpentier, 1938b, p. 164.

<u>A. birama</u> Maier, 1959, p. 304, pl. 29 fig. 2.   Oligocene, Germany (incorrectly as <u>A. biramum</u>).

<u>A. coronata</u> (O. Wetzel, 1933), p. 41, pl. 4 fig. 17   (as <u>Hystrichosphaera</u> <u>penicillata</u> forma
      coronata).U. Cretaceous, Germany ---, Lejeune-Carpentier, 1938b, p. B168.

<u>A. dermatica</u> Maier, 1959, p. 305, pl. 29 fig. 3.   Oligocene, Germany   (incorrectly as
      A. dermaticum).

<u>A. incerta</u> Klumpp, 1953, p. 389-10, pl. 17 figs. 1-2.   Eocene, Germany.

<u>A. medusettiformis</u> (O. Wetzel, 1932), pp. 41, 62,   pl.3 fig. 7 (as <u>Hystrichosphaera</u> <u>penicillata</u>
      forma <u>medusettiformis</u>).   U. Cretaceous, Germany.--- , Lejeune-Carpentier, 1938b,
      pp. B168-9.

<u>A. rhizopodiphora</u> (O. Wetzel, 1933), pp. 41, 62-3, pl. 4 fig. 18 (as <u>Hystrichosphaera</u> <u>penicillata</u>
      forma <u>rhizopodiphora</u>).   U. Cretaceous, Germany.--- , Lejeune-Carpentier, 1938b,
      p. B169.

* <u>A. senonensis</u> Lejeune-Carpentier, 1938b, pp. B164-6, text-figs. 1-3.   U. Cretaceous, Belgium.

<u>A. tenuicapillata</u> (O. Wetzel, 1933), p. 42, pl. 4 fig. 20 (as <u>Hystrichosphaera tenuicapillata</u>
      forma <u>irregularis</u>).   U. Cretaceous, Germany, --- , Lejeune-Carpentier, 1938b, p. B167.

<u>A. tenuicapillata</u> (O. We.) forma pinopollina O. Wetzel, 1933, pp. 42-3, pl. 4 fig. 22.
      U. Cretaceous, Belgium. (Lejeune-Carpentier, 1938b, p. 167, shows this assignation to be
      doubtful but does not propose transfer elsewhere).

<u>A. turbilineata</u> (O. Wetzel, 1933), p. 42, pl. 4 fig. 21 (as <u>Hystrichosphera tenuicapillata</u> forma
      turbilineata).   U. Cretaceous, Baltic.   --- , Lejeune-Carpentier, 1938b, p. B167.

ARNOLDIA Hovasse, 1956, pp. 2583-4.

* <u>A. antiqua</u> Hovasse,1956, pp. 2583-4, text-figs. 1-4.   Pre-Cambrian, Ivory Coast.

ASCODINIUM Cookson and Eisenack, 1960a, p. 5.

* <u>A. acrophorum</u> Cookson and Eisenack, 1960a, p. 5, pl. 1 figs. 19-20. U. Cretaceous, Australia.

A. parvum (Cookson and Eisenack, 1958), p. 28, pl. 4 figs. 12-13 (as Deflandrea parva).
    L. -U. Cretaceous, Australia. ---, Cookson and Eisenack, 1960a, p. 5.

A. serratum Cookson and Eisenack, 1960a, p. 5, pl. 1 figs. 21-2. U. Cretaceous, Australia.

BACISPHAERIDIUM Eisenack, 1962c, pp. 355-6.

*B. bacifer (Eisenack, 1934), p. 66, pl. 4 figs. 20-1 (as Bion (Ovum) bacifer). U. Ordovician,
    Baltic. Hystrichosphaeridium bacifer Eisenack, 1938a, p. 189. Veryhachium bacifer
    Deunff, 1954c, p. 306. --- , Eisenack, 1962c, p. 356.

BALTISPHAERIDIUM Eisenack, 1958c, p. 398, emend. Downie and Sarjeant, 1963, p. 89.

B. aculeatum (Timofeyev, 1959), p. 56, pl. 4 fig. 21 (as Hystrichosphaeridium). L. Ordovician,
    U.S.S.R. --- , Downie and Sarjeant, 1963, p. 89.

B. alloiteaui (Deunff, 1955a), p. 148, pl. 4 fig. 3 (as Micrhystridium). Devonian, Canada. --- ,
    Downie and Sarjeant, 1963, p. 89.

B. alperni Stockmans and Willière, 1962a, pp. 55-6, pl. 2 fig. 11, text-fig. 12. U. Devonian,
    Belgium.

B. andrewsi Stockmans and Willière, 1962b, pp. 88-9, pl. 2 fig. 16, text-fig. 7. U. Devonian,
    Belgium.

B. annulatum (Timofeyev, 1959), p. 56, pl. 4 fig. 22 (as Hystrichosphaeridium). L. Ordovician,
    U.S.S.R. --- , Downie and Sarjeant, 1963, p. 89.

B. anticum (Naumova, 1950), p. 188, pl. 5 fig. 2 (as Archaeletes). U. Cambrian, Baltic
    U.S.S.R. ---, comb. nov.

B. apiculatum (Timofeyev, 1959), p. 52, pl. 4 fig. 3 (as Hystrichosphaeridium). L. Ordovician,
    U.S.S.R. --- , Downie and Sarjeant, 1963, p. 89.

B. arbusculiferum Downie, 1963, p. 644, pl. 91 fig. 5, text-fig. 3d. M. Silurian, England.

B. armatum (Deflandre, 1937c), p. 76-7, pl. 16 figs. 6-7 (as Hystrichosphaeridium). U. Cretaceous
    France. --- , Downie and Sarjeant, 1963, p. 91.

B. arrectum (Timofeyev, 1959), p. 53, pl. 4 fig. 8 (as Hystrichosphaeridium). L. Ordovician,
    U.S.S.R. --- , Downie and Sarjeant, 1963, p. 89.

B. ashdodense (Rossignol, 1962), p. 132, pl. 2 fig. 2 (as Hystrichosphaeridium). Quaternary,
    Israel. --- , comb. nov.

B. asteroideum (Maslov, 1956), p. 262, pl. 86 fig. 13 (as Hystrichosphaera asteroidea)
    U. Cretaceous, Caucasus, U.S.S.R. Hystrichosphaeridium asteroideum. Deflandre and
    Deflandre-Rigaud, 1958, card 1359. Baltisphaeridium hirsutoides var. asteroidea
    Eisenack, 1959a, p. 196 --- , Downie and Sarjeant, 1963, p. 91.

B. biformoides (Eisenack, 1954b), pp. 68-9, pl. 11 figs. 16-20, (as Hystrichosphaeridium).
    Oligocene, East Prussia. --- , Downie and Sarjeant, 1963, p. 91.

B. bimarginatum (Timofeyev, 1959), p. 54, pl. 4 fig. 12, (as Hystrichosphaeridium).
    L. Ordovician, U.S.S.R. ---, Downie and Sarjeant, 1963, p. 89.

B. bohemicum (Eisenack, 1934), pp. 70-1, pl. 5 fig. 31 (as Ovum hispidum). Silurian,
    Bohemia. Hystrichosphaeridium bohemicum Eisenack, 1938a, p. 12. ---- ,
    Downie and Sarjeant, 1963, p. 89.

B. breviciliatum (Staplin, 1961), p. 408, pl. 48 fig. 16 (as Micrhystridium). U. Devonian,
  Canada. --- , Downie and Sarjeant, 1963, p. 90.

B. brevifurcatum (Eisenack, 1954a), p. 207-8, pl. 1 fig. 2, text-fig. 2 (as Hystrichosphaeridium).
  Lower Silurian, Sweden. --- , Downie and Sarjeant, 1963, p. 89.

B. brevispinosum (Eisenack, 1931), p. 111, pl. 5 figs. 3-5, (as Ovum hispidum).
  Baltic drift, Ordovician pebble. Hystrichosphaeridium brevispinosum, Eisenack, 1938,
  p. 12. --- , Eisenack, 1958b, p. 400.

B. brevispinosum (Eis. 1931) subsp. callosum Sannemann, 1955, pp. 325-6, pls. 1 figs. 1-4, 7;
  3 figs. 2-5, 10; 4 figs. 3-4; 6 figs. 11, 12; text-figs. 2a-d. L. Devonian, Germany.

B. brevispinosum (Eis. 1931) subsp. castaneoides Sannemann,1955, p. 326, pl. 4 figs. 13, 14,
  text-fig. 3. L. Devonian, Germany.

B. brevispinosum (Eis. 1931) var. granuliferum Downie, 1959, p. 59, pl. 10 fig. 5. M. Silurian,
  England.

B. cannosphaeropsisoides Stockmans and Willière, 1962b, pp. 90-1, pl. 1 fig. 17, text-fig. 9.
  U. Devonian, Belgium.

B. castaneum (Eisenack, 1934), p. 71, pl. 5 fig. 32 (as Ovum hispidum). Silurian, Bohemia.
  Hystrichosphaeridium castaneum Eisenack, 1938a, p. 12. ---, Downie and Sarjeant,
  1963, p. 90.

B. centrocarpum (Deflandre and Cookson, 1955), pp. 272-3, pl. 8 figs. 3-4 (as Hystrichosphaeridium). Miocene, Australia. ---, Gerlach, 1961, pp. 192-3.

B. circumscissum (Timofeyev, 1959), p. 53, pl. 4 fig. 9, (as Hystrichosphaeridium).
  L. Ordovician, U.S.S.R. ---, Downie and Sarjeant, 1963, p. 90.

B. cladum Downie, 1963, pp. 643-4, pl. 92 fig. 5, text-fig. 3a. M. Silurian, England.

B. claviculorum (Deflandre, 1938e), pp. 191-2, pl. 10 fig. 4 (as Hystrichosphaeridium).
  U. Jurassic, France. --- , Downie and Sarjeant, 1963, p. 91.

B. claviferum (Wilkinson, 1849), pp. 89-92, pl. 13 fig. 1 (as Xanthidium). U. Cretaceous,
  England. Hystrichosphaeridium claviferum Deflandre, 1946a, card 887. ---
  Downie and Sarjeant, 1963, p. 91.

B. clavispinulosum Churchill and Sarjeant, 1963, pp. 41-2, pl. 2 fig. 31, text-fig. 14.   Post-
  Pleistocene, Australia.

B. cognitum (Timofeyev, 1959), pp. 54-5, pl. 4 fig. 15 (as Hystrichosphaeridium). L. Ordovician,
  U.S.S.R. --- , Downie and Sarjeant, 1963, p. 90.

B. colligerum (Deflandre and Cookson, 1955), pp. 278-9, pl. 7 fig. 3 (as Hystrichosphaeridium).
  Eocene, Australia. ---, Downie and Sarjeant, 1963, p. 92.

B. coniferum (Sannemann, 1955), p. 327, pl. 4 fig. 2, text-figs. 4a-b (as Hystrichosphaeridium).
  --- , Downie and Sarjeant, 1963, p. 90.

B. conspersum (Naumova, 1950), p. 189, pl. 5 figs. 13-4 (as Archaeletes). U. Cambrian,
  Baltic U.S.S.R. ---, comb. nov.

B. conspicuum (Timofeyev, 1959), p. 54, pl. 4 fig. 14 (as Hystrichosphaeridium). U. Cambrian,
  U.S.S.R. --- , Downie and Sarjeant, 1963, p. 90.

B. corallinum Eisenack, 1959a, p. 201, pl. 16 figs. 15, 16.   U. Silurian, Sweden.

B. corollatum (Timofeyev, 1959), p. 54, pl. 4 fig. 11   (as Hystrichosphaeridium).   L. Ordovician,
U.S.S.R.   --- , Downie and Sarjeant, 1963, p. 90.

B. crassiechinatum (Staplin, 1961), p. 410, pl. 48 fig. 21   (as Micrhystridium).   U. Devonian,
Canada.   --- , Downie and Sarjeant, 1963, p. 90.

B. cretaceum (Merrill, 1895), pp. 15-16, text-fig. 12 (as ? Geodia).   L. Cretaceous, Texas,
U.S.A.   --- , Sarjeant, 1964 (in press).

B. cristatum (Downie, 1958), pp. 338-9, pl. 16 fig. 4, text-fig. 4f   (as Hystrichosphaeridium).
L. Ordovician, England.   --- , Eisenack, 1958b, p. 400.

B. cylindrosum Eisenack, 1963e, p. 213, pl. 20 figs. 4-5.   U. Ordovician, Baltic drift.

B. danicum (W. Wetzel, 1952), pp. 396-7, pl. A fig. 5, text-fig. 8, (as Areoligera).
U. Cretaceous, Denmark.   Hystrichosphaeridium danicum W. Wetzel, 1955, p. 34. --- ,
Downie and Sarjeant, 1963, p. 91.

B. densicomatum (Maier, 1959), pp. 307-8, pl. 29 figs. 708   (as Galea).   Oligocene, Germany.
--- , Gerlach, 1961, p. 193.

B. denticulatum (Courteville in Deflandre, 1946a), card 895 (as Hystrichosphaeridium).
U. Cretaceous, France.   --- , comb. nov.

B. denticulatum Stockmans and Willière, 1963   (non Courteville in Deflandre, 1946a), p. 458,
pl. 1 fig. 4, text-fig. 13.   Silurian, Belgium.

B. deunffii (Jansonius, 1962), p. 84, pl. 16 fig. 51, text-fig. 3-C   (as Multiplicisphaeridium).
L. Triassic, Canada.   --- , Sarjeant, 1964 (in press).

B. dictyophorum (Cookson and Eisenack, 1958), p. 44, pl. 11 fig. 14   (as Hystrichosphaeridium).
U. Jurassic, Papua.   --- , Downie and Sarjeant, 1963, p. 91.

B. differtum (Sannemann, 1955), p. 327, pl. 4 fig. 15, text-figs. 5a-c   (as Hystrichosphaeridium).
L. Devonian, Germany.   --- , Downie and Sarjeant, 1963, p. 90.

B. difforme (Pritchard, 1845), p. 188, pl. 12 figs. 513-4, (as ?Xanthidium).   U. Cretaceous,
England.   --- , Downie and Sarjeant, 1963, p. 92.

B. digitatum (Eisenack, 1938a), pp. 20-1, pl. 4 figs. 3-5, text-fig. 7   (as Hystrichosphaeridium).
Baltic drift, Ordovician pebble.   --- , Eisenack, 1959a, p. 200.

B. dignum (Sannemann, 1955), p. 327, pls. 1 fig. 5; 4 fig. 11; text-fig. 7   (as Hystrichosphaeridium).   L. Devonian, Germany.   --- , Downie and Sarjeant, 1963, p. 90.

B. dilatispinosum Downie, 1963, p. 642, pl. 92 fig. 4.   M. Silurian, England.

B. diploporum (Eisenack, 1951), p. 190-1, pl. 2 fig. 6   (as Hystrichosphaeridium).   Baltic drift,
Ordovician pebble.   --- , Downie and Sarjeant, 1963, p. 90.

B. downiei Sarjeant, 1960a, pp. 138-9.   U. Jurassic, England.   (Figured by Downie, 1957,
pl. 20 fig. 10, text-fig. 4c).

B. duvernayensis (Staplin, 1961), p. 410, pl. 49 fig. 8   (as Micrhystridium).   U. Devonian,
Canada.   --- , comb. nov.

B. echiniplax Churchill and Sarjeant, 1963, p. 46, pl. 2 fig. 26, text-fig. 1.   Post-Pleistocene,
Australia.

<u>B. echinodermum</u> Stockmans and Willière, 1963, pp. 460-2, pls. 2 figs. 5-8, 3 fig. 26 text-figs. 17-20. Silurian, Belgium.

<u>B. echinoides</u> (Maier, 1959), pp. 318-9, pl. 32 figs. 5-6 (as <u>Hystrichosphaeridium</u>). Oligocene, Germany. --- , Downie and Sarjeant, 1963, p. 91.

<u>B. echinosum</u> (Staplin, 1961), p. 408, pl. 48 fig. 14 (as <u>Micrhystridium</u>). U. Devonian, Canada. --- , Downie and Sarjeant, 1963, p. 90.

<u>B. ehrenbergi</u> (Deflandre, 1947d), text-fig. 1 no. 5 (as <u>Hystrichosphaeridium</u>). U. Jurassic, France. --- , Sarjeant, 1961a, p. 103.

<u>B. ehrenbergi</u> (Defl. 1947d) var. <u>brevispinosum</u> Sarjeant, 1961a, p. 103, pl. 15 fig. 8, text-fig. 8a. U. Jurassic, England.

<u>B. eisenacki</u> (Sannemann, 1955), pp. 327-8, pl. 4 figs. 10, 12, text-figs. 8a-d (as <u>Hystricho-sphaeridium</u>). L. Devonian, Germany. ---, Downie and Sarjeant, 1963, p. 90.

<u>B. eisenackianum</u> (Deunff, 1958), pp. 23-4, pl. 2 figs. 26, 30, 31 (as <u>Hystrichosphaeridium</u>) M. Ordovician, France. --- , Downie and Sarjeant, 1963, p. 90.

<u>B. eisenackianum</u> (Dff. 1958) var. <u>crozonensis</u> Deunff, 1958, p. 24, pl. 2 figs. 25-7, 29, 32. M. Ordovician, France.

<u>B. eoplanktonicum</u> (Eisenack, 1955), pp. 178-9, pl. 4 fig. 14 (as <u>Hystrichsphaeridium</u>). U. Silurian, Baltic. --- , Downie, 1959, p. 60.

<u>B. erraticum</u> (Eisenack, 1954a), p. 209, pl. 1 figs. 6-7, text-fig. 7 (as <u>Hystrichosphaeridium</u>). Baltic drift, Silurian pebble. --- , Downie and Sarjeant, 1963, p. 90.

<u>B. excisum</u> (Naumova, 1950), p. 188, pl. 5 fig. 7 (as <u>Archaeletes</u>). U. Cambrian, Baltic U.S.S.R. --- , comb. nov.

<u>B. ferox</u> (Deflandre, 1937a), p. 72, pl. 14 figs. 3-4 (as <u>Hystrichosphaeridium</u>). U. Cretaceous, France. --- , Downie and Sarjeant, 1963, p. 91.

<u>B. fimbriatum</u> (White, 1842), p. 35, pl. 4 fig. 3 (as <u>Xanthidium</u>). U. Cretaceous, England. <u>Hystrichosphaeridium fimbriatum</u> Deflandre 1946a, card 899. --- Sarjeant, 1959, p. 339.

<u>B. fissile</u> Stockmans and Willière, 1963, pp. 458-9, pl. 1 fig. 6, text-fig. 14. Silurian, Belgium.

<u>B. franconium</u> (Sannemann, 1955), p. 328, pls. 3 fig. 1; 5 figs. 1, 2 (as <u>Hystrichosphaeridium</u>). L. Devonian, Germany. --- , Downie and Sarjeant, 1963, p. 90.

<u>B. geometricum</u> (Pastiels, 1948), p. 41, pl. 3 figs. 1-11 (as <u>Hystrichosphaeridium</u>). Eocene, Belgium. --- , Downie and Sarjeant, 1963, p. 91.

<u>B. galeum</u> (Maier, 1959b,) p. 300, pl. 29 fig. 4 (as <u>Galea</u>). Oligocene, Germany. ---, Sarjeant, 1964 (in press).

<u>B. gilsonii</u> (Kufferath, 1950), pp. 33-4, text-fig. 8 (as <u>Micrhystridium</u>). Post-Pleistocene, Belgium. --- , Downie and Sarjeant, 1963, p. 91.

<u>B. gotlandicum</u> (Eisenack, 1954a), p. 209, pl. 1 fig. 5, text-fig. 6 (as <u>Hystrichosphaeridium</u>). L. Silurian, Sweden. --- , Downie and Sarjeant, 1963, p. 90.

<u>B. gracile</u> Timofeyev, 1962, pl. 9 fig. 1. M. Cambrian, U.S.S.R.

<u>B. granulatispinosum</u> Downie, 1963, pp. 640-1, pl. 91 figs. 1, 7. M. Silurian, England.

B. granulosum (Deflandre, 1937c), p. 29, pl. 16 fig. 4 (as Hystrichosphaeridium xanthiopyxides var. granulosum). U. Cretaceous, France. ---, Sarjeant, 1962a, p. 264.

B. grosjeani Stockmans & Willière, 1962b, pp. 87-8, pl. 2 fig. 17, text-fig.6. U. Dev., Belgium.

B. heteracanthum (Deflandre & Cookson, 1955), p. 276, pl. 2 figs. 5-6, text-figs. 40-1 (as Hystri-chosphaeridium). U. Cretaceous-L. Eocene, Australia. ---, Downie & Sarjeant,1963,p.91).

B. hippocrepicum (Timofeyev, 1959), p. 52, pl. 4 fig. 2 (as Hystrichosphaeridium). L. Ordovician, U.S.S.R. ---, Downie and Sarjeant, 1963, p. 90.

B. hirsutoides Eisenack, 1951, p. 189-90, pl. 3 fig. 8 (as Hystrichosphaeridium). L. Ordovician, Estonia, U.S.S.R. --- , Eisenack, 1958b, p. 400.

B. hirsutoides (Eis. 1951) var. hamatum Downie, 1958, p. 335, pl. 16 fig. 1, text-figs. 2j-k. L. Ordovician, England.

B. hirsutum (Ehrenberg, 1838), p. 109-36, pl. 1 fig. 13 (as Xanthidium). Cretaceous, Germany. Ovum hispidum hirsutum W. Wetzel, 1922, pp. 60-1. Hystrichosphaeridium hirsutum Deflandre, 1937c, p. 78. ---, Klement, 1960, p. 58.

B. hirsutum (Ehr. 1838) subsp. amplum W. Wetzel, 1955, p. 38, text-fig. 11. Danian, Germany.

B. hirsutum (Ehr. 1838) forma minor O. Wetzel, 1933, pp. 45-6, pl. 4 fig. 26. U. Cret.,Baltic.

B. hirsutum (Ehr. 1838) forma varians O. Wetzel, 1933, pp. 47-8, pl. 4 figs. 27-9. U. Cretaceous, Baltic.

B. horridum (Deflandre, 1957c), p. 74, pl. 15 figs. 7-8 (as Hystrichosphaeridium). U. Cretaceous, France. ---, Downie and Sarjeant, 1963, p. 91.

B. huguonioti (Valensi, 1955a), pp. 38-9, text-fig. 2a (as Hystrichosphaeridium). Cretaceous, France. ---, Downie and Sarjeant, 1963, p. 91.

B. hydraferum Stockmans & Willière, 1962b, pp. 93-4, pl. 2 fig.15, text-fig.13. U. Dev.,Belgium.

B. hymenoferum (Eisenack, 1938a), p. 19, pl. 3 figs. 2-5 (as Hystrichosphaeridium). Baltic drift, Ordovician pebble. ---, Eisenack, 1958b, p. 400.

B. hystrichoreticulatum (Eisenack, 1938a), p. 20, pl. 3 figs. 6a-b (as Hystrichosphaeridium). Baltic drift, Ordovician pebble. --- , Downie and Sarjeant, 1963, p. 90.

B. iaculigerum Klement, 1960, pp. 57-8, pl. 7 fig. 10. U. Jurassic, Germany.

B. inconspicuum (Timofeyev, 1959), p. 54, pl. 4 fig. 13 (as Hystrichosphaeridium). L. Ordovician, U.S.S.R. ---, Downie and Sarjeant, 1963, p. 90.

B. integrum (Sannemann, 1955), p. 329, pl. 5 fig. 12, text-fig. 12 (as Hystrichosphaeridium). ---, Downie and Sarjeant, 1963, p. 90.

B. intermedium (O. Wetzel, 1933), p. 46, text-fig. 14 (as Hystrichosphaera intermedia). U. Cretaceous, Baltic. Hystrichosphaeridium intermedium Deflandre, 1937c, p. 77. ---, Downie and Sarjeant, 1963, p. 91.

B. inusitatum Klement, 1960, pp. 60-1, pl. 7 fig. 9. U. Jurassic, Germany.

B. israelianum (Rossignol, 1962), p. 132, pl. 2 fig. 3 (as Hystrichosphaeridium). Quaternary, Israel. ---, comb. nov.

B. korykum (Maier, 1959), p. 310, pl. 30 figs. 7-8 (as Galea). Oligocene, Germany. ---, Sarjeant, 1964 (in press).

B. leve (Maier, 1959), p. 308, pl. 30 figs. 1-2 (as Galea). Oligocene-Miocene, Germany.
  ---, Sarjeant, 1964 (in press).

B. lewisi (Deunff, 1954a), p. 240, text-fig. 3 (as Hystrichosphaeridium). Silurian, France.
  --- Downie and Sarjeant, 1963, p. 90.

B. longifurcatum (Firtion, 1952), pp. 157-8, pl. 9 fig. 1, text-fig. 1 H-M (as Hystrichosphaeridium).
  U. Cretaceous, France. ---, Downie and Sarjeant, 1963, p. 91.

B. longispinosoides (Sannemann, 1955), pp. 329-30, pls. 2 fig. 10; 2 figs. 1-4; 3 figs. 6, 8;
  6 figs. 1-6; text-figs. 9a, b (as Hystrichosphaeridium). L. Devonian, Germany.

* B. longispinosum (Eisenack, 1931), pp. 110-1, pl. 5 figs. 6-17 (as Ovum hispidum). Baltic
  drift, Ordovician pebble. Hystrichosphaera longispinosa O. Wetzel, 1933, p. 44.
  Hystrichosphaeridium longispinosum Eisenack, 1938, p. 12-4. ---, Eisenack, 1958c,
  p. 398.

B. longispinosum (Eis. 1931) forma filifera Eisenack, 1959a, p. 195, pl. 15 fig. 1.
  L. Ordovician, Sweden.

B. longispinosum (Eis. 1931) forma latiradiata Eisenack, 1959a, p. 195, pl. 15 fig. 4.
  L. Ordovician, Sweden.

B. longispinosum (Eis. 1931) var. parvum Downie, 1963, p. 639, pl. 91 fig. 2.
  M. Silurian, England.

B. longispinosum (Eis. 1931) var. paucispinosum, Downie, 1959, p. 640, pl. 91 fig. 4.
  M. Silurian, England.

B. longispinosum (Eis. 1931) var. uncinatum Downie, 1958, p. 337, text-fig. 2a. L. Ordovician,
  England.

B. longofilum (Maier, 1959), p. 317, pl. 32 fig. 7 (as Hystrichosphaeridium). Oligocene,
  Germany. ---, Downie and Sarjeant, 1963, p. 91.

B. lophophorum Eisenack, 1959a, p. 204, pl. 17 fig. 14. U. Silurian, Sweden.

B. lucidum (Deunff, 1958), pp. 25-6, pl. 9 figs. 80, 82-3, 85-9 (as Hystrichosphaeridium).
  M. Ordovician France. ---, Downie and Sarjeant, 1963, p. 90.

B. lumectum Sarjeant, 1960a, pp. 139-40, pl. 6 fig. 1, text-fig. 2. U. Jurassic, England.

B. lychneum (Maier, 1959), p. 310, pl. 30 fig. 6 (as Galea). Miocene, Germany. ---,
  Sarjeant, 1964 (in press).

B. machaerophorum (Deflandre and Cookson, 1955), p. 274, pl. 9 figs 4, 8. (as Hystrichosphaeridium). Miocene, Australia. ---, Gerlach, 1961, p. 191.

B. macropylum Eisenack, 1959a, pl. 16 figs. 3-5, text-fig. 9. L. Ordovician, Sweden.

B. malleoferum (H.H. White, 1842), p. 37, pl. 4 fig. 7 (as Xanthidium). U. Cretaceous,
  England. Hystrichosphaeridium malleoferum, Deflandre, 1937c, p. 31. ---,
  Downie and Sarjeant, 1963, p. 91.

B. mariannae (Philippot, 1949), pp. 56-7, text-fig. 2 (as Hystrichosphaeridium). U. Cretaceous,
  France. ---, Downie and Sarjeant, 1963, p. 91.

B. meson (Eisenack, 1955), p. 179 (figured in Eisenack, 1954a, pl. 1 figs. 3-9, text-figs. 3-4)
  (as Hystrichosphaeridium). L. Silurian, Sweden. ---, Downie and Sarjeant, 1963, p. 90.

B. mespilanum (Maier, 1959), pp. 306-7, pl. 29 figs. 5-6.   (as Galea).   Miocene, Germany.
   ---, Sarjeant, 1964 (in press).

B. micranthum Eisenack, 1959a, p. 203, pl. 17 fig. 13. L. Ordovician, Estonia, U.S.S.R.

B. microcladum Downie, 1963, p. 645, pls. 91 fig. 3, 92 fig. 6, text-fig. 3g.   M. Silurian,
   England.

B. microfurcatum (Deunff, 1957), p. 6, fig. 2 (as Hystrichosphaeridium).   M. Devonian, Canada.
   ---, Stockmans and Willière, 1963b, p. 92.

B. mixtispinosum Klement, 1960, pp. 58-9, pl. 6 figs. 17-9. U. Jurassic, Germany.

B. molodovense Timofeyev, 1962, pl. 9 fig. 2. M. Ordovician, U.S.S.R.

B. multifurcatum (Deflandre, 1937c), p. 76, pl. 16 figs. 1-3 (as Hystrichosphaeridium).
   U. Cretaceous, France.   ---, Klement, 1960, p. 59.

B. multipilosum (Eisenack, 1931), p. 111, pl. 5 figs. 20-22 (as Ovum hospidum). Baltic drift,
   Ordovician pebble.   Hystrichosphaeridium multipilosum, Eisenack, 1938a, p. 12.   ---,
   Eisenack, 1958b, p. 400.

B. multipilosum (Eis. 1931) subsp. validum Sannemann, 1955, p. 330, pl. 5 figs. 9, 10, text-
   fig. 10.   L. Devonian, Germany.

B. mutabile (Sannemann, 1955), p. 331, pl. 5 figs. 5, 6, text-figs. 17a-d   (as Hystrichosphaeridium).   L. Devonian, Germany.   ---, Downie and Sarjeant, 1963, p. 90.

B. mutabilis (Naumova, 1950), p. 188, pl. 5 figs. 3, 4   (as Archaeletes). M. Cambrian,
   Baltic U.S.S.R. ---, comb. nov.

B. nanum (Deflandre, 1945a), pp. 62-3, pl. 1 figs. 5-7, ?18   (as Hystrichosphaeridium brevispinosum var. nanum).   Silurian, France.   ---, Stockmans and Willière, 1962a,
   pp. 54-5 (figured and named without description in Deflandre 1942b, text-fig. 1).

B. neptuni Eisenack, 1958a, p. 399, pl. 26 figs. 7-8, text-fig. 8.   L. Cretaceous, Germany.

B. nudatum (Timofeyev, 1959), p. 53, pl. 4 fig. 10   (as Hystrichosphaeridium).   L. Ordovician,
   U.S.S.R. ---, Downie and Sarjeant, 1963, p. 90.

B. octospinosum (Staplin, 1961), p. 410, pl. 48 fig. 18   (as Micrhystridium).   U. Devonian,
   Canada.   ---, Downie and Sarjeant, 1963, p. 90.

B. ohioensis (Winslow, 1962), p. 77, pls. 19 fig. 1, 22 fig. 9   (as Hystrichosphaeridium).
   U. Devonian, U.S.A.   ---, comb. nov.

B. oligacanthum (W. Wetzel, 1952), pp. 402-3, pl. A fig. 8, text-figs. 21, 22 (as Hystrichosphaeridium).   U. Cretaceous, Baltic.   ---, Downie and Sarjeant, 1963, p. 91.

B. oliganthum (W. We., 1952) subsp. complanatum W. Wetzel, 1952, pp. 404-5, pl. A
   figs. 11a, b.   U. Cretaceous, Baltic.

B. oliganthum (W. We., 1952) subsp. granulatum W. Wetzel, 1952, p. 404, text-fig. 25.

B. oliganthum (W. We., 1952) subsp. stella W. Wetzel, 1962, p. 403, pl. A fig. 4,
   text-fig. 23.   U. Cretaceous, Baltic.

B. oliganthum (W. We., 1952) subsp. velatum W. Wetzel, 1952, pp. 403-4, pl.   A
   fig. 7, text-fig. 24.   U. Cretaceous, Baltic.

B. oligofurcatum (Eisenack, 1954a), p. 208, pl. 1 fig. 4, text-fig. 5 (as Hystrichosphaeridium).
L. Silurian, Sweden. ---, Downie and Sarjeant, 1963, p. 90.

B. ordovicum (Timofeyev, 1959), p. 56, pl. 4 fig. 20 (as Hystrichosphaeridium). L. Ordovician,
U.S.S.R. ---, Downie and Sarjeant, 1963, p. 90.

B. paleozoicum Stockmans and Willière, 1962a, p. 56, pl. 1 fig. 12, text-fig. 13. U. Devonian,
Belgium.

B. palmatum (Deflandre and Courteville, 1939), pp. 101-2, pl. 3 fig. 1 (as Hystrichosphaeridium).
U. Cretaceous, France. ---, Downie and Sarjeant, 1963, p. 91.

B. panniforme Gerlach, 1961, pp. 196-8, pl. 28 fig. 13. Oligocene, Germany.

B. parvispinum (Deflandre, 1937c), p. 29, pl. 16 fig. 5 (as Hystrichosphaeridium xanthiopyxides
var. parvispinum). U. Cretaceous, France. Hystrichosphaeridium parvispinum, Cookson
and Eisenack, 1958, p. 45. ---, Klement, 1960, p. 59.

B. pastielsi Stockmans and Willière, 1960b, p. 91, pl. 1 fig. 14, text-fig. 10. U. Devonian,
Belgium

B. pateum(Timofeyev, 1959), p. 52, pl. 4 fig. 4 (as Hystrichosphaeridium). L. Ordovician,
U.S.S.R. ---, Downie and Sarjeant, 1963, p. 90.

B. pattei (Valensi, 1948), pp. 539-40, text-fig. 1 (as Hystrichosphaeridium). M. Jurassic,
France. ---, Sarjeant, 1960a, p. 139.

B. paucifurcatum (Cookson and Eisenack, 1961b), p. 44, pl. 2 fig. 15 (as Hystrichosphaeridium).
Eocene, Western Australia. ---, comb. nov.

B. paucispinum (Deunff, 1961b), p. 217, (as Micrhystridium). Devonian, Canada. (Figured and
named without description in Deunff, 1954a, text-fig. 14). ---, Downie and Sarjeant,
1963, p. 90.

B. pectiniforme Gerlach, 1961, p. 195, pl. 28 fig. 14, text-fig. 18. Oligocene, Germany.

B. piliferum Stockmans and Willière, 1962b, p. 89, pl. 2 fig. 14, text-fig. 8. U. Devonian,
Belgium.

B. pilosum (Ehrenberg, 1843) pp. 61-3, (as Xanthidium). U. Jurassic, Poland. (First figured by
Ehrenberg, 1854, pl. 37 sect. viii no. 4). Ovum hispidum pilosum, Lohmann, 1904,
pp. 21-5. Hystrichosphaera pilosa, O. Wetzel, 1933, p. 43. Hystrichosphaeridium
pilosum, Deflandre, 1937c, p. 79. ---, Sarjeant, 1961a, pp. 101-2.

B. pilosum (Ehr.) var. longispinosum Sarjeant, 1961a, p. 102, pl. 14 fig. 8. U. Jurassic, England.

B. piriferum (Eisenack, 1954a), p. 206, pl. 1 fig. 1, text-fig. 1 (as Hystrichosphaeridium).
L. Silurian, Sweden. ---, Downie and Sarjeant, 1963, p. 90.

B. placacanthum (Deflandre and Cookson, 1955), pp. 276-7, pl. 9 figs. 1-3 (as Hystrichosphaeridium). Miocene, Australia. ---, Downie and Sarjeant, 1963, p. 92.

B. plicatum (Maier, 1959), p. 318, pl. 33 fig. 1 (as Hystrichosphaeridium). Oligocene,
Germany. ---, Downie and Sarjeant, 1963, p. 92.

B. polygonale (Eisenack, 1931), p. 113, pls. 4 figs. 16-20; 5 fig. 18 (as Ovum hispidum
polygonale). Baltic drift, Silurian pebble. Hystrichosphaeridium polygonale,
Eisenack, 1938a, p. 12. ---, Eisenack, 1959a, p. 199.

B. polyozon Brosius 1963, p. 45, pls. 1 fig. 6; 6 fig. 5; text-fig. 2. Oligocene, Germany.

B. polytrichum (Valensi, 1947), p. 818, text-fig. 4 (as Hystrichosphaeridium). M. Jurassic, France. ---, Sarjeant, 1959, p. 339.

B. pseudhystrichodinium (Deflandre, 1937c), p. 73, pl. 15 figs. 3-4 (as Hystrichosphaeridium). U. Cretaceous, France. ---, Downie and Sarjeant, 1963, p. 92.

B. pseudhystrichodinium (Defl. 1937c) subsp. magnum W. Wetzel, 1955, pp. 36, 38, text-figs. 9, 10 and 14. U. Cretaceous, Baltic.

B. quadriradiatum (Timofeyev, 1959), p. 57, pl. 4 fig. 25 (as Hystrichosphaeridium). L. Ordovician, U.S.S.R. ---, Downie and Sarjeant, 1963, p. 90.

B. quaternarium Churchill and Sarjeant, 1963, pp. 46-7, pl. 2 fig. 33, text-fig. 16. Post-Pleistocene, Australia.

B. ramispinosum (Staplin, 1961), p. 411, pl. 48 fig. 24, text-figs. 9g-h (as Multiplicisphaeridium). ---, Downie and Sarjeant, 1963, p. 90.

B. ramusculosum (Deflandre, 1945a), p. 63, pl. 1 figs. 8-16, text-figs. 38-9 (as Hystrichosphaeridium). Silurian, France. ---, Downie, 1959, pp. 59-60. (Figured and named without description in Deflandre 1942b, text-figs. 2-6).

B. ramusculosum (Defl. 1945), var. macrocladum Deunff, 1955a, p. 146, text-fig. 21. M. Devonian, Canada.

B. ravum Downie, 1963, p. 643, pl. 91 fig. 6, text-fig. 3c. M. Silurian, England.

B. rectangulare Eisenack, 1963e, p. 211, pl. 20 figs. 1-3, 10. U. Ordovician, Baltic.

B. reginaldi (Mantell, 1844), pp. 239-42, text-fig. 53 (as Xanthidium). U. Cretaceous, England. Spiniferites reginaldi Mantell, 1854, text-figs. 77 no. 4, 78. ---, Downie and Sarjeant, 1963, p. 92.

B. rehdense (Maier, 1959), pp. 317-8, pl. 32 figs. 3-4 (as Hystrichosphaeridium). Miocene, Germany. ---, Downie and Sarjeant, 1963, p. 92.

B. rigens (Timofeyev, 1959), p. 55 pl. 4 fig. 18 (as Hystrichosphaeridium). L. Ordovician, U.S.S.R. ---, Downie and Sarjeant, 1963, p. 90.

B. rjabinini (Timofeyev, 1959), p. 56, pl. 4 fig. 24 (as Hystrichosphaeridium). L. Ordovician, U.S.S.R. ---, Downie and Sarjeant, 1963, p. 90.

B. robustispinosum Downie, 1959, p. 61, pl. 10 fig. 7. M. Silurian, England.

B. robustum (Sannemann, 1955), p. 331, pls. 1 figs. 6, 8, 9; 6 figs. 7, 8; text-fig. 13 (as Hystrichosphaeridium). L. Devonian, Germany. ---, Downie and Sarjeant, 1963, p.90.

B. robustum (Sann. 1955) subsp. fissum Sannemann, 1955, p. 331, pl. 6 fig. 9, text-figs. 14a-c. L. Devonian, Germany.

B. robustum (Eisenack, 1959, non Sannemann, 1955), p. 195, pls. 15 figs. 2, 3, 8; 17 figs. 16-17 (as Baltisphaeridium longispinosum forma robusta). L. Ordovician, Baltic. ---, Eisenack, 1963e, pp. 212-3.

B. sannemanni (Deunff, 1958), p. 6, fig. 1 (as Micrhystridium). M. Devonian, Canada. ---, Downie and Sarjeant, 1963, p. 90.

B. saturnium (Maier, 1959), pp. 319-20, pl. 32 fig. 8 (as Hystrichosphaeridium). Miocene, Germany. ---, Downie and Sarjeant, 1963, p. 92.

B. scaber (Naumova, 1950), p. 189, pl. 5 fig. 15   (as Archaeletes). U. Cambrian, Baltic,
U.S.S.R.   ---, comb. nov.

B. sedecimspinosum (Staplin, 1961), p. 414, pl. 49 fig. 12.   (as Veryhachium). U. Devonian,
Canada.   ---, Downie and Sarjeant, 1963, p. 90.

B. seminudum (W. Wetzel, 1952), p. 405, text-fig. 26   (as Hystrichosphaeridium).   U. Cretaceous,
Baltic.   ---, Downie and Sarjeant, 1963, p. 92.

B. sericum (Deunff,1961b), p. 217 (as Micrhystridium).   (figured in Deunff, 1954d, text-fig.16).I.
Devonian, Canada.   ---, Downie and Sarjeant, 1963, p. 90.

B. serratum (Naumova, 1950), p. 188, pl. 5 fig. 5   (as Archaeletes).   U. Cambrian, U.S.S.R.
---, comb. nov.

B. setigerfurcatum (Timofeyev, 1959), pp. 52-3, pl. 4 fig. 6   (as Hystrichosphaeridium).
L. Ordovician, U.S.S.R.   ---, Downie and Sarjeant, 1963, p. 90.

B. sexradiatum (Timofeyev, 1959), p. 53, pl. 4 fig. 7   (as Hystrichosphaeridium).   L. Ordovician,
U.S.S.R.   ---, Downie and Sarjeant, 1963, p. 90.

B. simplex Stockmans and Willière, 1962a, pp. 58-9, pl. 1 figs. 23-4, text-fig. 15.   U. Devonian,
Belgium.

B. snigirevskaiae Stockmans and Willière, 1963, pp. 459-60, pl. 1 fig. 5, text-fig. 15.
M. Silurian, Belgium.

B. spectatissimum (Naumova, 1950), p. 189, pl. 5 figs. 8-9   (as Archaeletes).   M. Cambrian,
U.S.S.R.   ---, comb. nov.

B. spicatum (Staplin, 1960), pp. 411-12, pl. 49 fig. 21, text-fig. 9i   (as Multiplicisphaeridium).
U. Devonian, Canada.   ---, Downie and Sarjeant, 1963, p. 90.

B. spiciferum (Deunff, 1955a), p. 146, pl. 3 fig. 1   (as Hystrichosphaeridium).   M. Devonian,
Canada.   ---, Downie and Sarjeant, 1963, p. 90.

B. spiculatum (H.H. White, 1844b), p. 87, pl. 19 fig. 4 (as Xanthidium tubiferum spiculatum).
U. Cretaceous, England.   Hystrichosphaeridium spiculatum Deflandre, 1937c, p. 31.
---, Downie and Sarjeant, 1963, p. 92.

B. spinellosum (Naumova, 1950), p. 188, pl. 5 fig. 6   (as Archaeletes).   U. Cambrian,
U.S.S.R.   ---, comb. nov.

B. spinescens (Timofeyev, 1959), p.56, pl. 4 fig. 23   (as Hystrichosphaeridium).   L. Ordovician,
U.S.S.R.   ---, Downie and Sarjeant, 1963, p. 90.

B. spinicurvatum (Merrill, 1895), p. 17, text-fig. 20 (as ?Geodia).   L. Cretaceous, U.S.A.
---, Sarjeant, 1964 (in press).

B. spinoglobosum (Staplin, 1961), p. 409, pl. 48 fig. 17 (as Micrhystridium).   U. Devonian,
Canada.   ---, Downie and Sarjeant, 1963, p. 90.

B. spinosum (H.H. White, 1842), p. 237, pl. 4 fig. 6   (as Xanthidium).   U. Cretaceous, England.
Hystrichosphaeridium spinosum, Deflandre, 1937a, p. 31   ---, Downie and
Sarjeant, 1963, p. 92.

B. spinosum (H.H. White, 1842), var. deflandrei Lejeune-Carpentier, 1941, p. 84, text-figs.6-7.
U. Cretaceous, Belgium.

B. spiralisetum (de Wit, 1942), p. 383, text-figs. 2, 11 (as Hystrichosphaeridium). U. Cretaceous, Netherlands. ---, comb. nov.

B. sprucegrovensis (Staplin, 1961), p. 411, pl. 42 fig. 22, pl. 49 fig. 6, text-fig. 9¡ (as Multiplicisphaeridium?). U. Devonian, Canada. ---, Downie and Sarjeant, 1963, p.90.

B. stellaeforme (Timofeyev, 1959), p. 57, pl. 4 fig. 26 (as Hystrichosphaeridium). L. Ordovician, U.S.S.R. ---, Downie and Sarjeant, 1963, p. 90.

B. stimuliferum (Deflandre, 1938c), p. 192, pl. 10 fig. 10 (as Hystrichosphaeridium). U. Jurassic, France. ---, Sarjeant, 1960c, p. 397.

B. striolatum (Deflandre, 1937c), pp. 72-3, pl. 15 figs. 1-2 (as Hystrichosphaeridium). U. Cretaceous, France. ---, Downie and Sarjeant, 1963, p. 92.

B. striatoconus (Deflandre and Cookson, 1955), pp. 275-6, pl. 2 fig. 10, text-fig. 36 (as Hystrichosphaeridium). U. Cretaceous, Australia. (Figured and named without description by Deflandre and Cookson, 1954, fig. 12). ---, Downie and Sarjeant, 1963, p. 92.

B. suecicum Eisenack, 1959a, p. 198, pls. 15 fig. 19; 16 figs. 1-2; text-figs. 6, 8. L. Ordovician, Sweden.

B. sylheti (Baksi, 1962), p. 17, pl. 2 fig. 26 (as Hystrichosphaeridium). Eocene, Assam, India. ---, comb. nov.

B. telmaticum Churchill and Sarjeant, 1963, pp. 44-5, pl. 2 fig. 32, text-fig. 13. Post-Pleistocene, Australia.

B. tenuiramusculosum Stockmans and Willière, 1963, p. 457, pl. 3 fig. 9, text-fig. 12. Silurian, Belgium.

B. texanum (Merrill, 1895), p. 16, text-fig. 18 (as ?Geodia texana). L. Cretaceous, Texas, U.S.A. ---, Sarjeant, 1964 (in press).

B. tiara (Klumpp, 1953), pp. 390-1, pl. 17 figs. 8-10 (as Hystrichosphaeridium). Eocene, Germany. ---, Downie and Sarjeant, 1963, p.92.

B. timofeevi Deunff, 1961, p. 39, pl. 2 fig. 6. L. Ordovician, Sahara.

B. tinglewoodense Churchill and Sarjeant, 1963, pp. 42, 44, pl. 2 fig. 29, text-fig. 12. Post-Pleistocene, Australia.

B. triangulare Stockmans and Willière, 1962a, p. 59, pl. 1 fig. 11, text-fig. 16. U. Devonian, Belgium.

B. triangulatum Gerlach, 1961, pp. 194-5, pl. 29 fig. 1. Miocene, Germany.

B. tribuliferum Sarjeant, 1962b, pp. 487-8, pl. 70 fig. 4, text-fig. 6c, 7. U. Jurassic, England.

B. tridactylites (Valensi, 1955a), pp. 37-8, text-fig. 10 (as Hystrichosphaeridium). Cretaceous, France. ---, Downie and Sarjeant, 1963, p. 92.

B. trifurcatum (Eisenack, 1931), p. 112, pl. 4 figs. 21-23 (as Ovum hispidum trifurcatum). ?Ordovician pebble, Baltic drift. Hystrichosphaeridium trifurcatum Eisenack, 1938a, pp. 12, 16-19. ---, Eisenack, 1958b, p. 400.

B. trifurcatum (Eis. 1931) forma breviradiata Eisenack, 1959a, pp. 202-3, pl. 17 fig. 7. L. Silurian, Estonia, U.S.S.R.

B. trifurcatum (Eis. 1931) subsp. consonum Sannemann, 1955, p. 332, pl. 5 fig. 7.
    L. Devonian, Germany.

B. trifurcatum (Eis. 1931) forma longiradiata Eisenack, 1959a, p. 202 (figured in Eisenack
    1938a, pl. 2 figs. 6-7). Ordovician pebble, Baltic drift.

B. trifurcatum (Eis. 1931) subsp. nudum Eisenack, 1959a, p. 203, pl. 17 figs. 4-6.
    M. Ordovician, Estonia, U.S.S.R.

B. trifurcatum (Eis. 1931) subsp. paucifurcatum Eisenack, 1959a, p. 203, pl. 17 figs. 8-10,
    text-fig. 10. L. Ordovician, Estonia, U.S.S.R.

B. trifurcatum (Eis. 1931) subsp. procerum Sannemann, 1955, p. 332, pl. 5 fig. 8, text-fig.18.
    L. Devonian, Germany.

B. triplicativum (Timofeyev, 1959), p. 55, pl. 4 fig. 16 (as Hystrichosphaeridium).
    L. Ordovician, U.S.S.R. ---, Downie and Sarjeant, 1963, p. 90.

B. truncatum (Staplin, 1961), p. 411, pl. 48 fig. 23, text-fig. 9f (as Multiplicisphaeridium).
    U. Devonian, Canada. ---, Downie and Sarjeant, 1963, p. 90.

B. tschunense (Timofeyev, 1962), pl. 11 fig. 1 (as Hystrichosphaeridium). M. Ordovician,
    U.S.S.R. ---, comb. nov.   No description; validity doubtful.

B. tuberatum (Downie, 1958) p. 338, pl. 17 fig. 3, text-fig. 3f (as Hystrichosphaeridium).
    L. Ordovician, England. ---, Downie and Sarjeant, 1963, p. 90.

B. tuberosum (Sannemann, 1955), p. 345, pl. 4 fig. 17, text-fig. 16 (as Hystrichosphaeridium).
    L. Devonian, Germany. --- Downie and Sarjeant, 1963, p. 91.

B. twistringense (Maier, 1959) p. 308-9, pl. 30 figs. 3-4. (as Galea).Oligocene-Miocene,
    Germany. --- Sarjeant, 1964 (in press).

B. varispinosum Sarjeant, 1959, pp. 338-40, pl. 13 fig. 7, text-fig. 6. M. Jurassic, England.

B. veliferum (Downie, 1958), p. 340, pl. 17 fig. 2 (as Hystrichosphaeridium). L. Ordovician,
    England. ---, comb. nov.

B. venustum (Sannemann, 1955), p. 345, pl. 5 fig. 11, text-fig. 15   (as Hystrichosphaeridium).
    L. Devonian, Germany. ---, Downie and Sarjeant, 1964, p. 91.

B. vestitum (Deflandre, 1938c), pp. 190-1, pl. 11 figs. 4-6 (as Hystrichosphaeridium).
    U. Jurassic, France. ---, Sarjeant, 1960c, p. 397.

B. vigintispinum (Staplin,1961), p. 409, pl. 48 fig. 13 (as Micrhystridium). U. Devonian,
    Canada. ---, Downie and Sarjeant, 1963, p. 91 (incorrectly as B. vigivitispinosum).

B. wenlockense (Downie, 1959), p. 59, pl. 10 fig. 4, (as B. brevispinosum var. wenlockensis.)
    M. Silurian, England. ---, Stockmans and Willière, 1962b, p. 90.

B. wepionense Stockmans and Willière, 1962b, p. 92, pl. 1 fig. 9, text-fig. 11. U. Devonian,
    Belgium.

B. whitei (Deflandre and Courteville, 1939), p. 103, pl. 3 figs. 5-6   (as Hystrichosphaeridium).
    U. Cretaceous, France. ---, Sarjeant, 1959, p. 339.

B. xanthiopyxides (O. Wetzel, 1933), p. 44-5, pl. 4 fig. 25 (as Hystrichosphaera).
    U. Cretaceous, Germany. Hystrichosphaeridium xanthiopyxides, Deflandre, 1937c,
    p. 77. ---, Klement, 1960, p. 59.

B. zonale (Timofeyev, 1959), p. 55, pl. 4 fig. 19 (as Hystrichosphaeridium). L. Ordovician, U.S.S.R. ---, Downie and Sarjeant, 1963, p. 91.

BELODINIUM Cookson and Eisenack, 1960b, p. 249.

* B. dysculum Cookson and Eisenack, 1960b, p. 250, pls. 37 fig. 14; 39 fig. 10. U. Jurassic, Australia.

BICARINELLUM Deflandre, 1948c, p. 212.

* B. castaninum Deflandre, 1948c, pp. 212-5, text-figs. 28-31, 34. Eocene, France.

BIECHELERELLA Deflandre, 1948c, pp. 209-10.

* B. jurassica Deflandre, 1948c, pp. 210-11, text-figs. 26-7, U. Jurassic, France.

BLEPHAROCYSTA Ehrenberg (Modern genus and type species).

B. splendor maris (Ehrenberg) Stein (Modern species recorded by W. Wetzel, 1922, p. 60, from U. Cretaceous, Baltic).

BROCHOPSOPHOSPHAERA Shepeleva in Shepeleva and Timofeyev, 1963, p. 1158.

* B. minimus Shepeleva in Shepeleva and Timofeyev, 1963, p. 1158, pl. 1 fig. 7. Pre-Cambrian, U.S.S.R.

BROOMEA Cookson and Eisenack, 1958, p. 41.

B. exigua Alberti, 1961, pp. 26-7, pl. 5 fig. 14.   L. Cretaceous, Germany.

B. gochti Alberti, 1961, p. 27, pl. 5 figs. 8-10.   L. Cretaceous, Germany.

B. jaegeri Alberti, 1961, p. 26, pl. 5 figs. 1-7. L. Cretaceous, Germany.

? B. longicornuta Alberti, 1961, pp. 27-8, pl. 5 figs. 18-21, 6 figs. 1-2. L. Cretaceous, Germany.

B. micropoda Eisenack and Cookson, 1960, pp. 7-8, pl. 2 figs. 8-9.   U. Cretaceous, Australia.

B. pellifera Alberti, 1961, p. 26, pl. 5 figs. 11-13. L. Cretaceous, Germany.

* B.ramosa Cookson and Eisenack, 1958, pp. 41-2, pl. 6 figs. 6-8. M.-U Jurassic, Australia.

B. simplex Cookson and Eisenack, 1958, p. 42, pl. 6 fig. 9. U. Jurassic, Papua.

? B. tricornoides Alberti, 1961, p. 28, pl. 5 fig. 17.   L. Cretaceous, Germany.

BUEDINGIISPHAERIDIUM Schaarschmidt, 1963, pp. 69-70.

* B. permicum Schaarschmidt, p. 70, pl. 20 figs. 4-5, text-fig. 26. U. Permian, Germany.

BULBODINIUM O. Wetzel, 1960, p. 82.

B. altipetax O. Wetzel, 1960, p. 83, pl. 1 figs. 3, 5, 9.   U. Cretaceous, Germany.

B. oistoides O. Wetzel, 1960, pp. 83-4, pl. 1 figs. 6-7.   U. Cretaceous, Germany.

* B. seitzi O. Wetzel, 1960, pp. 82-3, pl. 1 figs. 1-2, 4, 8, 10-13.   U. Cretaceous, Germany.

CALCICARPINUM Deflandre, 1948c, p. 216.

* C. tetraedricum Deflandre, 1948c, pp. 216, 218, text-figs. 35-7.   Eocene, France.

CALCIGONELLUM Deflandre, 1948c, p. 206.

* C. infula Deflandre, 1948c, pp. 206-7, text-figs. 13-18.   Miocene, Algeria.

CALCIODINELLUM Deflandre, 1947b, pp. 1781-2.

*C. operosum Deflandre, 1947b, pp. 1781-2, text-figs. 1-6.   Miocene, Algeria.

CALCIOGRANELLUM Deflandre, 1948c, p. 204.

*C. limbatum Deflandre, 1948c, pp. 204-6, text-figs. 10-12.   Miocene, Algeria.

CALCIPTERELLUM Deflandre, 1948c, p. 207.

* C. colomi Deflandre, 1948c, pp. 208-9, text-figs. 19-25.   Miocene, Algeria.

CALCISPHAERELLUM Deflandre, 1948c, p. 215.

* C. flosculus Deflandre, 1948c, pp. 215-6, text-figs. 32-3.   U. Jurassic, France.

CANNINGIA Cookson and Eisenack, 1960b, p. 251.

C. colliveri Cookson and Eisenack, 1960b, p. 251, pl. 38 figs. 3-4.   L. Cretaceous, Australia.

* C. reticulata Cookson and Eisenack, 1960b, p. 251, pl. 38 figs. 1-2.   U. Jurassic, Australia.

C. rotundata Cookson and Eisenack, 1961a, pp. 72-3, pl. 13 figs. 1-5.   U. Cretaceous,
        Australia.

CANNINGINOPSIS Cookson and Eisenack, 1962b, p. 488.

* C. denticulata Cookson and Eisenack, 1962b, p. 488, pl. 1 figs. 16-19, text-figs. 2a-b.
        U. Cretaceous, Australia.

CANNOSPHAEROPSIS O. Wetzel, 1932, p. 140, emend.   Deflandre 1947a, pp. 1574-6.

C. aemula (Deflandre, 1938a), pp. 187-9, pls. 9 fig. 12; 10 figs. 5-8; 11 figs. 1, 7.
        (as Hystrichosphaeridium).   U. Jurassic, France. ---, Deflandre, 1947a, p. 1574.

C. aemula subsp. integra Cookson and Eisenack, 1958, p. 47, pl. 7 figs. 6-7.   M.-U. Jurassic,
        Australia.

C. apiculata Cookson and Eisenack, 1960b, p. 254, pl. 39 fig. 15.   U. Jurassic -L. Cretaceous,
        Australia and Papua.

C. caulleryi (Deflandre, 1938e), p. 189, pl. 11 figs. 2-3   (as Hystrichosphaeridium).
        U. Jurassic, France.   ---, Deflandre, 1947a, p. 1574.

? C. choneta Cookson and Eisenack, 1962a, p. 493, pl. 4 figs. 8-10.   U. Cretaceous, Australia.

C. densa Cookson and Eisenack, 1962b, p. 493, pl. 4 figs. 1-3.   U. Cretaceous, Australia.

C. densiradiata Cookson and Eisenack, 1962b, p. 493, pl. 4 figs. 5-7.   U. Cretaceous, Australia.

C. eupeplos (Valensi, 1948), p. 542, text-fig. 3, nos. 1-6   (as Micrhystridium).   M. Jurassic,
        France.   ---, Deflandre, 1954, p. 258.

C. filamentosa Cookson and Eisenack, 1958, pp. 47-8, pls. 7 figs. 8-9; 8 figs. 1-2. M.-U. Jurassic, Australia.

C. filifera (Cookson and Eisenack, 1958), p. 46, pl. 7 fig. 4 (as C. utinensis var.filifera). U. Cretaceous, Australia. ---, Cookson and Eisenack, 1960a, pp. 8-9.

C. hyperacantha Cookson and Eisenack, 1960a, p. 9, pl. 2 figs. 14-15. U. Cretaceous, Australia.

C. mirabilis Cookson and Eisenack, 1958, p. 48, pl. 8 figs. 3-5. U. Jurassic, Papua.

C. paucispina Klement, 1960, p. 72, pl. 10 figs. 9-10. U. Jurassic, Germany.

C. perforata Alberti, 1961, p. 37, pl. 9 fig. 14. M. Jurassic, Germany.

C. peridictya Eisenack and Cookson, 1960, pp. 8-9, pl. 3 figs. 5-6. U. Cretaceous, Australia.

C. philippoti Deflandre, 1947a, pp. 1574-5, text-figs. 2-3. U. Cretaceous, France.

C. pulchra Alberti, 1961, p. 37, pl. 10 fig. 5. L. Cretaceous, Australia.

C. reticulensis Pastiels, 1948, p. 49, pl. 5 figs. 7-10. Eocene, Belgium.

C. scaffoldi (Baksi, 1962), p. 17, pl. 2 fig. 25 (as Hystrichosphaeridium). Eocene, Assam, India. ---, comb. nov.

C. speciosa Alberti, 1961, pp. 37-8, pl. 9 fig. 13. M. Jurassic, Germany.

C. tutulosa Cookson and Eisenack, 1960a, p. 8, pl. 2 figs. 12-13. U. Cretaceous, Australia.

* C. utinensis O. Wetzel, 1932, p. 140, pl. 1 fig. 14. U. Cretaceous, Baltic.

CANTULODINIUM Alberti, 1961, p. 23.

* C. speciosum Alberti, 1961, p. 23, pls. 3 figs. 20-3; 12 fig. 3. L. Cretaceous, Germany.

CARPODINIUM Cookson and Eisenack, 1962b, p. 489.

* C. granulatum Cookson and Eisenack, 1962b, p. 489, pl. 1 figs. 6-10. U. Cretaceous, Australia.

CAYEUXIPORA Graindor, 1957, pp. 2075-6. (Type species not specified).

C. dangeardi Graindor, 1957, p. 2076, text-fig. 3. Pre-Cambrian, France.

C. falloti Graindor, 1957, p. 2076, text-fig. 1. Pre-Cambrian, France.

C. pruvosti Graindor, 1957, p. 2076, text-fig. 2. Pre-Cambrian, France.

C. robloti Graindor, 1957, pp. 2076-7, text-fig. 4. Pre-Cambrian, France.

CERATIOPSIS Vozzhennikova, 1960. Name used in plate captions only; no diagnosis.

C. leptoderma ?Vozzh. forma minor Vozzhennikova, 1960, pl. 3 fig. 5 (no diagnosis). Eocene, U.S.S.R.

CERATIUM Schrank (Modern genus and type species).

Subgenus Amphiceratium. (Modern subgenus).

<u>Ceratium fusus</u> Ehrenberg (Modern species).

<u>Ceratium</u> cf. <u>fusus</u> Ehr. forma <u>filosum</u> O. Wetzel, 1933, p. 169, pl. 2 fig. 20.   U. Cretaceous,
Baltic.

<u>Ceratium</u> cf. <u>fusus</u> Ehr. forma <u>incerta</u> Deflandre, 1936c, p. 40, pl. 10 figs. 8-9.   U. Cretaceous,
France.

<u>Ceratium</u> cf. <u>fusus</u> Ehr. forma <u>nodosum</u> O. Wetzel, 1933, p. 169, pl. 2 fig. 20.   U. Cretaceous,
Baltic.

<u>Ceratium</u> cf. <u>fusus</u> Ehr. forma <u>ovatum</u> O. Wetzel, 1933, pp. 168-9, pl. 2 fig. 18.   U. Cretaceous,
Baltic.

<u>Ceratium</u> cf. <u>fusus</u> Ehr. forma <u>rhomboides</u> O. Wetzel, 1933, p. 168, pl. 2 fig. 17.   U. Cretaceous,
Baltic.

(The correctness of the generic assignation of these fossil forms has been questioned by Eisenack, 1961b,
pp. 300-1, and Evitt, 1961c, p. 402.   However, their transfer to other genera has not been
proposed to date.)

CERATOCORYS Stein 1883 (Modern genus).

<u>C. veligera</u> (Deflandre, 1937c), p. 81, pl. 12 fig. 9   (as <u>Micrhystridium</u>).   U. Cretaceous,
France.   ---, Lejeune-Carpentier, 1943, pp. 24-5.

CERATOCYSTIDIOPSIS Deflandre, 1937c, p. 89.

* <u>C. simplex</u> Deflandre, 1937c, pp. 89-90, pl. 17 fig. 1.   U. Cretaceous, France.

CHIROPTERIDIUM Gocht, 1960, pp. 221-2.

<u>C. aspinatum</u> (Gerlach, 1961), pp. 199-201, pl. 29 figs. 7-8 (as <u>Membranophoridium</u>).   Oligocene,
Germany.   ---, Brosius, 1963, p. 48.

<u>C. dispersum</u> Gocht, 1960, pp. 227-9, pl. 18 figs. 1-16, text-figs. 16-27.   Oligocene, Germany.

* <u>C. lobospinosum</u> (Gocht, in Weiler, 1956, p. 138-9, pl. 12 figs. 1-3, text-fig. 8   (as
<u>Hystrichosphaeridium</u>).   Oligocene, Germany.   ---, Gocht, 1960, pp. 222-3, 226-7.
<u>Baltisphaeridium lobospinosum</u> Downie and Sarjeant, 1963, p. 91.

<u>C. partispinatum</u> (Gerlach, 1961), pp. 201-3, pl. 29 figs. 3, 6 (as <u>Membranophoridium</u>).
Oligocene, Germany.   ---, Brosius, 1963, p. 48.

CHLAMYDOPHORELLA Cookson and Eisenack, 1958, p. 56.

* <u>C. nyei</u> Cookson and Eisenack, 1958, pp. 56-7, pl. 11 figs. 1-3.   L.-U. Cretaceous, Australia.

<u>C. urna</u> Cookson and Eisenack, 1960a, p. 10, pl. 3 fig. 7.   U. Cretaceous, Australia.

<u>C. wallala</u> Cookson and Eisenack, 1960b, p. 255, pls. 38 fig. 13; 39 fig. 11. U. Jurassic,
Australia.

CHONESPHAERA Klumpp, 1953, p. 395.

* <u>C. incerta</u> Klumpp, 1953, p. 395, pl. 19 fig. 9.   Eocene, Germany.

CHYTROEISPHAERIDIA Sarjeant, 1962b, pp. 492-3 (as subgenus of <u>Leiosphaeridia</u>). Raised to
generic status by Downie, Evitt and Sarjeant, 1963. p. 9.

* C. chytroeides Sarjeant, 1962b, pp. 493-4, pl. 70 figs. 13, 16, text-figs. 11-12. U. Jurassic, England.

CIRCULISPORITES   Jersey, 1962, p. 15.

* C. parvus   Jersey, 1962, p. 15, pl. 5 figs. 13-15.   M.-U. Triassic, Queensland, Australia.

CIRCULODINIUM Alberti, 1961, p. 28.

C. deflandrei Alberti, 1961, p. 29, pl. 4 figs. 7-13.   L. Cretaceous, Germany.

* C.hirtellum Alberti, 1961, pp. 28-9, pl. 4 fig. 20.   L. Cretaceous, Germany.

CIRRIFERA Cookson and Eisenack, 1960a, p. 10.

* C. unilateralis Cookson and Eisenack, 1960a, p. 10, pl. 3 fig. 8.   U. Cretaceous, Australia.

CODONIELLA Cookson and Eisenack, 1961, p. 75.

* C. campanulata (Cookson and Eisenack, 1960a), p. 11, pl. 3 figs. 1-3   (as Codonia).
     U. Cretaceous, Australia.   ---, Cookson and Eisenack, 1961a, p. 75 (implicitly in
     renaming of genus).

COMETODINIUM Deflandre and Courteville, 1939, p. 98.

* C. obscurum Deflandre and Courteville, 1939, p. 99, pl. 2 fig. 1.   U. Cretaceous, France.

CONCENTRICYSTES Rossignol, 1962, pp. 134-5.

* C. rubinus Rossignol, 1962, pp. 134-5, pl. 2 figs. 4-6.   Pleistocene, Israel.

CORDOSPHAERIDIUM Eisenack, 1963f, p. 261.

C. diktyoplokus (Klumpp, 1953), p. 392, pl. 18 figs. 3-7 (as Hystrichosphaeridium).   Eocene,
     Germany.   ---, Eisenack, 1963f, p. 262.

C. diktyoplokus (Klumpp) subsp. latum Klumpp, 1953, p. 392, pl. 18 figs. 8-10.   Eocene, Germany.

C. divergens (Eisenack, 1954b), p. 67, pl. 19 figs. 13-16 (as Hystrichosphaeridium).   Oligocene,
     East Prussia, U.S.S.R.   Baltisphaeridium divergens.   Downie and Sarjeant, 1963, p. 91.
     ---, Eisenack, 1963f, p. 262.

C. eoinodes (Eisenack, 1958c), p. 402, pl. 27 figs. 3-4 (as Hystrichosphaeridium).   L. Cretaceous,
     Germany.   ---, Eisenack, 1963f, p. 262.

C. floripes Deflandre and Cookson, 1955, p. 276, pl. 7 figs. 1-2, 7 (as Hystrichosphaeridium).
     Miocene, Australia.   ---,Eisenack, 1963f, p. 262.

C. floripes (Defl. & Cooks. 1955) subsp. breviradiatum Cookson and Eisenack, 1961b, p. 44,
     pl. 2 figs. 10-11.   Eocene, Australia.

* C. inodes (Klumpp, 1953), pp. 391-2, pl. 18 figs. 1-2 (as Hystrichosphaeridium).   Eocene,
     Germany.   ---, Eisenack, 1963f, p. 261.

C. inodes (Klumpp, 1953) subsp. gracilis Eisenack, 1954b, pls. 8 fig. 17, 10 figs. 3-8, 12 figs.
     7, 21.   Oligocene, East Prussia, U.S.S.R.

C. microtriaina (Klumpp, 1953), p. 390, pl. 17 figs. 6-7 (as Hystrichosphaeridium).   Eocene,
     Germany.   ---, Eisenack, 1963f, p. 263.

CORONIFERA Cookson and Eisenack, 1958, p. 45.

* C. oceanica Cookson and Eisenack, 1958, p. 45, pl. 12 figs. 5-6.   L. Cretaceous, Australia.

CORONOPSIS O. Wetzel, 1961, p. 343.

*C. digitata O. Wetzel, 1961, p. 343, pl. 3 fig. 11.   U. Cretaceous, Baltic.

CRASSOSPHAERA Cookson and Manum, 1960, pp. 5-6.

* C. concinna Cookson and Manum, 1960, pp. 6-7, pl. 1 figs. 1-3, 7-10, text-fig. 1.
        L. Cretaceous, Papua and L. Tertiary, Spitsbergen.

C. cooksoni Kriván Hutter, 1963a, pp. 74-5, pl. 3 figs. 7-11.   Oligocene, Hungary.

C. digitata Cookson and Manum, 1960, p. 7, pl. 1 figs. 4-6.   L. Cretaceous, Papua.

C. manumi Kriván Hutter, 1963a, p. 74, pls. 2 figs. 13-17; 3 fig. 3-4.   Oligocene, Hungary.

C. minor Kriván Hutter, 1963a, pp. 73-4, pl. 2 figs. 1-12.   Eocene-Oligocene, Hungary.

C. stellulata Cookson and Manum, 1960, pp. 7-8, pl. 2 figs. 1-4, text-fig. 2.   Eocene,
        Australia.

C. stellulata Cooks. and Manum, 1960 var. minor Kedves, 1962, p. 20, pl. 2 figs. 1-6.
        Eocene, Hungary.

CRIBROPERIDINIUM Neale and Sarjeant, p. 1962, p. 443.

* C. sepimentum Neale and Sarjeant, pp. 443-4, pl. 19 fig. 4, text-fig. 3.   L. Cretaceous,
        England.

CRYPTARCHAEODINIUM Deflandre, 1939b, p. 145.

* C. calcaratum Deflandre, 1939b, p. 145, pl. 6 fig. 6.   U. Jurassic, France.

CTENIDODINIUM Deflandre, 1938e, p. 181.

* C. ornatum (Eisenack, 1935), pp. 176-7, pl. 4 figs. 9-10, text-figs. 1-4   (as Lithodinia
        jurassica var. ornata).   M. Jurassic, Baltic.   ---, Deflandre, 1938e, pp. 181-2.
        Gonyaulax ornata Klement, 1960, pp. 30-33.

C. tenellum Deflandre, 1938e, pp. 182-3, pl. 9 figs. 8-10.   U. Jurassic, France.

CYCLODICTYON Cookson and Eisenack, 1958, p. 58.

* C. paradoxos Cookson and Eisenack, 1958, pp. 58-9, pl. 12 figs. 1-2.   U. Cretaceous,
        Australia.

CYCLONEPHELIUM Deflandre and Cookson, 1955, p. 285, emend. Cookson and Eisenack, 1962b,
        pp. 493-4.

C. areolatum Cookson and Eisenack, 1960b, p. 253, pl. 38 figs. 7-8.   U. Jurassic, Australia.
        (Figured and named without description in Defl. & Cooks. 1954, p. 1236).

? C. attadalicum Cookson and Eisenack, 1962b, p. 495, pl. 5 figs. 12-15.   L.-U. Cretaceous,
        Australia.

C. clathromarginatum Cookson and Eisenack, 1962b, p. 495, pl. 6 figs. 1-4.   U. Cretaceous,
        Australia.

* C. compactum Deflandre and Cookson, 1955, p. 285, pl. 2 figs. 11-13, text-figs. 44-6.
    L.-U. Cretaceous, Australia.

C. densebarbatum Cookson and Eisenack, 1960b, p. 253, pl. 38 figs. 9-10. U. Jurassic,
    Australia.

C. distinctum Deflandre and Cookson, 1955, pp. 285-6, pl. 2 fig. 14, text-figs. 47-8.
    U. Cretaceous, Australia.

C. exuberans Deflandre and Cookson, 1955, p. 281 (figured by Pastiels, 1948, pl. 5 figs. 11-14,
    as Membranilarna pterospermoides). Eocene, Belgium.

C. laciniiforme Gerlach, 1961, pp. 206-7, pl. 29 fig. 4. Oligocene, Germany.

C. membraniphorum Cookson and Eisenack, 1962b, p. 495, pl. 6 figs. 8-14. U. Cretaceous,
    Australia.

C. pastielsi Deflandre and Cookson, 1955, p. 285 (figured by Pastiels, 1948, pl. 5 fig. 5, as
    Membranilarnax cf. liradiscoides). Eocene, Belgium.

C. paucimarginatum Cookson and Eisenack, 1962b, p. 494, pl. 6 figs. 5-7. U. Cretaceous,
    Australia.

C. reticulosum Gerlach, 1961, pp. 204-5, pl. 29 fig. 2. Oligocene, Germany.

CYMATIOGALEA Deunff, 1961a, pp. 41-2.

C. bellicosa Deunff, 1961a, p. 42, pl. 1 fig. 13. L. Ordovician, Sahara.

* C. margaritata Deunff, 1961a, p. 42, pl. 1 fig. 1. L. Ordovician, Sahara.

C. membranispina Deunff, 1961a, p. 42, pl. 1 fig. 6. L. Ordovician, Sahara.

C. membrasnacea (Naumova, 1950), p. 189, pl. 5 figs. 10-1   (as Archaeletes). U. Cambrian,
    U.S.S.R. ---, comb. nov.

C. pudica Deunff, 1961a, p. 42, pl. 1 fig. 4. L. Ordovician, Sahara.

CYMATIOSPHAERA O. Wetzel, 1933, p. 27, emend. Deflandre, 1954, p. 257-8.

C. areolata (Deflandre, 1941b), pp. 21-2, pl. 6 figs. 4-5   (as Micrhystridium). U. Jurassic,
    France. ---, Deflandre, 1954, p. 258.

C. boulouardi Deunff, 1961a, p. 40, pl. 2 fig. 7. L. Ordovician, Sahara.

C. canadensis Deunff, 1961b, p. 217. M. Devonian, Canada. (Figured and named without
    description, Deunff, 1954d, text-fig. 10).

C. celtica Deunff, 1958, pp. 33-4, pl. 6 figs. 54-6. M. Ordovician, France.

C. chlamydea (Rust, 1885), p. 321, pl. 44 fig. 22 (as Dictyospyris chlamydea). U. Cretaceous,
    England. ---, Deflandre, 1954, p. 258.

C. cornifera Deunff, 1955a, p. 147, text-fig. 23. M. Devonian, Canada.

C. cubus Deunff, 1961b, p. 217. M. Devonian, Canada. (Figured and named without description
    in Deunff, 1954d, text-fig. 1).

C. deanei Deflandre, 1954, p. 258 (figured by Deane, 1845, pl. 9 fig. 5). U. Cretaceous, England.

C. dictyophora (Valensi, 1953), p. 56, pls. 2 fig. 15; 10, fig. 1   (as Micrhystridium). M. Jurassic, France.   ---, Downie and Sarjeant, 1963, p. 93.

C. dictyospyroides O. Wetzel, 1933, p. 28, pl. 4 fig. 11.   U. Cretaceous, Baltic.

C. elgassiensis Deunff, 1961a, p. 40, pl. 2 fig. 9.   L. Ordovician, Sahara   (as C. el _gassiensse, corrected by author on reprints).

C. eupeplos (Valensi, 1948), pp. 542-3, text-fig. 3   (as Micrhystridium).   M. Jurassic, France.   ---, Deflandre, 1954, p. 258.

C. exilissima (Deflandre, 1947d), p. 9, text-fig. 20-1 (as Micrhystridium).   M. Jurassic, France. ---, Deflandre, 1954, p. 258.

C. fagoni Deunff, 1961b, p. 217.   M. Devonian, Canada.   (Named without description in Deunff, 1954d, text-fig. 5.)

C. flosdevonica Stockmans and Willière, 1960, p. 5, pl. 2 figs. 38, 41.   U. Devonian, Belgium.

C. kraeuseli Stockmans and Willière, 1960, p. 5, pl. 1 fig. 20.   U. Devonian, Belgium.

C. imitata Deflandre and Cookson, 1955, pp. 288-9, text-fig. 55.   U. Cretaceous, Australia. (Figured and named, without description, in Defl. and Cookson, 1954, fig. 16.)

C. miloni Deunff, 1957, p. 7, fig. 14.   M. Devonian, Canada.

C. mirabilis Deunff, 1958, p. 34, pl. 6 figs. 53, 63.   M. Ordovician, France.

C. multisepta Deunff, 1955a, p. 147, text-fig. 25.   M. Devonian, Canada.

C. nebulosa Deunff, 1954b, p. 241, text-fig. 8.   M. Devonian, France.

C. octoplana Downie, 1959, p. 63, pl. 11 fig. 2.   M. Silurian, England.

C. pachytheca Eisenack, 1957, p. 244-5, pls. 19 figs. 4-5; 20, fig. 11.   L. Jurassic, Germany.

C. parva Sarjeant, 1959, pp. 342-3, pl. 13 fig. 6, text-fig. 8,   emend.   Sarjeant, 1961a, p. 108. M. Jurassic, England.

C. pavimenta (Deflandre, 1945a), p. 68, pl. 3 figs. 20-21, text-fig. 41   (as Micrhystridium). Silurian, France.   ---, Deflandre, 1954, p. 258.

C. pentaster Staplin, 1961, p. 416, pl. 49 fig. 18.   U. Devonian, Canada.

C. perimembrana Staplin, 1961, p. 417, pl. 49 figs. 16-17.   U. Devonian, Canada.

C. placophora (Valensi, 1948), pp. 543-4, text-fig. 4   (as Micrhystridium).   M. Jurassic, France.   ---, Downie and Sarjeant, 1963, p. 93.

C. prismatica Deunff, 1961b, p. 217.   M. Devonian, Canada.   (Figured and named without description in Deunff, 1954d, text-fig. 6).

C. pterophora (Deflandre and Courteville, 1939), p. 102, pl. 2 figs. 4-5   (as Hystrichosphaer- idium).   U. Cretaceous, France.   ---, Downie and Sarjeant, 1962, p. 92.

C. pterota Cookson and Eisenack, 1958, p. 50, pl. 11 fig. 7.   ?L.-U. Cretaceous, Australia.

C. punctifera Deflandre and Cookson, 1955, p. 289, pl. 7 fig. 14, text-fig. 50.   ?Eocene, Australia.

C. pygmaeis Deunff, 1958, p. 33, pl. 6 figs. 49-50.   M. Ordovician, France.

* C. radiata O. Wetzel, 1933, p. 27, pl. 4 fig. 8.   U. Cretaceous, Baltic.

C. radiata O. We., forma serratocyclus O. Wetzel, 1933, pp. 27-8, pl. 4 fig. 9. U. Cret., Germany.

C. reticulata (Deflandre,1937c), pp. 82-3, pl. 17 figs. 5-6.   U. Cretaceous, France   (as
      Micrystridium).   ---, Downie and Sarjeant, 1963, p. 93.

C. stigmata Cookson and Eisenack, 1958, p. 50, pl. 9 fig. 14.   L. Cretaceous, Australia.

C. striata Eisenack and Cookson, 1960, p. 9, pl. 3 figs. 10-11.   U. Cretaceous, Australia.

C. teichophera Sarjeant, 1961a, pp. 107-8, pl. 15 fig. 9, text-figs. 9a-b.   U. Jurassic, England.

C. tetraster Staplin, 1961, p. 416, pl. 49 fig. 15.   U. Devonian, Canada.

C. wenlockia Downie, 1959, pp. 63-4, pl. 11 fig. 4.   M. Silurian, England.

C. wetzeli Deflandre, 1954, p. 258 (figured by O. Wetzel, 1933, pl. 4 fig. 7).

DAPCODINIUM Evitt, 1961b, p. 996.

* D. priscum Evitt, 1961b, pp. 996-1001, pl. 119 figs. 1-14, text-figs. 1-20.   L. Jurassic, Denmark.

DASYDIACRODIUM Timofeyev, 1959, p. 88, emend.   Deflandre and Deflandre-Rigaud, 1961, p.10.

D. angulare Timofeyev, 1959, p. 91, pl. 8 figs. 6, 6a.   U. Cambrian-L. Ordovician, U.S.S.R.

D. angulatum (Timofeyev, 1959), pp. 92-3, pl. 8 fig. 12   (as Dasyrytidodiacrodium).
      U. Cambrian, U.S.S.R.   ---, Deflandre and Deflandre-Rigaud, 1961, p. 10
      (by implication).

D. argutum (Naumova, 1950), p. 186, pl. 4 figs. 4-5 (as Azonomonoletes).   U. Cambrian,
      Baltic U.S.S.R.   ---, comb. nov.

D. asymmetricum (Timofeyev, 1959), p. 93, pl. 8 fig. 14 (as Dasyrytidodiacrodium). U. Cambrian,
      U.S.S.R.   ---, Deflandre and Deflandre-Rigaud, 1961, p. 10 (by implication).

*D. eichwaldi Timofeyev, 1959, p. 92, pl. 8 fig. 8.   L. Ordovician, U.S.S.R.

D. gibbum (Timofeyev, 1959), p. 93, pl. 8 figs. 15, 15a (as Dasyrytidodiacrodium).   U. Cambrian
      -L. Ordovician, U.S.S.R.   ---, Deflandre and Deflandre-Rigaud, 1961, p. 10
      (by implication).

D. imperfectum (Naumova, 1950), p. 186, pl. 4 figs. 8-9 (as Azonomonoletes).   U. Cambrian,
      Baltic U.S.S.R.   ---, comb. nov.

D. inaequilaterale (Timofeyev, 1959), p. 92, pl. 8 fig. 11   (as Dasyrytidodiacrodium).   ---,
      Deflandre and Deflandre-Rigaud, 1961, p. 10 (by implication).

D. monstrorsum Timofeyev, 1959, p. 90, pl. 8 fig. 3.   U. Cambrian, U.S.S.R.

D. mutilatum (Timofeyev, 1959), p. 93, pl. 8 figs. 13-13a (as Dasyrytidodiacrodium).
      L. Ordovician, U.S.S.R.   ---, Deflandre and Deflandre-Rigaud, 1961, p. 10
      (by implication).

D. palmatilobum Timofeyev, 1959, p. 91, pl. 8 figs. 5-5b.   U. Cambrian-L. Ordovician,
      U.S.S.R.

107

D. palmatiobatum Timofeyev, 1959, p. 90, pl. 8 fig. 2.   U. Cambrian, U.S.S.R.

D. prominens Timofeyev, 1959, p. 91, pl. 8 fig. 7.   L. Ordovician, U.S.S.R.

D. sewergini (Timofeyev, 1959), p. 92, pl. 8 fig. 9 (as Dasyrytidodiacrodium).   U. Cambrian,
   U.S.S.R.   ---, Deflandre and Deflandre-Rigaud, 1961, p. 10 (by implication).

D. singulare (Naumova, 1950), p. 186, pl. 4 fig. 7 (as Azonomonoletes).   U. Cambrian,
   Baltic U.S.S.R.   ---, comb. nov.

D. stellare (Timofeyev, 1959), p. 92, pl. 8 fig. 10 (as Dasyrytidodiacrodium).   M. Cambrian,
   U.S.S.R.   ---, Deflandre and Deflandre-Rigaud, 1961, p. 10 (by implication).

D. trapezoideum Timofeyev, 1959, p. 88, pl. 8 fig. 1.   M. Cambrian, U.S.S.R.

D. tricorne Timofeyev, 1959, pp. 90-1, pl. 8 fig. 4.   U. Cambrian, U.S.S.R.

DEFLANDREA Eisenack, 1938c, p. 187.

D. acuminata Cookson and Eisenack, 1958, p. 27, pl. 4 figs. 5-8.   U. Cretaceous, Australia.

D. bakeri Deflandre and Cookson, 1955, p. 251, pl. 4 figs. 1-24.   Paleocene-Eocene,
   Australia.

D. balmei Cookson and Eisenack, 1962b, p. 486   (figured as Deflandrea minor n. sp. in
   Cookson and Eisenack, 1960a, pl. 1 figs. 1-4). U. Cretaceous, Australia.

D. belfastensis Cookson and Eisenack, 1961a, p. 71, pl. 11 figs. 4-6.   U. Cretaceous, Australia.

D. cincta Cookson and Eisenack, 1958, p. 26, pl. 4 figs. 1-3.   L. Cretaceous, Australia.

D. conica Vozzhennikova, 1960, pl. 3 fig. 4 (no diagnosis).   Eocene, Siberia, U.S.S.R.

D. cooksoni Alberti, 1959b, pp. 97-8, pl. 9 figs. 1-6,   U. Cretaceous, Germany.

D. cretacea Cookson, 1956, pp. 184-5, pl. 1 figs. 1-7.   U. Cretaceous, Australia.

D. denticulata Alberti, 1959b, pp. 102-3, text-fig. 1.   Eocene, Germany.

D. diebeli Alberti, 1959b, pp. 99-100, pl. 9 figs. 18-21.   U. Cretaceous, Germany.

D. echinoidea Cookson and Eisenack, 1960a, p. 2, pl. 1 figs. 5-6.   U. Cretaceous, Australia.

D. foliacea Eisenack and Cookson, 1960, p. 2, pl. 1 fig. 3.   U. Cretaceous, Australia.

D. granulifera Manum, 1963, pp. 61-4, pl. 3 figs. 5-9.   Cretaceous, Graham Island, Arctic
   Canada.

D. heterophlycta Deflandre and Cookson, 1955, pp. 249-50, pl. 5 fig. 6, text-fig. 5.   Eocene,
   Australia.   (Figured and named without description in Deflandre and Cookson, 1954,
   text-fig. 3.).

D. korojenensis Cookson and Eisenack, 1958, pp. 27-8, pl. 4 figs. 10-11.   U. Cretaceous,
   Australia.

D. macrocysta Cookson and Eisenack, 1960a, p. 3, pl. 1 figs. 7-8.   U. Cretaceous, Australia.

D. micracantha Cookson and Eisenack, 1960a, p. 3, pl. 1 fig. 9.   U. Cretaceous, Australia.

D. minor Alberti, 1959b, p. 98, pl. 9 figs. 9-11. U. Cretaceous, Germany.

D. nucula Cookson and Eisenack, 1962b, p. 486, pl. 1 fig. 13.   U. Cretaceous, Australia.

D. obliquipes Deflandre and Cookson, 1955, p. 252, pl. 4 fig. 6.   Paleocene-Eocene, Australia.

D. oebisfeldensis Alberti, 1959b, pp. 95-6, pl. 8 figs. 10-13.   Eocene, Germany.

D. pachyceros Deflandre and Cookson, 1955, p. 252, pl. 4 fig. 7.   Eocene, Australia.

D. pellucida Deflandre and Cookson, 1955, p. 251, pl. 4 fig. 3 (as D. bakeri forma pellucida.) Paleocene-Eocene, Australia.   ---, Cookson and Eisenack, 1958, p. 27.

D. perlucida Alberti, 1959b, p. 102, pl. 9 figs. 16-7.   L. Cretaceous, Germany.

* D. phosphoritica Eisenack, 1938c, p. 187, text-fig. 6.   Oligocene, East Prussia, U.S.S.R.

D. phosphoritica Eis., 1938c subsp. phosphoritica Cookson and Eisenack, 1961b, p. 39. (figured in Eisenack, 1938c, text-fig. 6).   Oligocene, East Prussia, U.S.S.R.

D. phosphoritica subsp. australis Cookson and Eisenack, 1961b, pp. 39-40, pl. 1 fig. 2-3. Eocene, Australia.

D. pirnaensis Alberti, 1959b, p. 100, pl. 8 figs. 1-5.   U. Cretaceous, Germany.

D. rectangularis Cookson and Eisenack, 1962b, p. 486, pl. 1 figs. 14-5.   U. Cretaceous, Australia.

D. robusta Deflandre and Cookson, 1955, p. 250, pl. 4 fig. 9.   Eocene, Australia.

D. rotundata Eisenack and Cookson, 1960, p. 2, pl. 1 figs. 1-2.   U. Cretaceous, Australia.

D. scheii Manum, 1963, pp. 56-8, pl. 1 figs. 1-16, text-fig. 1.   Cretaceous, Graham Island, Arctic Canada.

D. serratula Cookson and Eisenack, 1958, p. 28, pl. 4 fig. 4.   U. Cretaceous, Australia.

D. speciosa Alberti, 1959b, p. 97, pl. 9 figs. 12-13.   Paleocene, Germany.

D. spectabilis Alberti, 1959b, p. 99, pl. 9 figs. 7-8.   U. Cretaceous, Germany.

D. spinulosa Alberti, 1959b, p. 95, pl. 8 figs. 8-9.   Oligocene, Germany.

D. sverdrupiana Manum, 1963, pp. 59-60, pl. 2 figs. 6-15, text-fig. 3.   Cretaceous, Graham Island, Arctic Canada.

?D. tenera Krutzsch, 1962, pp. 44-5, pl. 11 figs. 20-22, text-fig. 1e.   Eocene, Germany.

D. thomasi Cookson and Eisenack, 1961a, pp. 71-2, pl. 11 figs. 7-10.   Eocene, Australia.

D. tripartita Cookson and Eisenack, 1960a, pp. 2-3, pl. 1 fig. 10.   U. Cretaceous, Australia.

D. ventriosa Alberti, 1959b, p. 101, pl. 9 figs. 14-15.   L. Cretaceous, Germany.

D. verrucosa Manum, 1963, pp. 60-1, pl. 3 figs. 1-4.   Cretaceous, Graham Island, Arctic Canada.

D. wellingtoniana Tasch, 1963a, p. 336, pl. 1 figs. 10-11.   L. Permian, U.S.A.

DEUNFFIA Downie, 1960, p. 198.

D. brevispinosa Downie, 1960, pp. 198-9, pl. 1 figs. 4, 6.   M. Silurian, England.

D. furcata Downie, 1960, p. 199, pl. 1 figs. 1, 9.   M. Silurian, England.

D. monacantha (Deunff, 1951), p. 323, text-fig. 4   (as Hystrichosphaeridium)   M. Ordovician,
       France.   Veryhachium monacanthum Deunff, 1954c, p. 306.   ---, Downie, 1960, p. 198

* D. monospinosa Downie, 1960, p. 198, pl. 1 fig. 8.   M. Silurian, England.

D. ramusculosa Downie, 1960, p. 199, pl. 1 fig. 2, text-figs. 1-5.   M. Silurian, England.

DICONODINIUM Eisenack and Cookson, 1960, p. 3.

D. dispersum (Cookson and Eisenack, 1958), p. 39, pl. 10 figs. 12, 14   (as Palaeohystrichophora).
       L. Cretaceous, Australia.   ---, Eisenack and Cookson, 1960, p. 3.

D. glabrum Eisenack and Cookson, 1960, pp. 3-4, pl. 1 fig. 11.   U. Cretaceous, Australia.

D. inflatum Eisenack and Cookson, 1960, p. 4, pl. 1 figs. 12-3.   U. Cretaceous, Australia.

* D. multispinum (Deflandre and Cookson, 1955), p. 257, pl. 1 fig. 5   (as Palaeohystrichophora).
       U. Cretaceous, Australia.   ---, Eisenack and Cookson, 1960, p. 3.

D. pelliferum (Cookson and Eisenack, 1958), pp. 38-9, pl. 10 fig. 11   (as Palaeohystrichophora).
       L. Cretaceous - Eocene ,   Australia.   ---, Eisenack and Cookson, 1960, p. 3.

D. tenuistriatum Eisenack and Cookson, 1960, p. 4, pl. 1 figs. 14-16.   U. Cretaceous, Australia.

DICTYOPYXIDIA Eisenack, 1961b, p. 316.

* D. areolata (Cookson and Eisenack, 1960b), pp. 255-6, pl. 39, figs. 12-14   (as Dictyopyxis).
       U. Jurassic, Australia.   ---, Eisenack, 1961b, p. 316 (by implication).

DICTYOSPHAERIDIUM W. Wetzel, 1952, p. 406.

* D. deflandrei W. Wetzel, 1952, p. 406, pl. A fig. 12.   U. Cretaceous, Baltic.

DICTYOTIDIUM Eisenack, 1955, p. 179, emend.   Staplin, 1961, p. 417.

* D. dictyotum (Eisenack, 1938a), pp. 27-8, pl. 3 fig. 8a-c   (as Leiosphaera). Baltic drift,
       Silurian pebble.   ---, Eisenack, 1955, pp. 179-80.

D. polosymmetrium Staplin, 1961, p. 417, pl. 49 fig. 13.   U. Devonian, Canada.

D. polygonium Staplin, 1961, p. 417, pl. 49 fig. 14.   U. Devonian, Canada.

D. tenuiornatum Eisenack, 1955, p. 180, pl. 4 fig. 11, text-fig. 4.   U. Silurian, Baltic.

DIMASTIGOBOLUS Deflandre, 1935a, p. 224.

* D. longifilus Deflandre, 1935a, p. 224, pl. 5 fig. 12, text-figs. 1-2.   U. Cretaceous, France.
       (as D. longifilum , here corrected).

DINGODINIUM Cookson and Eisenack, 1958, p. 39.

D. cerviculum Cookson and Eisenack, 1958, p. 40, pl. 1 figs. 12, 14.   L. Cretaceous, Australia.

D. europaeum Eisenack, 1958c, pp. 392-3, pl. 24 fig. 4.   L. Cretaceous, Germany.

* D. jurassicum Cookson and Eisenack, 1958, p. 39, pl. 1 figs. 10, 11.   Papua and Australia.

DINOBRYON Ehrenberg (Modern genus)
Forms attributed to this genus by O. Wetzel, 1933, pp. 173-4.   No named fossil taxa.

DINOPTERYGIUM Deflandre, 1935, p. 231.

* D. cladoides Deflandre, 1935, p. 231, pl. 8 fig. 6.   U. Cretaceous, France.

DIOXYA Cookson and Eisenack, 1958, p. 59.

* D. armata Cookson and Eisenack, 1958, p. 59, pl. 11 fig. 11, text-fig. 20.   L. Cretaceous, Papua.

D. villosa Eisenack and Cookson, 1960, p. 10, pl. 2 figs. 15-16.   L. Cretaceous, Australia.

DIPLOFUSA Cookson and Eisenack, 1960a, p. 10.

* D. gearlensis Cookson and Eisenack, 1960a, p. 10, pl. 3 fig. 10.   U. Cretaceous, Australia.

DIPLOTESTA Cookson and Eisenack, 1960b, p. 256.

* D. glaessneri Cookson and Eisenack, 1960b, p. 256, pl. 39 figs. 4-6.   U. Jurassic, Australia.

D. krutzschi Alberti, 1961, pp. 21-3, pls. 7 figs. 19-21; 12 figs. 6-7.   L. Cretaceous, Germany.

D. luna Cookson and Eisenack, 1960a, pp. 10-11, pl. 3 fig. 21.   U. Cretaceous, Australia.

DISPHAERIA Cookson and Eisenack, 1960a, p. 11.

* D. macropyla Cookson and Eisenack, 1960a, p. 11, pl. 3 figs. 13-14.   U. Cretaceous, Australia.

DISPHAEROGENA O. Wetzel, 1933, p. 51.

* D. carposphaeropsis O. Wetzel, 1933, p. 51, pl. 4 fig. 34.   U. Cretaceous, Baltic.

DOMASIA Downie, 1960, p. 199.

D. bispinosa Downie, 1960, p. 200, pl. 1 fig. 3.   M. Silurian, England.

D. discophora Cookson and Eisenack, 1962b, pp. 492-3, pl. 7 figs. 17-21.   ?L. -U. Cretaceous, Australia.

D. elongata Downie, 1960, p. 200, pl. 1 fig. 5.   M. Silurian, England.

* D. trispinosa Downie, 1960, pp. 199-200, pl. 1 fig. 7.   M. Silurian, England.

DRACODINIUM subgen. of Wetzeliella, q.v.

DUVERNAYSPHAERA Staplin, 1961, pp. 414-5.

D. krauseli (Stockmans and Willière, 1960), p. 5, pl. 1 fig. 20. (as Cymatiosphaera).   U. Devonian, Belgium.   ---, Stockmans and Willière, 1962a, pp. 70-1.

* D. tenuicingulata Staplin, 1961, pp. 415-6, pl. 49 figs. 10-11, text-fig. 9d.   U. Devonian, Canada.

EISENACKIA Deflandre and Cookson, 1955, p. 258.   (Named without description by Deflandre and Cookson, 1954, p. 1236).

* E. crassitabulata Deflandre and Cookson, 1955, pp. 258-61, pl. 5 fig. 2, text-figs. 6-16.
    Paleocene-Eocene. Australia.   (Figured and named without description by Deflandre , and Cookson, 1954, figs. 8-11).

ELLIPSOIDICTYUM Klement, 1960, p. 78.

* E. cinctum Klement, 1960, pp. 78-80, pls. 6 figs. 15-16; 7 figs. 1-2; text-figs. 36-7.
    U. Jurassic, Germany.

EMSLANDIA Gerlach, 1961, p. 171.

* E. emslandensis Gerlach, 1961, pp. 172-3, pl. 26 figs. 13-14.   Miocene, Germany.

ENDOSCRINIUM subgen. of Scriniodinium, q.v.

EODINIA Eisenack, 1936b, pp. 73-5.

* E. pachytheca Eisenack, 1936b, pp. 73-5, text-figs. 1-5.   M. Jurassic, Baltic.

EOPSEUDOCERATIUM subgen. of Pseudoceratium, q.v.

EPICEPHALOPYXIS Deflandre, 1935, p. 234.

* E. adhaerens Deflandre, 1935, p. 234, pl. 9 figs. 5-6.   U. Cretaceous, France.

E. indentata Deflandre and Cookson, 1955, pp. 292-3, pl. 9 figs. 5-7, text-fig. 56.
    Paleocene-Eocene, Australia.

EPIPLOSPHAERA Klement, 1960, p. 73.

E. areolata Klement, 1960, pp. 76-7, pl. 8 figs. 5-9.   U. Jurassic, Germany.

* E. bireticulata Klement, 1960, pp. 74-5, pl. 8 figs. 1-4.   U. Jurassic, Germany.

E. reticulospinosa Klement, 1960, pp. 75-6, pl. 8 figs. 10-12.   U. Jurassic, Germany.

ESTIASTRA Eisenack, 1959a, p. 201.

E. barbata Downie, 1963, p. 638, pl. 92 fig. 8.   M. Silurian, England.

E. granulata Downie, 1963, p. 638, pl. 91 fig. 8.   M. Silurian, England.

* E. magna Eisenack, 1959a, pp. 201-2, pl. 16 figs. 17-20.   L. Silurian, Estonia, U.S.S.R.

FROMEA Cookson and Eisenack, 1958, p. 55.

* F. amphora Cookson and Eisenack, 1958, p. 56, pl. 5 figs. 10-11.   L.-U. Cretaceous, Australia.

GALEACORNEA Stover, 1963, p. 86.

G. acuminata Stover, 1963, p. 89, pl. 2 figs. 8-10, text-fig. 6.   U. Cretaceous, Portuguese Guinea.

G. causea Stover, 1963, pp. 87-8, pls. 1 figs. 16-17; 2 figs. 1-7; text-fig. 4.   U. Cretaceous, Portuguese Guinea.

* G. clavis Stover, 1963, pp. 86-7, pl. 1 figs. 1-5, text-figs. 2-3.   U. Cretaceous, Senegal.

G. protensa Stover, 1963, pp. 88-9, pl. 2 figs. 11-15, text-fig. 5.   U. Cretaceous, Senegal.

GARDODINIUM Alberti, 1961, p. 18.

G. albertii Neale and Sarjeant, 1962, pp. 445-6, pl. 19 fig. 6, text-fig. 4.   L. Cretaceous, England.

* G. eisenacki Alberti, 1961, p. 18, pl. 3 figs. 8-13.   L. Cretaceous, Germany.

G. trabeculosum (Gocht, 1959), pp. 62-3, pls. 4 fig. fig. 5; 8 fig. 2 (as Scriniodinium.) L. Cretaceous, Germany.   ---, Alberti, 1961, p. 18.

GEISELODINIUM Krutzsch, 1962, p. 42.

G. eocenicum Krutzsch, 1962, p. 44, pl. 11 figs. 17-19, text-fig. 1d.   Eocene, Germany.

* G. geiseltalense Krutzsch, 1962, p. 43, pl. 11 figs. 8-13, text-fig. 1b.   Eocene, Germany.

G. hallense Krutzsch, 1962, p. 44, pl. 11 figs. 14-16, text-fig. 1c.   Eocene, Germany.

GILLINIA Cookson and Eisenack, 1960a, pp. 11-12.

* G. hymenophora Cookson and Eisenack, 1960a, p. 12, pl. 3 figs. 4-6, text-fig. 5. U. Cretaceous, Australia.

GINGINODINIUM Cookson and Eisenack, 1960a, p. 7.

* G. spinulosum Cookson and Eisenack, 1960a, p. 7, pl. 2 fig. 9.   U. Cretaceous, Australia.

GLENODINIUM Stein   (Modern genus and type species).

G. smreczyniense Woloszynska (Modern species recorded by Macko, 1957, p. 117, pls. A fig. 1; 73 figs. 15-16, from Miocene, Poland).

GONYAULAX Diesing (Modern genus and type species).

G. acanthosphaera Sarjeant, 1961a, pp. 94-5, pl. 13 fig. 14, text-fig. 4.   U. Jurassic, England.

G. aceras Eisenack, 1958c, pp. 391-2, pl. 21 figs. 1, 2.   L. Cretaceous, Germany.

G. aculeata Klement, 1960, pp. 42-4, pl. 5 figs. 6-9, text-fig. 21.   U. Jurassic, Germany.

G. amabilis Deflandre, 1939b, p. 143, pl. 6 fig. 8.   U. Jurassic, France.

G. ambigua Deflandre, 1939b, p. 144, pl. 6 fig. 2.   U. Jurassic, France.

G. apionis Cookson and Eisenack, 1958, p. 36, pl. 3 fig. 7, text-figs. 3-4.   L. Cretaceous, Australia.

G. areolata Sarjeant, 1961a, pp. 95-7, pl. 13 fig. 13, text-fig. 5.   U. Jurassic, England.

G. bulloidea Cookson and Eisenack, 1960b, p. 247, pl. 37 fig. 11, text-fig. 4.   U. Jurassic, Australia.

G. cassidata Eisenack and Cookson, 1960 , p. 3, pl. 1 figs. 5-6 (as G. helicoidea subsp. cassidata).   U. Cretaceous, Australia.   ---, Cookson and Eisenack, 1962b, pp. 486-7.

G. caytonensis Sarjeant, 1959, pp. 330-2, pl. 13 fig. 1, text-fig. 1.   M. Jurassic, England.

G. chaloneri Sarjeant, 1963c, p. 354, text-figs. 2 (right), 3.   U. Triassic, England.

G. cladophora Deflandre, 1938e, pp. 173-6, pl. 7 figs. 105, text-figs. 5-6.   U. Jurassic, France.

G. cladophora Defl., 1938e subsp. cladophora Klement, 1960, p. 35, pl. 3 figs. 1-9,
        text-figs. 11-13.   U. Jurassic, France.

G. cladophora Defl., 1938e subsp. extensa Klement, pp. 36-7, pl. 4 figs. 1-4,
        text-fig. 16.   U. Jurassic, Germany.

G. cladophora Defl., 1938e subsp. hemipolyedrica Klement, 1960, p. 36, pl. 3 figs. 10-12, ∴.
        text-figs. 14-5.   U. Jurassic, Germany.

G. cladophora Defl., 1938e subsp. isovalvata Klement, 1960, pp. 37-8, pl. 4 figs. 5-9,
        text-fig. 17.   U. Jurassic, Germany.

G. clathrata Cookson and Eisenack, 1960b, pp. 246-7, pl. 37 fig. 5, text-fig. 2.   U. Jurassic,
        Australia.

G. cornigera Valensi, 1953, p. 27   pls. 1 figs. 4, 8, 10; 2 figs. 1, 2; 13 fig. 5; text-fig. 2a.
        M. Jurassic, France (incorrectly as G. cornigerum; altered to correct form by Sarjeant,
        1962b, p. 481).

G. crassicornuta Klement, 1960, pp. 38-9, pl. 5 figs. 1-3.   U. Jurassic, Germany.

G. cretacea Neale and Sarjeant, 1962, pp. 441-3, pl. 19 figs. 1-2, text-fig. 2.   L. Cretaceous,
        England.

?G. cristulata Sarjeant, 1959, pp. 332-4, pl. 13 fig. 2, text-fig. 2.   M. Jurassic, England.

G. diaphanis Cookson and Eisenack, 1958, pp. 36-7, pl. 3 figs. 13-14, text-figs. 10-11.
        L. Cretaceous, Australia.

G. edwardsi Cookson and Eisenack, 1958, pp. 32-3, pl. 3 figs. 5-6, text-fig. 7.   U. Cretaceous,
        Australia.

G. eisenacki Deflandre, 1938e, pp. 171-3, pl. 6 figs. 7-10, text-figs. 3-4.   U. Jurassic, France.

G. eisenacki Defl., 1938e subsp. oligodentata Cookson and Eisenack, 1958, p. 30, pl. 2
        fig. 11.   U. Jurassic, Australia.

G. eumorpha Cookson and Eisenack, 1960b, p. 246, pl. 37 figs. 1-3, text-fig. 3.   U. Jurassic,
        Australia.

G. freakei Sarjeant, 1963d, pp. 85-6, pl. 1 figs. 1-3.   U. Jurassic, England.

G. granulata Klement, 1960, pp. 39-41, pl. 4 figs. 10-13, text-figs. 18-20.   U. Jurassic,
        Germany.

G. granuligera Klement, 1960, pp. 41-2, pl. 5 figs. 4-5.   U. Jurassic, Germany.

G. helicoidea Eisenack and Cookson, 1960, pp. 2-3, pl. 1 figs. 4, 9.   L. Cretaceous, Australia.

G. heslertonense Neale and Sarjeant, 1962, pp. 440-1, pls. 19 fig. 5; 20, fig. 5; text-fig. 1.
        L. Cretaceous, England.

G. hyalodermopsis Cookson and Eisenack, 1958, p. 34, pl. 3 figs. 11-12, text-figs. 5-6.
  L. Cretaceous, Australia.

G. jurassica Deflandre, 1938e, pp. 168-70, pl. 6 figs. 2-5, text-figs. 1-2. U. Jurassic, France.

G. jurassica Defl., 1938e var. longicornis Deflandre, 1938e, p. 171, pl. 6 fig. 6. U. Jur., France.

G. longicornis Downie, 1957, p. 420, pl. 20 fig. 8, text-figs. 2a-b. U. Jurassic, England.

G. mamillifera Deflandre, 1939b, p. 143, pl. 6 fig. 1. U. Jurassic, France.

G. margaritifera Cookson and Eisenack, 1960a, pp. 5-6, pl. 2 figs. 1-2, text-fig. 1. U. Cretaceous, Australia.

G. microceras Eisenack, 1958c, p. 391, pl. 21 figs. 12-13. L. Cretaceous, Germany.

G. millioudi Sarjeant, 1963d, pp. 86, 88, pl. 1 figs. 4-7. U. Jurassic, Switzerland.

G. muderongensis Cookson and Eisenack, 1958, p. 32, pl. 3 figs. 3-4, text-fig. 15.
  L. Cretaceous, Australia.

G. nannotrix Deflandre, 1939b, p. 143, pl. 6 fig. 7. U. Jurassic, France.

G. nealei Sarjeant, 1962b, pp. 480-1, pl. 69 fig. 1, text-fig. 2. U. Jurassic, England.

G. nuciformis (Deflandre, 1938c), p. 180, pl. 8 figs. 4-6 (as Palaeoperidinium nuciforme).
  U. Jurassic, France. ---, Sarjeant, 1962b, pp. 482-3.

G. obscura Lejeune-Carpentier, 1946, pp. 191-3, text-figs. 3-5. U. Cretaceous, Belgium.

G. orthoceras Eisenack, 1958c, pp. 388-9, pls. 21 figs. 3-11; 24 fig. 1; text-figs. 2-3.
  L. Cretaceous, Germany.

G. pachyderma Deflandre, 1938e, pp. 176-8, pl. 7 figs. 6-10, text-figs. 7-10. U. Jurassic,
  France.

G. paliuros Sarjeant, 1962a, p. 260, pl. 1 fig. 7, text-fig. 5. U. Jurassic, England.

G. perforans Cookson and Eisenack, 1958, pp. 30-2, pl. 2 figs. 1-4, 7, 8, text-figs. 8-9.
  U. Jurassic, Papua.

G. porosa Lejeune-Carpentier, 1946, pp. 193, 196, text-fig. 6. U. Cretaceous, Belgium.

G. rhaetica Sarjeant, 1963c, pp. 353-4, text-figs. 1, 2 (left). U. Triassic, England.

G. scotti Cookson and Eisenack, 1958, p. 30, pl. 2 figs. 5-6. U. Jurassic, Australia.

G. serrata Cookson and Eisenack, 1958, p. 34, pl. 3 fig. 2, text-figs. 12-14. U. Jurassic
      - L. Cretaceous, Papua.

G. tenuiceras Eisenack, 1958c, pp. 389-91, pls. 21 figs. 14-15; 22, figs. 1-3 24; fig. 2 text-
  figs. 4-5. L. Cretaceous.

G. tenuitabulata Gerlach, 1961, pp. 159-61, pl. 25 figs. 10-11, text-figs. 1-3. Oligocene,
  Germany.

?G. transparens Sarjeant, 1959, pp. 334-5, pl. 13 fig. 3, text-fig. 3. M. Jurassic, England.

G. venusta Klement, 1960, pp. 44-5, pl. 5 figs. 10-13, text-fig. 22. U. Jurassic, Germany.

G. wetzeli Lejeune-Carpentier, 1939, pp. 526-9, text-figs. 1-2.   U. Cretaceous, Baltic.

GRANOMARGINATA ° Naumova, 1961, p. 114.

* G. prima° Naumova, 1961, p. 114, pl. 5 fig. 10.   L. Cambrian, U.S.S.R.

GYMNODINIUM Stein, 1878 (Modern genus and type species).

G. australiense Deflandre and Cookson, 1955, pp. 248-9, pl. 5 fig. 1.   Miocene, Australia.

? G. avellana Lejeune-Carpentier, 1951, p. 309, text-fig. 3.   U. Cretaceous, Belgium.

G. cretaceum Deflandre, 1935a, p. 225, pl. 5 figs. 6-8, text-figs. 4-5.   U. Cretaceous, France.
(Figured and named without description in Deflandre, 1934, text-figs. 9-10).

G. dabendorfense Alberti, 1961, p. 5, pl. 3 fig. 4.   L. Cretaceous, Germany.

G. decorum Deflandre, 1943a, pp. 503-4, pl. 17 fig. 2, text-figs. 8-9.   U. Cretaceous, France.

G. denticulatum Alberti, 1961, p. 5 pl. 3 figs. 2-3.   U. Cretaceous, Germany.

G.digitum Deflandre, 1935a, p. 225, text-figs. 7-8.   U. Cretaceous, France.

G. dorsispirale Churchill and Sarjeant, 1963, pp. 33-4, pl. 1 fig. 18, text-fig. 2.   Post-
Pleistocene, Australia.

G. heterocostatum Deflandre, 1935a, p. 225, text-fig. 6.   U. Cretaceous, Australia.

G. hexagonum Deflandre-Rigaud, 1954, p. 58, text-figs.1-2.   U. Cretaceous, France.

G. laticinctum Deflandre, 1943a, pp. 501-3, pl. 17 fig. 3, text-fig. 11.   U. Cretaceous, France.

G. marthae Deflandre, 1943a, p. 500, pl. 17 fig. 1, text-figs. 1-4.   U. Cretaceous, France.

G. nelsonense Cookson, 1956, pp. 183-4, pl. 1 figs. 8-11.   U. Cretaceous, Australia.

G. pontis-mariae Deflandre, 1936c, pp. 19-20, pl. 2 figs. 7-9.   U. Cretaceous, France.

G. strombomorphum Deflandre, 1943a, p. 501, pl. 17 figs. 4-6, text-figs. 5-7.   U. Cretaceous,
France.

G. torulosum Deflandre, 1943a, pp. 504-5, pl. 17 figs. 7-8, text-figs. 17-25.   U. Cretaceous,
France.

G. ventriosum Alberti, 1961, pp. 5-6, pl. 3 fig. 5.   U. Cretaceous, Germany.

G. westralium Cookson and Eisenack, 1958, pp. 25-6, pl. 1 fig. 9.   U. Cretaceous, Australia.

HALOPHORIDIA Cookson and Eisenack, 1962a, p. 271.

* H. xena Cookson and Eisenack, 1962a, p. 271, pl. 37 figs. 6-8.   U. Cretaceous, Australia.

HELIODINIUM Alberti, 1961, p. 33.

H. patriciae Neale and Sarjeant, 1962, pp. 451-2, pl. 19 fig. 3, text-fig. 7.   L. Cretaceous,
England.

* H. voigti Alberti, 1961, p. 33, pl. 8 figs. 1-5.   L. Cretaceous, Germany.

HEXAGONIFERA Cookson and Eisenack, 1961a, p. 73, emend.   Cookson and Eisenack, 1962b, pp. 495-6.

H. chlamydata Cookson and Eisenack, 1962b, p. 496, pl. 7 figs. 1-3, 5-8.   L.-?U. Cretaceous, Australia.

* H. glabra Cookson and Eisenack, 1961a, p. 74, pl. 12 figs. 9-13.   U. Cretaceous, Australia.

H. vermiculata Cookson and Eisenack, 1961a, p. 74, pl. 12 figs. 6-8.   U. Cretaceous, Australia.

HISTIOPHORA Klement, 1960, p. 51.

* H. ornata Klement, 1960, pp. 51-3, pl. 6 figs. 11-14, text-figs. 28-30.   U. Jurassic, Germany.

HOEGISPHAERA Staplin, 1961, p. 419.

* H. glabra Staplin, 1961, pp. 419-20, pl. 50 figs. 5-7.   U. Devonian, Canada.

HOROLOGINELLA Cookson and Eisenack, 1962a, p. 271.

H. apiculata Cookson and Eisenack, 1962a, p. 272, pl. 37 fig. 4.   U. Cretaceous, Australia.

? H. extrema Cookson and Eisenack, 1962a, pp. 272-3, pl. 37 fig. 10.   U. Cretaceous, Australia.

H. incurvata Cookson and Eisenack, 1962a, p. 272, pl. 37 fig. 5.   Eocene, Australia.

* H. lineata Cookson and Eisenack, 1962a, p. 272, pl. 37 figs. 1-3.   L. Cretaceous, Australia.

? H. obliqua Cookson and Eisenack, 1962a, p. 273, pl. 37 fig. 9.   ?L.-U.Cretaceous, Australia.

HUNGARODISCUS Kriván Hutter, 1963a, p. 76.

* H. fragilis Kriván Hutter, 1963a, p. 77, pls. 15 figs. 1-6; 16 figs. 1-13.   Oligocene, Hungary.

HYSTRICHODINIUM Deflandre, 1935a, p. 229.

H. alatum Cookson and Eisenack, 1962b, pp. 487-8, pl. 2 figs. 1-4.   L. Cretaceous, Australia.

H. amphiacanthum Cookson and Eisenack, 1958, p. 37, pl. 5 fig. 9.   U. Jurassic - L. Cretaceous, Papua.

H. compactum Alberti, 1961, p. 15, pl. 9 figs. 5-6.   L. Cretaceous, Germany.

H. furcatum Alberti, 1961, p. 16, pl. 9 figs. 7-8.   L. Cretaceous, Germany.

H. oligacanthum Deflandre and Cookson, 1955, pp. 255-7, pl. 1 fig. 1, text-figs. 2-3.
         L. Cretaceous, Australia.   (Figured and named without description in Deflandre and
         Cookson, 1954, text-fig. 1).

? H. parvum Alberti, 1961, pp. 16-17, pl. 9 figs. 1-4.   L. Cretaceous, Germany.

* H. pulchrum Deflandre, 1935a, pp. 229-30, pl. 5 fig. 1, text-figs. 9-11.   U. Cretaceous, France.

H. pulchrum Defl., 1935a var. densispinum Deflandre, 1936c, pp. 35-6, pl. 9 fig. 3.
         U. Cretaceous, France.

H. pulchrum Defl., 1935a var. globosum Deflandre, 1936c, p. 35, pl. 9 figs. 1-2.
         U. Cretaceous, France.

H. ramoides Alberti, 1961, pp. 15-16, pl. 8 figs. 11-13.   L. Cretaceous, Germany.

HYSTRICHOKIBOTIUM Klumpp, 1953, pp. 387-8.

* H. pseudofurcatum Klumpp, 1953, p. 388, pl. 16 figs. 12-14.   Eocene, Germany.

H. trabeculiferum Deflandre and Cookson, 1955, p. 269, pl. 8 fig. 6.   Miocene, Australia.

HYSTRICHOKOLPOMA Klumpp, 1953, pp. 388-9.

* H. cinctum Klumpp, 1953, p. 389, pl. 17 figs. 305.   Eocene, Germany.

H. poculum Maier, 1959, pp. 312-3, pl. 31 fig. 3.   Miocene, Germany.

H. rigaudae Deflandre and Cookson, 1955, pp. 279-81, pl. 6 figs. 6, 10, text-fig. 42.   Eocene-
    ?Miocene, Australia.   (Figured and named without description in Deflandre and Cookson,
    1954, fig. 15.)

H. sequanaportus Deflandre and Deflandre-Rigaud, 1958, cards 1352-3, 4 figs.   U. Cretaceous,
    France.

HYSTRICHOSPHAERA O. Wetzel, 1932, pp. 136-7, restr. Deflandre, 1937c, p. 64.

HYSTRICHOSPHAERA subgen. Hystrichosphaera Deflandre, 1937c, p. 13.

H. bentori Rossignol, 1962, p. 132 (figured in Rossignol, 1961, pl. 1 figs. 7-8).   Pleistocene,
    Israel.

H. bulloidea Deflandre and Cookson, 1955, p. 264, pl. 5 figs. 3-4.   Eocene-Miocene, Australia.

H. ceratioides Deflandre, 1937c, pp. 66-7, pl. 12 figs. 7-8.   U. Cretaceous, France.

H. cingulata (O. Wetzel, 1933), p. 28, pl. 4 fig. 10 (as Cymatiosphaera cingulata).
    U. Cretaceous, Baltic.   ---, Deflandre and Cookson, 1955, p. 267.

H. cornigera O. Wetzel, 1933, p. 39, pl. 5 fig. 6.   U. Cretaceous, Baltic.

H. cornuta Gerlach, 1961, pp. 180-1, pl. 27 figs. 10-12.   Oligocene, Germany.

H. crassipellis Deflandre and Cookson, 1955, p. 265, pl. 6 figs. 2-3, text-fig. 20.   Eocene,
    Australia (Figured and named without description by Defl. and Cookson, 1954, text-fig. 5)

H. cristata Conrad, 1941, p. 4-5, pl. 1 fig. D, text-fig. 2D.   U. Cretaceous, Belgium.

? H. dentata Gocht, 1959, pp. 75-6, pls. 4 fig. 11 7 fig. 19.   L. Cretaceous, Germany.

* H. furcata (Ehrenberg, 1838a), pl. 1 figs. 12, 14 (as Xanthidium).   U. Cretaceous, Germany.
    Ovum hispidum (Xanthidium) furcatum Lohmann, 1904, pp. 21-25.   ---, O. Wetzel,
    1932, p. 144.

H. furcata (Ehr.) forma aulosphaeropsis O. Wetzel, 1933, p. 35, pl. 5 fig. 5.   U. Cret., Baltic.

H. furcata (Ehr.) subsp. angusta W. Wetzel, 1952, p. 394, pl. A fig. 2, text-fig. 2.
    U. Cretaceous, Baltic.

H. furcata (Ehr.) forma multibrachiata de Wit, 1943, p. 376, text-fig. 3f.   U. Cretaceous,
    Netherlands.

H. hyperacantha Deflandre and Cookson, 1955, pp. 264-5, pl. 6 fig. 7.   Miocene, Australia.

H. mirabilis Rossignol, 1963, pl. 2 figs. 16-21 (named without description in Rossignol, 1961, p. 322; described in Rossignol, 1962, p. 132). Pleistocene, Israel.

? H. pedata O. Wetzel, 1933, pp. 55-6, pl. 4 fig. 35. U. Cretaceous, Baltic.

H. ramosa (Ehrenberg, 1838a), pl. 1 pt. 15 figs. 1-5 (as Xanthidium ramosum). U. Cretaceous, Germany. Spiniferites ramosus Mantell, 1854, text-fig. 77 nos. 4 & 6. Ovum hispidum (Xanthidium) ramosum Lohmann, 1904, pp. 21, 25. ---, O. Wetzel, 1932, p. 144.

H. setosa Philippot, 1949, p. 56, text-fig. 1. U. Cretaceous, France.

H. speciosa Deflandre, 1937c, p. 65, pl. 11 fig. 2. U. Cretaceous, France. (Named without description in Deflandre, 1934, text-fig. 4.)

H. tertiaria Eisenack and Gocht, 1960, pp. 515-7, text-fig. 4. Oligocene, East Prussia, U.S.S.R.

H. wetzeli Deflandre, 1935a, p. 232, pl. 8 fig. 5. U. Cretaceous, France.

HYSTRICHOSPHAERA subgen. Hystrichosphaeropsis Deflandre, 1935a, p.232 (originally described as a separate genus; reduced to subgeneric status by Deflandre, 1937c, p. 61).

* H. ovum (Deflandre, 1935a), p. 232, pl. 8 fig. 11 (as Hystrichosphaeropsis). U. Cretaceous, France.

HYSTRICHOSPHAERIDIUM Deflandre, 1937c, p. 68, restr. Eisenack, 1958c, pp. 399-400.

H. albertense Pocock, 1962, p. 82, pl. 15 figs. 226-7. L. Cretaceous, Canada.

H. alcicornu Eisenack, 1954b, pp. 65-6, pl. 10 figs. 1-2, text-fig. 5. Oligocene, E. Prussia, U.S.S.R.

H. ancoriferum Cookson and Eisenack, 1960a, p. 8, pl. 2 fig. 11. U. Cretaceous, Australia.

H. anthophorum Cookson and Eisenack, 1958, pp. 43-4, pl. 11 figs. 12-13, text-figs. 16-18. U. Jurassic, Australia and Papua.

H. arundum Eisenack and Cookson, 1960, p. 8 pl. 3 figs. 7-9, U. Cretaceous, Australia.

H. aquitanicum Deunff, 1961a, p.39, pl. 2 figs. 12-13. L. -U.Cretaceous, France.

H. asperum Maier, 1959, p. 519, pl. 33 fig. 2. Miocene, Germany.

H. astartes Sannemann, 1955, p. 325, pl. 4 fig. 1, text-fig. 1a, b. L. Devonian, Germany.

H. asterigerum Gocht, 1959, p. 67-8, pls. 3 fig. 1; 5 figs. 1-4. L. Cretaceous, Germany.

H. asymmetricum Deflandre and Courteville, 1939, pp. 100-1, pl. 4 figs. 1-2. U. Cretaceous, France.

H. biforme (Wiesner, 1936), p. 154, pl. 7 fig. 9 (as Hystrichosphaera biformis). U. Cretaceous, Czechoslovakia. ---, Deflandre, 1946a, card 881.

H. bulbosum (Ehrenberg, 1838), pl. 1 fig. 17 (as Xanthidium). U. Cretaceous, Germany. Ovum hispidum bulbosum, Lohmann, 1904, pp. 21, 25. Hystrichosphaera bulbosa. O. Wetzel, 1932, p. 144. ---, Deflandre, 1937c, p. 80.

H. cantharellum Brosius, 1963, pp. 40-1, pl. 6 fig. 1, text-fig. 2, nos. 11a-c. Oligocene, Germany.

<u>H. capitatum</u> Cookson and Eisenack, 1960b, p. 252, pl. 39 fig. 5.   U. Jurassic, Australia.

<u>H. choanophorum</u> Deflandre and Cookson, 1955, pp. 271-2, text-figs. 23-9.   Miocene,
    Australia.   (Figured and named in Deflandre and Cookson, 1954, text-fig. 7.)

<u>H. clavigerum</u> Deflandre, 1937c, p. 71, pl. 14 figs. 1-2.   U. Cretaceous, France.   <u>Baltisphae-</u>
    <u>ridium clavigerum</u>.   Downie and Sarjeant, 1963, p. 91.   ---, Sarjeant, 1964 (in press)

<u>H. complex</u> (H.H. White, 1842), p. 39, pl. 4 div. 3 fig. 11 (as <u>Xanthidium tubiferum complex</u>).
    U. Cretaceous, England.   <u>H. elegantulum</u>, Lejeune-Carpentier, 1940, p. 222.   ---.
    Deflandre, 1946b, p. 11.

<u>H. crassipes</u> (Reade, 1839), pl. 9 figs. 2, 5 (as <u>Xanthidium</u>).   U. Cretaceous, England.   ---,
    Lejeune-Carpentier, 1941, pp. 79-80.

<u>H. cribrotubiferum</u> Sarjeant, 1960a, pp. 137-8, pl. 6 figs. 2-3, text-fig. 1.   U. Jurassic,
    England.

<u>H. cruciatum</u> (O. Wetzel, 1933), pp. 48-9, pl. 4 fig. 30 (as <u>Hystrichosphaera</u>).   U. Cretaceous,
    Baltic.   ---, Deflandre, 1937c, p. 79.

<u>H. deflandrei</u> Valensi, 1947, p. 817-8, text-fig. 3.   M. Jurassic, France.

<u>H. dissimilare</u> Isagulova, 1963, pl. 1 fig. 17 No description; validity doubtful.
    Jurassic, Lvov-Volyu region, U.S.S.R.

<u>H. equispinosum</u> Tasch, 1963a, p. 336, pl. 1 fig. 12.   L. Permian, U.S.A.

<u>H. flosculus</u> Deflandre, 1937c, pp. 75-6, pl. 15 figs. 5-6.   U. Cretaceous, France.

<u>H. fucosum</u> (Valensi, 1955a), p. 40, text-fig. 2b (as <u>Micrhystridium</u>).   Cretaceous, France.
    ---, Downie and Sarjeant, 1963, p. 93.

<u>H. gliwicense</u> Macko, 1957, p. 113, pls. 71 figs. 11-15 72 fig. 1.   Miocene, Poland.

<u>H. grallaeforme</u> Brosius, 1963, p. 42, pl. 5 fig. 3, text-fig. 2 nos. 3a-b.   Oligocene, Germany.

<u>H. hilli</u> (Merrill, 1895), p. 17, text-fig. 21 (as ?<u>Geodia</u>).   L. Cretaceous, Texas, U.S.A.   ---,
    Sarjeant, 1964 , (in press).

<u>H. hirundo</u> Eisenack, 1958c, pp. 404-5, pl. 24 fig. 12.   L. Cretaceous, Germany.

<u>H. irregulare</u> (Merrill, 1895), p. 16, text-fig. 14 (as ?<u>Geodia</u>).   L. Cretaceous, U.S.A.   ---,
    Sarjeant, 1964 (in press).

<u>H. irregulare</u> Pocock, 1963 (non Merrill, 1895), pp. 82-3, p. 115, figs. 228-9.   L. Cretaceous,
    Canada.

<u>H. isocalamus</u> Deflandre and Cookson, 1955, p. 272, pl. 2 figs. 7-8, text-figs. 30-35.
    L. Cretaceous, Australia.

<u>H. lacunosum</u> Isagulova, 1963, pl. 1 fig. 3 No description; validity doubtful.
    U. Jurassic, Lvov-Volyu Region, U.S.S.R.

<u>H. leonardium</u> Tasch, 1963a, p. 336, pl. 1 figs. 10-11.   Permian, U.S.A.

<u>H. leptodermum</u> Maier, 1959, pp. 321-2, pl. 33 figs. 5-6.   Oligocene, Germany.

<u>H. macrotubulum</u> Neale and Sarjeant, 1962, pp. 452-5, pl. 20 fig. 7, text-fig. 8a.
    L. Cretaceous, England.

H. major Lejeune-Carpentier, 1940, pp. 220-1, text-fig. 13.   U. Cretaceous, Belgium.

H. membranaceum Philippot, 1949, pp. 57-8, text-fig. 3.   U. Cretaceous, France.

H. pachydermum Cookson and Eisenack, 1960b, pp. 251-2, pl. 38 fig. 5.   U. Jurassic, Australia.

H. paradoxum Brosius, 1963, pp. 41-2, pl. 4 fig. 6, text-fig. 2 nos. 1a-c.   Oligocene, Germany.

H. paulinae (Valensi, 1953), p. 48, pl. 12 fig. 6 (as Micrhystridium).   M. Jurassic, France.   ---,
    Downie and Sarjeant, 1963, p. 93.

H. penicillatum (Ehrenberg, 1843), pp. 61-3 (as Xanthidium penicillatum).   Ovum hispidum
    _penicillatum Lohmann, 1904, pp. 21-5.   Hystrichosphaera penicillata O. Wetzel, 1933,
    p. 41.   ---, Deflandre, 1937c, p. 27.

H. perceptibile Isagulova, 1963, pl. 1 fig. 5 No description; validity doubtful.
    Jurassic, Lvov-Volyu Region, U.S.S.R.

H. perforatum Gocht, 1959, pp. 68-9, pls. 3 fig. 7; 7 figs. 13-16.   L. Cretaceous, Germany.

H. polyplasium Maier, 1959, pp. 322-3, pl. 33 figs. 7-8.   Miocene, Germany.

H. pulcherrimum Deflandre and Cookson, 1955, pp. 270-1, pl. 1 fig. 8, text-figs. 21-2.
    L. Cretaceous, Australia.   (Figured and named, without description,in Deflandre and
    Cookson, 1954, text fig. 6).

H. recurvatum(H.H. White, 1842), pp. 39-40, pl. 4 div. 3 fig. 12 (in text as Xanthidium recurvatum
    or palmaforme, in plate caption as X. palmatum).   Xanthidium palmatum Bronn, 1848,
    p. 1375.   Spiniferites palmatus.   Mantell, 1854, p. 251.   Hystrichosphaeridium
    recurvatum Lejeune-Carpentier, 1940, pp. 221-2.

H. recurvatum(H.H. White, 1842), subsp. polypes Cookson and Eisenack, 1962b, pp. 491-2, pl. 4
    figs. 11-13.   L. -?U. Cretaceous, Australia.

H. rhabdophorum Valensi, 1955b, pp. 593-4, pl. 3 fig. 7.   Cretaceous, France.

H. rhopalophorum Valensi, 1955a, pp. 36-7, text-fig. 1c.   Cretaceous, France.

H. rubinum Rossignol, 1962, p. 134.   Pleistocene, Israel.   Never figured: validity doubtful.

H. salpingophorum (Deflandre, 1935a), p. 232, pl. 9 fig. 1   (as Hystrichosphaera).
    U. Cretaceous, France.   ---, Deflandre, 1937c, p. 80.

H. simplex (White, 1842), pp. 38-9, pl. 4 div. 3 fig. 10   (as Xanthidium tubiferum simplex).
    U. Cretaceous, England.   ---, Deflandre, 1946a, card 934.

H. siphoniphorum Cookson and Eisenack, 1958, p. 44, pl. 11 figs. 8-10.   ?L.-U. Cretaceous,
    Australia.

H. spini-pansatum (Merrill, 1895), p. 17, text-fig. 20 (as ?Geodia spini-pansata).   L. Cretaceous,
    Texas, U.S.A.   ---, Sarjeant, 1964   (in press).

H. stellatum Maier, 1959, pp. 320-1, pl. 33 figs. 3-4.   Oligocene, Germany.

H. tiara Klumpp, 1953, pp. 390-1, pl. 17 figs. 8-10.   Eocene, Germany.

H. torynum Cookson and Eisenack, 1960b, p. 252, pl. 38 figs. 6, 15.   ?U. Jurassic-L.Cretaceous.
    Australia and Papua.

H. truncigerum Deflandre, 1937c, pp. 71-2, pl. 13 figs. 6-7.   U. Cretaceous, France.

* H. tubiferum (Ehrenberg, 1838a), pl. 1 fig. 16 (as Xanthidium).   U. Cretaceous, Germany.
    Ovum hispidum (Xanthidium) tubiferum, Lohmann, 1904, pp. 21 and 25.   Hystrichos-
    phaera tubifera O. Wetzel, 1933, pp. 40-1.   ---, Deflandre, 1937c, p. 96.

H. vasiformum Neale and Sarjeant, 1962, p. 452, pl. 20 fig. 1, text-fig. 8b.

H. verbinense Courteville in Deflandre, 1946a, card 945, 1 text-fig.   U. Cretaceous, France.

H. xipheum Maier, 1959, p. 309, pl. 30 fig. 5 (as Galea xiphea).   Oligocene, Germany.   ---,
    Sarjeant, 1964 (in press).

H. zoharyi Rossignol, 1962, p. 132, pl. 2 fig. 10.   Pleistocene, Israel.

HYSTRICHOSPHAEROPSIS subgen. of Hystrichosphaera q.v.

KALYPTEA Cookson and Eisenack, 1960b, p. 256.

* K. diceras Cookson and Eisenack, 1960b, pp. 256-7, pl. 39 fig. 1.   U. Jurassic, Australia.

K. jurassica Alberti, 1961, p. 21, pl. 7 fig. 8.   M. Jurassic, Germany.

K. monoceras Cookson and Eisenack, 1960b, p. 257, pl. 39 figs. 2-3.   U. Jurassic, Australia
    and Papua.

KILDINELLA Timofeyev in Shepeleva and Timofeyev, 1963, p. 1158.

* K. giperboreica Timofeyev in Shepeleva and Timofeyev, 1963, p. 1158, pl. 1 figs. 2, 3, 5, 6, 8
    9, 11, 12.   Pre-Cambrian, North U.S.S.R.

KISELEVIA Vozzhennikova, 1960.   No diagnosis; validity doubtful.

K. major Vozzhennikova, 1960, pl. 3 fig. 1 No description; validity doubtful. Eoc., U.S.S.R.

K. ornata Vozzhennikova, 1960, pl. 3 fig. 2 No description; validity doubtful. Eoc., U.S.S.R.

KOFOIDOPSIS Tasch, 1963, p. 333.

* K. coronata Tasch, 1963, pp. 333-4, pl. 1 figs. 7-8.   L. Permian, Kansas, U.S.A.

KOMEWUIA Cookson and Eisenack, 1960b, p. 257.

* K. glabra Cookson and Eisenack, 1960b, p. 257-8, pl. 39 figs. 7-8.   U. Jurassic, Australia
    and Papua.

KOROJONIA Cookson and Eisenack, 1958, p. 54.

* K. dubiosa Cookson and Eisenack, 1958, p. 54, pl. 12 fig. 13.   U. Cretaceous, Australia.

LECANIELLA Cookson and Eisenack, 1962a, p. 269.

L. dictyota Cookson and Eisenack, 1962a, p. 270, pl. 37 figs. 18-20.   ?L. -U. Cretaceous,
    Australia.

* L. margostriata Cookson and Eisenack, 1962a, pp. 269-70, pl. 37 figs. 16-17.   U. Cretaceous,
    Australia.

LEIOFUSA Eisenack, 1938a, p. 28.

L. bacillum Deunff, 1955a, p. 148, pl. 4 fig. 2.　M. Devonian, Canada.

L. filifera Downie, 1959, p. 65, pl. 11 figs. 6-7.　M. Silurian, England.

* L. fusiformis (Eisenack, 1934), p. 65, pl. 4 fig. 19　(as Ovum hispidum fusiformis).
　　　? Ordovician, Baltic.　---, Eisenack, 1938a, p. 28.

L. jurassica Cookson and Eisenack, 1958, p. 51, pl. 10 figs. 3-4.　U. Jurassic, Australia.

L. lidiae Gorka, 1963, pp. 37-8, pl. 5 fig. 6.　U. Cretaceous, Poland.

L. minuta Deunff, 1955a, p. 148, pl. 4 fig. 5.　M. Devonian, Canada.

L. navicula Eisenack, 1951, p. 192-3, pl. 1 fig. 8.　M. Ordovician, Estonia, U.S.S.R.

L. navis (Eisenack, 1938b), p. 229, pl. 16 fig. 8 (as Bion).　Ordovician, in Baltic drift.
　　　---, Eisenack, 1938a, p. 28.

L. oblonga Eisenack, 1959a, p. 205, pl. 17 fig. 23.　L. Ordovician, Sweden.

L. ovalis Eisenack, 1938a, p. 28, pl. 4 fig. 9.　Ordovician, Baltic.

L. squama Deunff, 1961a, p. 40, pl. 2 fig. 8.　L. Ordovician, Sahara.

L. tenuis Eisenack, 1951, p. 192, pl. 4 fig. 17.　L. Ordovician, Estonia, U.S.S.R.

L. tumida Downie, 1959, p. 65, pl. 11 fig. 5.　M. Silurian, England.

LEIOMARGINATA° Naumova, 1961, p. 114.

* L. simplex° Naumova, 1961, p. 114, pl. 3 fig. 9.　L. Cambrian, Estonia.

LEIOMINUSCULA° Naumova, 1961, p. 110.

* L. minuta° Naumova, 1961, p. 110, pl. 3 fig. 1.　Pre-Cambrian, U.S.S.R.

L. rugosa° Naumova, 1961, p. 112.　Pre-Cambrian, U.S.S.R.

LEIOPSOPHOSPHAERA° Naumova, 1961, p. 112.

* L. microrugosa° Naumova, 1961, p. 112, pl. 3 fig. 7.　Pre-Cambrian, U.S.S.R.

L. perlucidus Shepeleva in Shepeleva and Timofeyev, 1963, p.1158, pl.(1) fig. 1. Pre-Camb. U.S.S.R.

LEIOSPHAERIDIA Eisenack, 1958a, p. 2-5. emend Downie and Sarjeant, 1963, pp. 94-5.

LEIOSPHAERIDIA subgen.　Leiosphaeridia Sarjeant, 1962b, p. 492.　(The second subgenus,
　　　Chytroeisphaeridia, has since been given generic status).

L. aptiana Eisenack, 1958c, p. 409, pl. 27 figs. 10-11.　L. Cretaceous, Germany.

L. aurata (Deflandre, 1945a), p. 71, figured by Eisenack, 1938a, pl. 3 fig. 11　(as Leiosphaera).
　　　Ordovician, in Baltic drift.　---, Eisenack, 1958a, p. 9.

* L. baltica Eisenack, 1958a, p. 8, pl. 2 fig. 5.　Ordovician, in Baltic drift.

L. belloyense (Jansonius, 1962), p. 84, pl. 16 fig. 34 (as ?Leiosphaeridium).　M. Permian,
　　　Canada.　---, comb. nov.

L. cambriense (Timofeyev, 1959), p. 25, pl. 1 fig. 4 (as Protoleiosphaeridium). M. Cambrian, U.S.S.R. ---, Downie and Sarjeant, 1963, p. 95.

L. communis (Naumova, 1950), p. 181, pl. 2 fig. 10 (as Azonomonoletes). L. Ordovician, Baltic U.S.S.R. ---, comb. nov.

L. conglutinata (Timofeyev, 1959), p. 26, pl. 1 fig. 6 (as Protoleiosphaeridium). Pre-Cambrian, U.S.S.R. ---, Downie and Sarjeant, 1963, p. 95.

L. cryptogranulosa (Staplin, 1961), p. 407, pl. 48 fig. 7 (as Protoleiosphaeridium). U. Devonian, Canada. ---, Downie and Sarjeant, 1963, p. 95.

L. deflandrei Stockmans and Willière, 1963, pp. 474-5, pl. 1 figs. 2-3. Silurian, Belgium.

L. diaphania (Staplin, 1961), p. 406, pl. 48 fig. 8 (as Protoleiosphaeridium). U. Devonian, Canada. ---, Downie and Sarjeant, 1963, p. 95.

L. disca (Timofeyev, 1962), pl. 6 fig. 2 (as Leiosphaeridium). U. Silurian, U.S.S.R. ---, comb. nov.

L. eisenacki (Timofeyev, 1959), p. 28 pl. 2 fig. 1 (as Leiosphaeridium). L.-M. Ordovician, U.S.S.R. ---, Downie and Sarjeant, 1963, p. 95.

L. fastigatirugosa (Staplin, 1961), p. 408, pl. 50 fig. 9 (as Leiosphaeridium). U. Devonian, Canada. ---, Downie and Sarjeant, 1963, p. 95.

L. faveolata (Timofeyev, 1959), p. 26, pl. 1 fig. 7 (as Protoleiosphaeridium). L.-M. Cambrian, U.S.S.R. ---, Downie and Sarjeant, 1963, p. 95.

L. fragile Downie, 1958, pp. 344-5, pl. 17 fig. 6. L. Ordovician, England.

L. ? globosa (White, 1842), p. 36, pl. 4 div. 2 no. 1 (as Xanthidium). U. Cretaceous, England. Leiosphaera globosa Deflandre, 1946a, card 993. ---, comb. nov.

L. granulata (Eisenack, 1938a), p. 27, pl. 3 fig. 10 (as Leiosphaera). ?Ordovician, Baltic. ---, Eisenack, 1958a, p. 9.

L. hyalina (Deflandre, 1941b), p. 24, pl. 6 figs. 12-13 (as ?Leiosphaera). U. Jurassic, France. -- Eisenack, 1958a, p. 9.

L. indefinita (Timofeyev, 1959), p. 26, pl. 1 fig. 9 (as Protoleiosphaeridium). Pre-Cambrian, U.S.S.R. ---, Downie and Sarjeant, 1959, p. 95.

L. laevigata Stockmans and Willière, 1963, pp. 473-4, pl. 3 fig. 28. Silurian, Belgium.

L. major (Staplin, 1961), p. 406, pl. 48 fig. 6 (as Protoleiosphaeridium). U. Devonian, Canada. ---, Downie and Sarjeant, 1963, p. 95.

L. megacystis (Eisenack, 1938b), p. 228 (as Bion). Ordovician, in Baltic drift. Leiosphaera megacystis Eisenack, 1938a, p. 26. ---, Eisenack, 1958a, p. 9. (Never figured; validity doubtful).

L. microcystis (Eisenack, 1938b), p. 229 (as Bion). Ordovician, in Baltic drift. Leiosphaera microcystis Eisenack, 1938a, p. 26. ---, Eisenack, 1958a, p. 9.

L. microgranifera (Staplin, 1961), p. 405, pl. 48 fig. 4 (as Protoleiosphaeridium). U. Devonian, Canada. ---, Downie and Sarjeant, 1963, p. 95 (incorrectly as L. microgranulifera).

L. microsaetosa (Staplin, 1961), p. 407, pl. 48 figs. 2, 5   (as Protoleiosphaeridium).
    U. Devonian, Canada.   ---, Downie and Sarjeant, 1963, p. 95.

L. minuta (Staplin, 1961, p. 405, pl. 48 fig. 3 (as Protoleiosphaeridium).   U. Devonian,
    Canada.   ---, Downie and Sarjeant, 1963, p. 95.

L. muitscha (Timofeyev, 1962), pl. 6 fig. 1   (as Leiosphaeridium).   M. Silurian, Poland.
    ---, comb. nov.

L. nervata (Timofeyev, 1959), p. 26, pl. 1 fig. 8 (as Protoleiosphaeridium).   Pre-Cambrian,
    U.S.S.R.   ---, Downie and Sarjeant, 1963, p. 95.

L. oelandica Eisenack, 1962a, pp. 60-1, pl. 3 figs. 2-3.   L. Ordovician, Sweden.

L. orbiculata (Staplin, 1961), p. 405, pl. 48 fig. 12   (as Protoleiosphaeridium).   U. Devonian,
    Canada.   ---, Downie and Sarjeant, 1963, p. 95.

L. papillata (Staplin, 1961), pp. 406-7, pl. 48 figs. 10-11   (as Protoleiosphaeridium).
    U. Devonian, Canada.   ---, Downie and Sarjeant, 1963, p. 95.

L. parvigranulosa (Staplin, 1961), p. 407, pl. 48 fig. 9   (as Protoleiosphaeridium).   U. Devonian,
    Canada.   ---, Downie and Sarjeant, 1963, p. 95.

L. pestovi (Timofeyev, 1962), pl. 5 fig. 1   (as Leiosphaeridium).   L. Ordovician, U.S.S.R.
    ---, comb. nov.

L. punctulosa (Naumova, 1950), p. 182, pl. 2 fig. 11   (as Azonomonoletes).   L. Ordovician,
    Baltic U.S.S.R.   ---, comb. nov.

L. reticulata (Eisenack, 1938a), p. 27, pl. 3 figs. 7a-b   (as Leiosphaera).   Silurian, in Baltic
    drift.   ---, Eisenack, 1958 , p. 9.

L. retigera (Deflandre, 1945a), p. 70, pl. 2 fig. 12   (as Leiosphaera).   M. Silurian, France.
    ---, Eisenack, 1958a, p. 9.

L. similis Cookson and Eisenack, 1960b, pp. 254-5, pl. 38 fig. 14.   U. Jurassic, Australia
    and Papua.

L. sorediformis (Timofeyev, 1959), p. 26, pl. 1 fig. 5   (as Protoleiosphaeridium).   Pre-Cambrian,
    U.S.S.R.   ---, Downie and Sarjeant, 1963, p. 95.

L. tenuissima Eisenack, 1958b, pp. 391-2, pl. 1 figs. 2, 3.   L. Ordovician, U.S.S.R.

L. trivialis (Naumova, 1950), p. 188, pl. 5 fig. 11   (as Archaeletes).   Ordovician, Baltic
    U.S.S.R.   ---, comb. nov.

L. tubulosa Eisenack, 1963e, p. 213, pl. 20 figs. 6-7.   M. -U. Ordovician, Baltic.

L. voigti Eisenack, 1958b, p. 392, pl. 1 figs. 4-6.   L. Ordovician, U.S.S.R.

L. wenlockia Downie, 1959, p. 65, pl. 12 figs. 2-4.   M. Silurian, England.

L. wimani (Timofeyev, 1960), pl. 2 fig. 1   (as Protoleiosphaeridium).   Pre-Cambrian, Sweden.
    ---, Downie and Sarjeant, 1963, p. 95.

LEJEUNIA Gerlach, 1961, p. 169.

* L. hyalina Gerlach, 1961, pp. 169-71, pl. 26 figs. 10-11.   Oligocene, Germany.

<u>L. kozlowskii</u> Górka, 1963, p. 41, pl. 5 fig. 4.   U. Cretaceous, Poland.

<u>L. tricuspis</u> (O. Wetzel, 1933), p. 166, pl. 2 fig. 14 (as <u>Peridinium</u>).   U. Cretaceous, Baltic. (Figured and named, without description, in O. Wetzel, 1932, pl. 2 fig. 10).   ---, Górka, 1963, p. 40.

LEPTODINIUM Klement, 1960, pp. 45-6.

<u>L. arcuatum</u> Klement, 1960, p. 48, pl. 6 figs. 5-6.   U. Jurassic, Germany.

<u>L. membranigerum</u> Gerlach, 1961, pp. 162-4, pl. 26 figs. 1-4, 7. text-figs. 4-5.   Oligocene, Germany.

<u>L. mirabile</u> Klement, 1960, pp. 48-50, pl. 6 figs. 7-10, text-figs. 25-7.   U. Jurassic, Germany.

* <u>L. subtile</u> Klement , 1960, pp. 46-7, pl. 6 figs. 1-4, text-figs. 23-4.   U. Jurassic, Germany.

? <u>L. tenuicornutum</u> Cookson and Eisenack, 1962b, p. 487, pl. 3 figs. 12-13, text-fig. 1. ?U. Cretaceous, Australia.

LINOTOLYPA Eisenack, 1962d, p. 136.

* <u>L. arcuata</u> Eisenack, 1962d, p. 137, pl. 5 fig. 2.   M. Triassic, Germany.

LITHODINIA Eisenack, 1935, pp. 175-7.

* <u>L. jurassica</u> Eisenack, 1935, pp. 175-7, pl. 4 figs. 5-10, text-figs. 1-4.   M. Jurassic, Baltic.

LOPHODIACRODIUM Timofeyev, 1958, p. 830 emend. Deflandre and Deflandre-Rigaud, 1961, pp. 8-9.

<u>L. abnorme</u> (Timofeyev, 1959), p. 64, pl. 5 fig. 21   (as <u>Lophorytidodiacrodium</u>).   M. Cambrian, U.S.R.   ---, Deflandre and Deflandre-Rigaud, 1961, p. 8   (by implication).

<u>L. aculeatum</u> (Naumova, 1950), p. 183, pl. 3 fig. 1   (as <u>Azonomonoletes</u>).   L. Ordovician, Baltic U.S.S.R.   ---, comb. nov.

<u>L. angustum</u> (Downie, 1958), pp. 345-6, pl. 17 figs. 7-8, text-figs. 3e   (as <u>Diornatosphaera</u>). L. Ordovician, England.   --- Deflandre and Deflandre-Rigaud, 1961, p. 8.

<u>L. arbustum</u> Timofeyev, 1959, p. 61, pl. 5 fig. 7.   M. Cambrian, U.S.S.R.

<u>L. atavum</u> (Timofeyev, 1959), p. 64, pl. 5 fig. 20   (as <u>Lophorytidodiacrodium</u>).   M. Cambrian, U.S.S.R.   ---, Deflandre and Deflandre-Rigaud, 1961, p. 8   (by implication).

<u>L. bilaterale</u> (Timofeyev, 1959), p. 66, pl. 5 fig. 29   (as <u>Lophorytidodiacrodium</u>).   L. Ordovician U.S.S.R.   ---, Deflandre and Deflandre-Rigaud, 1961, p. 8   (by implication).

* <u>L. bubnoffi</u> (Timofeyev, 1958b), p. 831, pls. 2 fig. 1; 3 fig. 10   (as <u>Lophorytidodiacrodium</u>). L. Cambrian, Germany.   ---, Deflandre and Deflandre-Rigaud, 1959, p. 9.

<u>L. doliumsimile</u> (Timofeyev, 1959), p. 67, pl. 5 fig. 33   (as <u>Lophozonodiacrodium</u>).   L. Cambrian, U.S.S.R.   ---, Deflandre and Deflandre-Rigaud, 1961, p. 8   (by implication).

<u>L. ellipticum</u> (Timofeyev, 1959), p. 64, pl. 5 fig. 19   (as <u>Lophorytidodiacrodium</u>).   M. Cambrian, U.S.S.R.   ---, Deflandre and Deflandre-Rigaud, 1961, p. 8   (by implication).

<u>L. filiforme</u> (Timofeyev, 1959), p. 66, pl. 5 fig. 30   (as <u>Lophorytidodiacrodium</u>).   L. Ordovician, U.S.S.R.   ---, Deflandre and Deflandre-Rigaud, 1961, p. 8   (by implication).

L. gibberosum (Naumova, 1950), p. 185, pl. 3 figs. 6-7 (as Azonomonoletes). U. Cambrian, U.S.S.R. ---, comb. nov.

L. gibbosum (Timofeyev, 1959), p. 63, pl. 5 fig. 14 (as Lophorytidodiacrodium). M. Cambrian, U.S.S.R. ---, Deflandre and Deflandre-Rigaud, 1961, p. 8 (by implication).

L. gracile Timofeyev, 1959, p. 61, pl. 5 fig. 9. M. Cambrian, U.S.S.R.

L. inane (Timofeyev, 1959), pp. 63-4, pl. 5 fig. 18 (as Lophorytidodiacrodium). M. Cambrian, U.S.S.R. ---, Deflandre and Deflandre-Rigaud, 1961, p. 8 (by implication).

L. intertextum (Timofeyev, 1959), pp. 65-6, pl. 5 fig. 27 (as Lophorytidodiacrodium). U. Cambrian, U.S.S.R. ---, Deflandre and Deflandre-Rigaud, 1961, p. 8 (by implication).

L. introrsum (Timofeyev, 1959), p. 65, pl. 5 fig. 26 (as Lophorytidodiacrodium). U. Cambrian, U.S.S.R. ---, Deflandre and Deflandre-Rigaud, 1961, p. 8 (by implication).

L. lutkevischi (Timofeyev, 1959), p. 62, pl. 5 fig. 12 (as Lophorytidodiacrodium). M. Cambrian, U.S.S.R. ---, Deflandre and Deflandre-Rigaud, 1961, p. 8 (by implication).

L. maljavkinae (Timofeyev, 1959), p. 63, pl. 5 fig. 16 (as Lophorytididiacrodium). M. Cambrian, U.S.S.R. ---, Deflandre and Deflandre-Rigaud, 1961, p. 8 (by implication).

L. meniscatum (Timofeyev, 1959), p. 66, pl. 5 fig. 28 (as Lophorytidodiacrodium). U. Cambrian, U.S.S.R. ---, Deflandre and Deflandre-Rigaud, 1961, p. 8 (by implication).

L. monomorphum (Timofeyev, 1959), p. 65, pl. 5 fig. 24 (as Lophorytidodiacrodium). L. Ordovician, U.S.S.R. ---, Deflandre and Deflandre-Rigaud, 1961, p. 8 (by implication).

L. notatum (Naumova, 1950), p. 183 pl. 3 fig. 2 (as Azonomonoletes). L. Ordovician, Baltic U.S.S.R. ---, comb. nov.

L. oblatum (Timofeyev, 1959), p. 67, pl. 5 fig. 34 (as Lophozonodiacrodium). L. Cambrian, U.S.S.R. ---, Deflandre and Deflandre-Rigaud, 1961, p. 8 (by implication).

L. obtusum Timofeyev, 1958b, p. 831, pls. 1 fig. 1; 3 fig. 1. L. Cambrian, Germany.

L. obversum (Timofeyev, 1959), p. 65, pl. 5 fig. 23 (as Lophorytidodiacrodium). L. Ordovician, U.S.S.R. ---, Deflandre and Deflandre-Rigaud, 1961, p. 8 (by implication).

L. palmatum (Timofeyev, 1959), p. 66, pl. 5 fig. 31 (as Lophorytidodiacrodium). U. Cambrian, U.S.S.R. --- Deflandre and Deflandre-Rigaud, 1961, p. 8 (by implication).

L. parvimammum (Naumova, 1950), p. 184, pl. 3 fig. 10 (as Azonomonoletes). L. Ordovician, Baltic U.S.S.R. ---, comb. nov.

L. parvispinum (Naumova, 1950), p. 182, pl. 2 fig. 14 (as Azonomonoletes). L. Ordovician, Baltic, U.S.S.R. ---, comb. nov.

L. primarium (Timofeyev, 1959), pp. 62-3, pl. 5 fig. 13 (as Lophorytidodiacrodium). M. Cambrian, U.S.S.R. ---, Deflandre and Deflandre-Rigaud, 1961, p. 8 (by implication).

L. rotundum (Naumova, 1950), p. 182, pl. 2 fig. 15 (as Azonomonoletes). L. Ordovician, Baltic U.S.S.R. ---, comb. nov.

L. rotundum (Timofeyev, 1959, non Naumova, 1950), p. 64, pl. 5 fig. 22 (as Lophorytidodiacr-odium). L. Ordovician, U.S.S.R. ---, Deflandre and Deflandre-Rigaud, 1961, p. 8 (by implication).

<u>L. salebrosum</u> (Timofeyev, 1959), p. 63,pl. 5 fig. 15 (as <u>Lophorytidodiacrodium</u>). M. Cambrian,
U.S.S.R. ---, Deflandre and Deflandre-Rigaud, 1961, p. 8 (by implication).

<u>L. simile</u> Timofeyev, 1959), p. 61, pl. 5 fig. 9. M. Cambrian, U.S.S.R.

<u>L. striatum</u> (Naumova, 1950), pp. 185-6, pl. 4 fig. 102   (as <u>Azonomonoletes</u>). L. Ordovician,
Baltic, U.S.S.R. ---, comb. nov.

<u>L. sinutum</u> (Naumova, 1950), pp. 182-3, pl. 2 fig. 16 (as <u>Azonomonoletes</u>). L. Ordovician,
Baltic U.S.S.R. ---, comb. nov.

<u>L. spectabile</u> (Timofeyev, 1959), pp. 67-8, pl. 5 fig. 36 (as <u>Lophozonodiacrodium</u>).
M. Cambrian, U.S.S.R. ---, Deflandre and Deflandre-Rigaud, 1961, p. 8 (by implicatio

<u>L. subspinellosum</u> (Naumova, 1950), p. 182, pl. 2 fig. 13 (as <u>Azonomonoletes</u>). L. Ordovician,
Baltic U.S.S.R. ---, comb. nov.

<u>L. torulosum</u> (Naumova, 1950), p. 185, pl. 3 fig. 12 (as <u>Azonomonoletes</u>). L. Ordovician,
Baltic U.S.S.R. ---, comb. nov.

<u>L. tosnaense</u> (Timofeyev, 1959), p. 62, pl. 5 fig. 10 (as <u>Lophorytidodiacrodium</u>). L. Cambrian,
U.S.S.R. ---, Deflandre and Deflandre-Rigaud, 1961, p. 8 (by implication).

<u>L. totum</u> (Timofeyev, 1959), p. 65, pl. 5 fig. 25 (as <u>Lophorytidodiacrodium</u>). U. Cambrian,
U.S.S.R. ---, Deflandre and Deflandre-Rigaud, 1961, p. 8 (by implication).

<u>L. tuber</u> Deunff, 1961a, p. 44 pl. 3 fig. 15 (as <u>Diornatosphaera</u>). L. Ordovician, Sahara.
---, Deflandre and Deflandre-Rigaud, 1961, p. 10.

<u>L. tuberculatum</u> (Naumova, 1950), p. 185, pl. 3 fig. 3 (as <u>Azonomonoletes</u>). L. Ordovician,
Baltic U.S.S.R. ---, comb. nov.

<u>L. tuberculatum</u> (Timofeyev, 1959, non Naumova, 1950), p. 62, pl. 5 fig. 11 (as <u>Lophorytid-
odiacrodium</u>). M. Cambrian, U.S.S.R. ---, Deflandre and Deflandre-Rigaud, 1961,
p. 8 (by implication).

<u>L. tumidum</u> (Timofeyev, 1959), p. 67, pl. 5 fig. 35 (as <u>Lophozonodiacrodium</u>). M. Cambrian,
U.S.S.R. ---, Deflandre and Deflandre-Rigaud, 1961, p. 8 (by implication).

<u>L. turulosum</u> (Timofeyev, 1959), p. 67, pl. 5 fig. 32 (as <u>Lophorytidodiacrodium</u>). M. Cambrian,
U.S.S.R. ---, Deflandre and Deflandre-Rigaud, p. 8 (by implication).

<u>L. valdaicum</u> (Timofeyev, 1959), p. 163, pl. 5 fig. 17 (as <u>Lophorytidodiacrodium</u>).
L. Ordovician, U.S.S.R. ---, Deflandre and Deflandre-Rigaud, 1961, p. 8 (by
implication).

LOPHOMINUSCULA Naumova, 1961, p. 112.

* <u>L. prima</u> ° Naumova, 1961, p. 112, pl. 3 fig. 3. Pre-Cambrian, U.S.S.R.

<u>L. rugosa</u> Naumova? (in Naumova and Pavlovski, 1961, p. 182, text-fig. 1). Pre-Cambrian,
Scotland.

LOPHOSPHAERIDIUM Timofeyev, 1959, p. 29. Type species designated by Downie, 1963, p.630.

<u>L. citrinum</u> Downie, 1963, pp. 630-1, pl. 92 fig. 3. M. Silurian, England.

<u>L. granulosum</u> (Staplin, 1961), p. 406, pl. 48 fig. 1 (as <u>Protoleiosphaeridium</u>). U. Devonian,
Canada. <u>Leiosphaeridia granulosa.</u> Downie and Sarjeant, 1963, p. 95. ---
Downie, 1963, p. 630.

128

L. microspinosum (Eisenack, 1954a), p. 209, pl. 1 fig. 8   (as Hystrichosphaeridium).   L. Silurian,
    Sweden.   Baltisphaeridium microspinosum.   Downie, 1959, p. 60. ---, Downie,
    1963, p. 632.

L. parvum Stockmans and Willière, 1963, p. 472, pls. 2 fig. 2; 3 fig. 27, text-fig. 34.
    Silurian, Belgium.

L. parverarum Stockmans and Willière, 1963, p. 473, pl. 3 fig. 21, text-fig. 35.   Silurian,
    Belgium.

L. pilosum Downie, 1963, p. 631, pl. 92 fig. 2.   M. Silurian, England.

L. plicatum Timofeyev, 1959, p. 29, pl. 2 fig. 6.   L. Ordovician, U.S.S.R.

* L. rarum Timofeyev, 1959, p. 29, pl. 2 fig. 5.   L. Ordovician, U.S.S.R.

L. triangulatum Downie, 1963, p. 631, pl. 92 fig. 1.   M. Silurian, England.

LUNULIDIA Eisenack, 1958b, p. 391.

* L. lunula (Eisenack, 1951), pp. 193-4, pl. 4 fig. 1   (as Leiofusa).   L. Ordovician, Inger-
    manland, U.S.S.R.   ---, Eisenack, 1958b, p. 391.

MARGOMINUSCULA Naumova, 1961, pp. 110, 112.

* M. rugosa 1961, pp. 110-2, pl. 3 fig. 4.   Pre-Cambrian, U.S.S.R.

M. antiqua Naumova, 1961, p. 112, pl. 3 fig. 5.   Pre-Cambrian, U.S.S.R.

M. tennela ° Naumova? (in Naumova and Pavlovski, 1961, p. 182, fig. 1, Pre-Cambrian,
    Scotland).

M. crassa ° Naumova ? (in Naumova and Pavlovski, 1961, p. 182, fig. 1, Pre-Cambrian,
    Scotland).

M. prisca ° Naumova ? (in Naumova and Pavlovski, 1961, p. 182, fig. 1, Pre-Cambrian,
    Scotland).

M. tremata ° Naumova ? (in Naumova and Pavlovski,1961, p. 182, fig. 1, Pre-Cambrian,
    Scotland).

MEGASACCULINA Naumova, 1961, p. 113.

* M. atava Naumova, 1961, p. 113, pl. 3 fig. 15.   Pre-Cambrian, U.S.S.R.

MEMBRANILARNACIA Eisenack, 1963b, pp. 99-100.

* M. leptoderma (Cookson and Eisenack, 1958), pp. 50-1, pl. 10 figs. 7-9   (as Membranilarnax).
    L. Cretaceous, Papua. ---, Eisenack, 1963b, p. 99.

? M. liradiscoides (O. Wetzel, 1933), pp. 52-3, pl. 6 figs. 3a-b   (as Membranilarnax).
    U. Cretaceous, Baltic.   ---, comb. nov.

? M. liradiscoides (O. We., 1933)   forma gulpensis de Wit, 1943, pp. 384-5, text-figs. 12a-b.
    U. Cretaceous, Netherlands.

? M. marina (Kufferath, 1950), p. 34, text-fig. 40   (as Membranilarnax).   Post-Pleistocene,
    North Sea.   ---, comb. nov.

? M pira (Deunff, 1958), pp. 35-6, pl. 10 figs. 90-3 (as ?Membranilarnax). M. Ordovician, France. ---, comb. nov.

M. polycladiata Eisenack, 1963b, p. 100 (figured in Cookson and Eisenack, 1958, pl. 10 fig. 8). L. Cretaceous, Papua.

M. pterococcoides (O. Wetzel, 1933), pp. 53-4, pl. 6 fig. 4 (as Membranilarnax). U. Cretaceous France. ---, Eisenack, 1963b, p. 102.

? M. pterospermoides (O. Wetzel, 1933), p. 52, pl. 6 figs. 1-2 (as Membranilarnax). U. Cretaceous, Baltic. ---, comb. nov.

MEMBRANOLIMBUS Maliavkina in Maliavkina et al., 1961, p. 257.

M. limbatus Maliavkina in Maliavkina et al., 1961, p. 258, pl. 84 fig. 5. U. Jurassic, Siberia, U.S.S.R.

* M. triangulatus Maliavkina in Maliavkina et al., 1961, p. 258, pl. 84 figs. 6a-b. U. Jurassic, Siberia, U.S.S.R.

MEMBRANOSPHAERA Samoilovitch in Maliavkina et al., 1961, p. 251.

M. bulluliniformis Maliavkina in Maliavkina et al., 1961, p. 253, pl. 84 figs. 1a-b, 2a-b, 3. U. Jurassic - U. Cretaceous, Siberia, U.S.S.R.

M. bulluliniformis Mal. forma sphaerica Maliavkina in Maliavkina et al., 1961, p. 253, pl. 84 fig. 4. U. Jurassic, Siberia, U.S.S.R.

* M. maestrichtica Samoilovitch in Maliavkina et al., 1961, p. 253, pl. 83 figs. 1a-d, 2a-d. U. Cretaceous, Siberia, U.S.S.R.

M. maestrichtica Sam. var. pilata Samoilovitch in Maliavkina et al., 1961, p. 253, pl. 83 figs. 3, 4a-d. U. Cretaceous, Siberia, U.S.S.R.

M. tuberculata Maliavkina in Maliavkina et al., 1961, p. 253, pl. 84 figs. 7a-b, 8. U. Jurassic, Siberia, U.S.S.R.

MICRHYSTRIDIUM Deflandre, 1937c, pp. 79-80, emend. Downie and Sarjeant, 1963, p. 92.

M. albertensis Staplin, 1961, p. 409, pl. 48 fig. 19. U. Devonian, Canada.

M. ambiguum Deflandre, 1937c, p. 81, pl. 16 figs. 8-9. U. Cretaceous, France.

M. angustum Staplin, 1961, p. 409, pl. 48 fig. 20. U. Devonian, Canada.

M. arachnoides Valensi 1953, p. 45, pls. 5 figs. 16, 20; 6, fig. 16. M. Jurassic, France.

M. bacilliferum Deflandre, 1946d, text-fig. 5. L. Carboniferous, France. (No description; validity doubtful).

M. bigoti Deflandre, 1947d, p. 6, text-figs. 5-6. M. Jurassic, France.

M. biornatum Deflandre, 1937c, p. 82, pl. 13 fig. 9. U. Cretaceous, France.

M. bistchoensis Staplin, 1961, p. 409, pl. 48 fig. 15. U. Devonian, Canada.

M. breve Jansonius, 1962, p. 85, pl. 16 figs. 62-3, 66, text-fig. 3m. L. Triassic, Canada.

M. castaninum Valensi, 1953, p. 52, pls. 7 figs. 2-5, 10, 11; 14 fig. 3. M. Jurassic, France.

M. chattoni Stockmans and Willière, 1962a, pp. 59-60, pl. 1 fig. 19, text-fig. 17.
    U. Devonian, Belgium.

M. comatum Stockmans and Willière, 1962a, p. 65, pl. 2 figs. 2-3, 6-7, text-fig. 25.
    U. Devonian, Belgium.

M. cometes Valensi, 1948, p. 547, text-fig. 5 no. 6. M. Jurassic, France.

M. coronatum Stockmans and Willière, 1963, p. 467, pl. 2 fig. 9, text-fig. 28. Silurian,
    Belgium.

M. cortracumense Stockmans and Willière, 1963, pp. 468-9, pls. 2 fig. 11; 3 fig. 13;
    text-fig. 29. Silurian, Belgium.

M. deflandrei Valensi, 1948, pp. 545-6, text-fig. 5 nos. 3, 5. M. Jurassic, France.

M. densispinum Valensi, 1953, pp. 52-3, pls. 7 fig 6-9; 13 figs. 17-18; 14 fig. 4.
    M. Jurassic, France.

M. duodeciaster (Staplin, 1961), p. 414, pl. 49 fig. 7 (as Veryhachium). U. Devonian,
    Canada. ---, Downie and Sarjeant, 1963, p. 92.

M. eatonensis Downie, 1959, p. 62, pl. 11 fig. 15. Silurian, England.

M. echinoides Valensi, 1948, pp. 544-5, text-fig. 5 no. 1. M. Jurassic, France.

M. echinoides Val., 1948 forma minor Valensi, 1953, p. 40, pl. 4 figs. 7-8, 14; 13 figs. 13, 15.
    M. Jurassic, France.

M. filigerum Valensi, 1953, pp. 45-6, pl. 6 figs. 13-15. M. Jurassic, France.

M. flandrianum Stockmans and Willière, 1963, p. 464, pl. 2 fig. 12, text-fig. 22. Silurian,
    Belgium.

M. fragile Deflandre, 1947d, p. 8, text-figs. 13-18. M. Jurassic, France.

M. geniculatum Rossignol, 1962, p. 134. Pleistocene, Israel. (Never figured; validity
    doubtful).

M. heteracanthum Deflandre, 1937c, p. 80, pl. 14 fig. 7. U. Cretaceous, France.

M. heurcki Stockmans and Willière, 1962a, p. 63, pl. 2 fig. 8, text-fig. 22. U. Devonian,
    Belgium.

M. imitatum Deflandre, 1945a, p. 67, pl. 3 figs. 1-4. M. Silurian, France. (Figured and
    named without description in Deflandre, 1942b, text-fig. 14).

? M. incertum Deunff, 1958, p. 31, pl. 6 figs. 57-9. M. Ordovician, France.

* M. inconspicuum (Deflandre, 1935a), p. 233, pl. 9 figs. 11-12 (as Hystrichosphaera).
    U. Cretaceous, France. ---, Deflandre, 1937c, p. 80.

M. inconspicuum (Defl., 1935a) forma bullosa Valensi, 1953, p. 55, pls. 7 figs. 14-15;
    14 fig. 10. M. Jurassic, France.

M. inconspicuum (Defl., 1935a) forma helios Valensi, 1953, p.54, pl.2 fig.10. M. Jur., France.

M. kufferathi Stockmans and Willière, 1962a, pp. 60-1, pl. 2 fig. 9, text-fig. 18.
U. Devonian, Belgium.

M. lagynophorum Valensi, 1953, pp. 46-7, pls. 7 figs. 12, 16; 14 fig. 20. M. Jurassic, France.

M. lejeunei Stockmans and Willière, 1962b, p. 95, pl. 1 fig. 11, text-fig. 14. U. Devonian,
Belgium.

M. leptothrix Valensi, 1953, p. 51, pl. 10 fig. 9. M. Jurassic, France.

M. lucasi Valensi, 1953, p. 39, pl. 6 fig. 20. M. Jurassic, France.

M. mastigophorum Valensi, 1948, pp. 547-8, text-fig. 5 nos. 7-8. M. Jurassic, France.

M. mendax Deflandre, 1945a, p. 68, pl. 3 fig. 22. M. Silurian, France.

M. micropolygonale Stockmans and Willière, 1961, p. 4, pl. 1 fig. 12. U. Devonian, Belgium.

M. multispinosum Pastiels, 1948, p. 45, pl. 5 figs. 1-3. Eocene, Belgium.

M. nannacanthum Deflandre, 1945a, p. 66, pl. 3 figs. 5-7. M. Silurian, France. (Figured and
named without description in Deflandre, 1942b, text-fig. 13).

M. oceanicum Stockmans and Willière, 1962b, p. 66, pl. 2 fig. 18, text-fig. 27. U. Devonian,
Belgium.

M. operosum Deflandre, 1937c, p. 82, pl. 15 figs. 9-10. U. Cretaceous, France.

M. ornatum Stockmans and Willière, 1963, p. 466, pl. 3 fig. 19, text-fig. 27. Silurian,
Belgium.

M. pachydermum Deflandre and Cookson, 1955, p. 282, text-fig. 37. L. Cretaceous, Australia.

M. parinconspicuum Deflandre, 1945a, pp. 65-6, pl. 3 figs. 8-13. M. Silurian, France.
(Figured and named without description in Deflandre, 1942b, text-figs. 11-21).

M. parveroquesi Stockmans and Willière, 1963, p. 471, pl. 2 fig. 10, text-fig. 33. Silurian,
Belgium.

M. parvidumeti Stockmans and Willière, 1962c, p. 30, fig. a. U. Carboniferous, Belgium.

M. parvispinum Deflandre, 1946d, text-figs. 6-9. L. Carboniferous, France. (No description;
validity doubtful).

M. parvispinum Defl., 1946d forma major Deflandre, 1946d, text-fig. 10. L. Carboniferous,
France. (No description; validity doubtful).

M. pascheri Stockmans and Willière, 1962a, p. 64, pl. 2 fig. 13, text-fig. 24. U. Devonian,
Belgium.

M. pelagicum Stockmans and Willière, 1962a, pp. 62-3, pl. 2 fig. 4, text-fig. 21.
U. Devonian, Belgium.

M. pentagonale Stockmans and Willière, 1963, pp. 470-1, pl. 3 fig. 18, text-fig. 32.
Silurian, Belgium.

M. piliferum Deflandre, 1937c, pp. 80-1, pl. 15 fig. 11. U. Cretaceous, France.

M. piveteaui Valensi, 1953, pp. 56-7, pl. 7 fig. 37.   M. Jurassic, France.

M. polyedricum Valensi, 1948, pp. 548-9, text-fig. 6.   M. Jurassic, France.

M. pumile (O. Wetzel, 1932), p. 144, pl. 3 fig. 12   (as Hystrichosphaera longispinosa var.
     pumilis). U. Cretaceous, Baltic.   Hystrichosphaeridium pumile Deflandre, 1937c,
     p. 30.   ---, Downie and Sarjeant, 1963, p. 93.

M. radians Stockmans and Willière, 1963, p. 463, pls. 2 fig. 18; 3 fig. 15, text-fig. 21.
     Silurian, Belgium.

M. rarispinum Sarjeant, 1960c, p. 400, pl. 14 figs. 6-8, text-fig. 11.   U. Jurassic, England.

M. rectangulare Stockmans and Willière, 1962a, p. 62, pl. 2 fig. 10.   U. Devonian, Belgium.

M. recurvatum Valensi, 1953, pp. 43-4, pls. 6 figs. 1-10; 13 fig. 16.   M. Jurassic, France.

M. recurvatum Val., 1953 f. brevispinosa Valensi, 1953, p.44, pl.6 figs.9-10.   M. Jur., France.

M. recurvatum Val., 1953 f. longispinosa Valensi, 1953, p. 44, pl.6 fig. 6.   M. Jur., France.

M. recurvatum Val., 1953 f. multispinosa Valensi, 1953, p.44, pl. 6 fig. 5.   M. Jur., France.

M. recurvatum Val., 1953 f. reducta Valensi, 1953, p.44, pls. 6 fig. 8; 13 fig. 16.   M. Jur.,France.

M. rhopalicum Sarjeant, 1962b, pp. 490-1, pl. 70 fig. 14, text-fig. 9f.   U. Jurassic, England.

M. robustum Downie, 1958, p. 344, pl. 17 fig. 5, text-fig. 3b.   L. Ordovician, England.

M. roquesi Valensi, 1948, p. 545, text-fig. 5 no. 2.   M. Jurassic, France.

M. scutospinum Valensi, 1947, pp. 817-8, text-fig. 6.   M. Jurassic, England.

M. setasessitante Jansonius, 1962, p. 85, pl. 16 figs. 40-1, 50, text-fig. 3d.   L. Triassic, Canada.

M. shinetonensis Downie, 1958, p. 342, text-fig. 5a-g.   L. Ordovician, England.

M. singulare Firtion, 1952, p. 160, pl. 8 figs. 1-2.   U. Cretaceous, France.

M. stellatum Deflandre, 1945a, p . 65 , pl. 3 figs. 16-19.   M. Silurian, France.   (Figured
     and named, without description, in Deflandre, 1942b, text-fig. 7-8).

M. stellatum var.inflatum Downie, 1959, p. 61, pl. 11 fig. 12.   M. Silurian, England.

? M. stipulatum Jansonius, 1962, pl. 16 figs. 38-9, text-figs. 3a-b.   L. Triassic, Canada.

M. sydus Valensi, 1953, pp. 59-60, pls. 8 fig. 40; 9 figs. 3-5, 11, 17, 23-4;   14 figs. 11-12.
     M. Jurassic, France.

M. tenuissimum Deflandre, 1945a, pp. 68-9, pl. 3 figs. 14-15.   M. Silurian, France.

M. tenuissimum Defl., 1945a f. major Deflandre,1946a,text-fig. 3.   L. Carbon., France.

M. tornacense Stockmans and Willière, 1961, p. 4, pl. 1 fig. 4.   U. Devonian, Belgium.

M. triassicum Jansonius, 1962, p. 85, pl. 16 fig. 57, text-fig. 3h.   L. Triassic, Canada.

M. variabile Valensi, 1953, p. 47, pls. 3 figs. 12-13, 17, 4 figs. 1-2, 13 fig. 8.
     M. Jurassic, France.

M. varians Stockmans and Willière, 1963, pp. 465-6, pl. 2 fig. 15, text-figs. 25-6.   Silurian, Belgium.

M. vulgare Stockmans and Willière, 1962a, pp. 63-4, pl. 2 figs. 12, 14-15, text-figs. 23. U. Devonian, Belgium.

M. westphalienum Stockmans and Willière, 1962c, p. 30, fig. c.   U. Carboniferous, Belgium.

MICROCONCENTRICA Naumova, 1961, pp. 113, 115.

* M. avata Naumova, 1961, p. 115, pl. 3 fig. 13.   Pre-Cambrian, U.S.S.R.

MICRODINIUM Cookson and Eisenack, 1960a, p. 6.

* M. ornatum Cookson and Eisenack, 1960a, pp. 6-7, pl. 2 figs. 3-8, text-figs. 2-4. U. Cretaceous, Australia.

MINUTISSIMA Naumova and Pavlovski, 1961, p. 182.   Type species not designated.

M. atava Naumova and Pavlovski, 1961, p. 182, fig. 1.   Pre-Cambrian, Scotland.

M. prima Naumova and Pavlovski, 1961, fig. 1.   Pre-Cambrian, Scotland.   No desc. val. doubtful.

MUDERONGIA Cookson and Eisenack, 1958, pp. 40-1.

M. crucis Neale and Sarjeant, 1962, pp. 449-50, pl. 20 figs. 2, 6, text-fig. 6.   L. Cretaceous, England.

* M. mcwhaei Cookson and Eisenack, 1958, p. 41, pl. 6 figs. 1-5.   L. Cretaceous, Australia.

M. perforata Alberti, 1961, p. 13, pl. 2 figs. 7-9.   U. Cretaceous, Germany.

M. simplex Alberti, 1961, p. 12, pls. 2 figs. 1-6; 12 figs. 1-2; text-fig. 15a.   L. Cretaceous, Germany.

M. tetracantha (Gocht, 1957), pp. 168-9, pl. 18 figs. 7-9, text-fig. 5   (as ?Pseudoceratium). L. Cretaceous, Germany.   ---, Alberti, 1961, p. 14.

M. tomaszowensis Alberti, 1961, pp. 12-13, pl. 2 figs. 12-13.   L. Cretaceous, Germany.

MUIRIELLA Churchill and Sarjeant, 1963, pp. 36-7.

* M. plioplax Churchill and Sarjeant, 1963, pp. 37-8, pl. 1 figs. 20-1, text-fig. 4.   Post-Pleistocene, Australia.

NANNOCERATOPSIELLA Tasch, 1963, p. 333.

* N. permiana Tasch, 1963, p. 333, pl. 1 figs. 4-6.   L. Permian, Kansas, U.S.A.

NANNOCERATOPSIS Deflandre, 1938e, p. 183, emend. Evitt, 1961a, pp. 306-7.

? N. gracilis Alberti, 1961, p. 30, pl. 7 figs. 16-17.   M. Jurassic, Germany.

* N. pellucida Deflandre, 1938e, pp. 183-4, pl. 8 figs. 8-12, emend. Evitt, 1961a, p. 34. Evitt, 1961a, p. 34. U. Jurassic, France.

NELSONIELLA Cookson and Eisenack, 1960a, p. 4.

* N. aceras Cookson and Eisenack, 1960a, p. 4, pl. 1 figs. 12-13.   U. Cretaceous, Australia.

N. semireticulata Cookson and Eisenack, 1960a, pp. 4-5, pl. 1 fig. 15.   U. Cretaceous,
    Australia.

N. tuberculata Cookson and Eisenack, 1960a, p. 4, pl. 1 fig. 14.   U. Cretaceous, Australia.

NEMATOSPHAEROPSIS Deflandre and Cookson, 1955, p. 268.   (Named without description,
    Deflandre and Cookson, 1954, pp. 123-6).

* N. balcombiana Deflandre and Cookson, 1955, pp. 268-9, pl. 8 fig. 5.   Miocene, Australia.

NETRELYTRON Sarjeant, 1961a, pp. 113-4.

* N. stegastum Sarjeant, 1961a, pp. 114-5, pl. 15 fig. 15, text-fig. 14.   U. Jurassic, England.

NOREMIA Kedves, 1962, pp. 20, 22.

* N. major Kedves, 1962, p. 20, pl. 1 figs. 1-3.   Eocene, Hungary.

ODONTOCHITINA Deflandre, 1935a, p. 234.

O. athabaskensis Pocock, 1962, p. 78, pl. 14 figs. 209-10.   L. Cretaceous, Canada.

O. costata Alberti, 1961, p. 31, pl. 6 figs. 10-13.   U. Cretaceous, Germany.

O. cribropoda Deflandre and Cookson, 1955, p. 292, pl. 3 figs. 7-11, text-fig. 58.
    U. Cretaceous, Australia.   (Figured and named without description in Deflandre and
    Cookson, 1954, text-fig. 17).

* O. operculata (O. Wetzel, 1933), pp. 170-1, pl. 11 figs. 21-22, text-fig. 3.   (as Ceratium
    (Euceratium)).   U. Cretaceous, Baltic.   O. silicorum Deflandre, 1935a, p. 234.
    Palaeoceratium operculatum O. Wetzel, 1948a, p. ---, Deflandre and Cookson, 1955,
    pp. 291-2.

O. porifera Cookson, 1956, p. 188, pl. 1 fig. 17.   U. Cretaceous, Australia.

O. striatoperforata Cookson and Eisenack, 1962b, p. 490, pl. 3 figs. 14-19.   U. Cretaceous,
    Australia.

ODONTOCHITINOPSIS Eisenack, 1961b, pp. 298-9, 308.

O. incerta (Deflandre-Rigaud, 1954), p. 59, text-fig. 3   (as Ceratocystidiopsis).   U. Cretaceous,
    France.   ---, Eisenack, 1961b, p. 299.

* O. molesta (Deflandre, 1937c), p. 90, pl. 17 figs. 1-2   (as Ceratocystidiopsis).   U. Cretaceous,
    France.   ---, Eisenack, 1961b, pp. 298-9.

OMATIA Cookson and Eisenack, 1958, p. 60.

* O. montgomeryi Cookson and Eisenack, 1958, p. 60, pl. 8 figs. 7-9.   U. Jurassic, Papua.

O. pisciformis Cookson and Eisenack, 1958, p. 61, pl. 8 fig. 6.   U. Jurassic, Papua.

OOIDIUM Timofeyev, 1958, p. 281.   Type species not designated.

? O. barbatum Jansonius, 1962, p. 86, pl. 16 fig. 52, text-fig. 3n.   L. Triassic, Canada.

O. bicorne Timofeyev, 1958, pl. 1 fig. 10.   M. Cambrian, U.S.S.R.

O. invisum Timofeyev, 1958, pl. 1 fig. 9.   M. Cambrian, U.S.S.R.

O. rossicum Timofeyev, 1958, pl. 1 figs. 1-5.　M. Cambrian, U.S.S.R.

O. sablincaense Timofeyev, 1958, pl. 1 figs. 6-8.　U. Cambrian, U.S.S.R.　(Spelled in error as O. sablincaene).

OODNADATTIA Eisenack and Cookson, 1960, p. 6.

* O. tuberculata Eisenack and Cookson, 1960, pp. 6-7, pl. 2 figs. 10-14, text-fig. 1.
　　U. Cretaceous, Australia.

OPHIOBOLUS O. Wetzel, 1933, p. 176.

* O. lapidaris O. Wetzel, 1933, pp. 176-85, pl. 2 figs. 30-34, text-figs. 5-7.　U. Cretaceous,
　　Baltic.

ORYCMATOSPHAERIDIUM Timofeyev, 1959, p. 29.

*O. ruminatum Timofeyev, 1959, p. 30, pl. 2 fig. 7.　L. Ordovician, U.S.S.R.

PALAEO3ION O. Wetzel, 1961, p. 338.

* P. catenatum O. Wetzel, 1961, pp. 338-9, pl. 1 figs. 12-13.　U. Cretaceous, Baltic.

PALAEOCRYPTIDIUM Deflandre, 1955, p. 183.

* P. cayeuxi Deflandre, 1955, pp. 183-4　(Figured in Deflandre, 1946c, card no. 1182).
　　Pre-Cambrian, France.

PALAEOCYSTODINIUM Alberti, 1961, p. 20.

? P. denticulatum Alberti, 1961, pp. 20-1, pl. 7 fig. 9.　U. Cretaceous, Germany.

* P. golzowense Alberti, 1961, p. 20, pls. 7 figs. 10-12, 12 fig. 16.　Oligocene, Germany.

P. hyperxantha Vozzhennikova, 1960, pl. 3 fig. No description; validity doubtful. Paleocene, Siberia

PALAEOGLENODINIUM Deflandre, 1935a, p. 227.

* P. cretaceum Deflandre, 1935a, p. 227, pl. 7 figs. 2-3.　U. Cretaceous, France.　(Figured
　　and named without description, in Deflandre, 1934, text-fig. 2).

PALAEOHYSTRICHOPHORA Deflandre, 1935a, pp. 230-1, emend.　Deflandre and Cookson,
　　1955, p. 257.

P. brevispinosa Pocock, 1962, p. 81, pl. 14 figs. 222-3.　L. Cretaceous, Germany.

* P. infusorioides Deflandre, 1935a, p. 230-1, pl. 8 fig. 4.　U. Cretaceous, France.　(Figured
　　and named without description, in Deflandre, 1934, text-fig. 8).

P. isodiametrica Cookson and Eisenack, 1958, p. 38, pl. 12 figs. 11-12.　U. Cretaceous,
　　Australia.

P. minuta Deflandre and Cookson, 1955, pp. 257-8, text-fig. 4.　U. Cretaceous, Australia.
　　(Figured and named without description in Deflandre & Cookson, 1954, text-fig. 4).

P. myalupensis Churchill and Sarjeant, 1963, pp. 38-40, pl. 1 figs. 22-3, text-fig. 5.　Post-
　　Pleistocene, Australia.

P. paucisetosa Deflandre, 1943a, pp. 507-8, text-fig. 26.　U. Cretaceous, France.

P. paucispina Alberti, 1961, pp. 19-20, pl. 3 fig. 25.   U. Cretaceous, Germany.

P. pikei Churchill and Sarjeant, 1963, pp. 40-1, pl. 1 fig. 24, text-fig. 6.   Post-Pleistocene, Australia.

P. spinosissima (Deflandre, 1938e), p. 179, pl. 9 fig. 11   (as Palaeoperidinium).   U. Jurassic, France.   ---, Deflandre and Cookson, 1955, p. 258.

PALAEOPERIDINIUM Deflandre, 1934, p. 968   No specified type species; validity doubtful.

P. alatum Conrad, 1941, pp. 5-7, pl. 1 fig. c.   U. Cretaceous, Belgium.

P. bicuneatum Deflandre, 1938e, p. 180, pl. 8 fig. 7.   U. Jurassic, France.

P. castanea Deflandre, 1935a, p. 229, pl. 6 fig. 8.   U. Cretaceous, France.

P. caulleryi Deflandre, 1935a, pl. 6 fig. 4.   U. Cretaceous, France.   (Named without description in Deflandre, 1934, text-fig. 7).

P. crassinervum Deflandre, 1939b, p. 144, pl. 6 fig. 5.   U. Jurassic, France.

P. cretaceum Pocock, 1962, p. 80, pl. 14 figs. 219-21.   Cretaceous, Canada.

P. dictyophorum Deflandre, 1938c, pp. 178-9, pl. 8 figs. 1-3.   U. Jurassic, France.

P. ellipsoideum Deflandre, 1936c, p. 178, pl. 6 figs. 5-7.   U. Cretaceous, France.

P. hyalodermum Deflandre, 1939b, p. 144, pl. 6 figs. 3-4.   U. Jurassic, France.

P. monocanthum Deflandre, 1935a, p. 228, pl. 6 fig. 1.   U. Cretaceous, France.

P. mosaicum Downie, 1957, p. 424, pl. 20 fig. 7, text-fig. 2f.   U. Jurassic, England.

P. muriciforme Conrad, 1941, pp. 7-8, pl. 1 fig. K, text-fig. 2K.   U. Cretaceous, Belgium.

P. nudum Downie, 1957, p. 424, pl. 20 fig. 11, text-fig. 2e.   U. Jurassic, England.

P. pilum Gocht, 1959, pp. 56-7, pls. 6 fig.14, 8 fig. 8.   L. Cretaceous, Germany.

P. piriforme Conrad, 1941, p. 9 pl. 1 fig. G.   U. Cretaceous, Belgium.

P. reticulatum Valensi, 1953, p. 28, pls. 2 figs. 4, 5, 14, 19; 13 fig. 6, text-fig. 2d.   M. Jurassic, France.

P. velatum Conrad, 1941, pp. 8-9, pl. 1 fig. A.   U. Cretaceous, Belgium.

P. ventriosum (O. Wetzel, 1933), pp. 161-2, pl. 2 figs. 4-6, text-figs. 1, 8   (as Peridinium).   U. Cretaceous, Baltic.   --- Deflandre, 1935a, p. 228.

PALAEOSTOMOCYSTIS Deflandre, 1935a, p. 234.

P. apiculata Cookson and Eisenack, 1960a, p. 12, pl. 3 fig. 15.   U. Cretaceous, Australia.

P. cretacea (O. Wetzel, 1933), p. 175, pl. 2 figs. 28-9.   (as ?Trachelomonas).   U. Cretaceous, Baltic.   ---, Deflandre, 1935a, p. 234.

P. cylindrica Cookson and Eisenack, 1960b, p. 258, pl. 38 fig. 16.   U. Jurassic-L. Cretaceous, Australia and Papua.

137

P. fragilis Cookson and Eisenack, 1962b, pp. 496-7, pl. 4 fig. 17.   U. Cretaceous, Australia.

P. decora Deflandre, 1945b, card 850.   U. Cretaceous, France.

P. echinulata Deflandre, 1937c, p. 55, pl. 11 fig. 9.   U. Cretaceous, France.

P. oblonga Deflandre, 1945b, card 852.   U. Cretaceous, France.

P. pulchella Conrad, 1941, p. 10, text-fig. 3.   U. Cretaceous, Belgium.

P. punctulosa Deflandre, 1941b, pp. 22-3, pl. 6 fig. 11.   U. Jurassic, France.

* P. reticulata Deflandre, 1935a, p. 234, pl. 9 fig. 13.   U. Cretaceous, France.

P. sinuosa Cookson and Eisenack, 1960b, pp. 258-9, pl. 38 figs. 16-17.   U. Jurassic, Australia.

P. sphaerica Deflandre, 1935a, p. 234, pl. 9 fig. 14.   U. Cretaceous, France.

P. volvocina (Ehrenberg, 1854), pl. 37 no. 8 fig. 2   (as ?Trachelomonas).   U. Jurassic,
     Poland.   ---, Deflandre, 1935a, p. 234 (by implication).

PALAEOTETRADINIUM Deflandre, 1935a, p. 231.

P. hermesinoides O. Wetzel, 1940, pp. 138-40, pl. 5 fig. 7.   U. Cretaceous, Denmark.

* P. silicorum Deflandre, 1935a, pl. 6 fig. 11.   U. Cretaceous, France.   (Figured and named
     without description in Deflandre, 1934, text-fig. 6).

PALEOPEDICYSTUS Staplin, 1961, p. 418.

* P. rodeoensis Staplin, 1961, p. 418, pl. 50 figs. 1-3, text-fig. 9b.   U. Devonian, Canada.

PALMNICKIA Eisenack, 1954b, pp. 69-70.

* P. lobifera Eisenack, 1954b, p. 70, pl. 11 figs. 10-11.   Oligocene, East Prussia.

PAREODINIA Deflandre, 1947d, pp. 4-5.

P. aphelia Cookson and Eisenack, 1958, p. 60, pl. 12 figs. 3-4, 9.   M. Jurassic -L. Cretaceous,
     Australia.

* P. ceratophora Deflandre, 1947d, pp. 4-5, text-figs. 1-3.   M. Jurassic, France.

P. ceratophora Defl., 1947d, var. pachyceras Sarjeant, 1959, p. 337, pl. 13 fig. 10,
     text-fig. 5a.   M. Jurassic, England.

P. moderna Kufferath, 1950, pp. 37-8, text-fig. 34.   Post-Pleistocene, North Sea.

P. prolongata Sarjeant, 1959, pp. 335-6, pl. 13 fig. 8, text-fig. 4.   M. Jurassic, England.

P. spinosa Alberti, 1961, p. 24, pl. 4 fig. 16.   L. Cretaceous, Germany.

PENTADINIUM Gerlach, 1961, pp. 164-5.

* P. laticinctum Gerlach, 1961, pp. 165-6, pl. 26 figs. 5-6, text-figs. 6-7.   Oligocene, Germany.

P. taeniagerum Gerlach, 1961, pp. 167-8, pl. 26 figs. 8-9, 12, 15, text-fig. 8.   Oligocene,
     Germany.

PERIDINITES Lefèvre, 1933b, p. 418   (Type species selected by Deflandre, 1945b, card 800).

P. barbadensis Lefèvre, 1933b, p. 416 (figured in Lefèvre, 1933c, text-figs. 9-12).   L. Tertiary, Barbados.

P. diodon Lefèvre, 1933b, pp. 417-8 (figured in Lefèvre, 1933c, text-fig. 23).   L. Tertiary, Barbados.

P. globosus Lefèvre, 1933b, p. 416 (figured in Lefèvre, 1933c, text-figs. 15-16).   L. Tertiary, Barbados.

P. oamaruensis (Deflandre, 1933), p. 265, text-figs. 1-7   (as Lithoperidinium).   Tertiary, New Zealand.   ---, Deflandre, 1945b, cards 806-9.

P. ovalis Lefèvre, 1933b, p. 417 (figured in Lefèvre, 1933c, text-figs. 21-2).   L. Tertiary, Barbados.

* P. parvulus Lefèvre, 1933b, p. 416 (figured in Lefèvre, 1933c, text-figs. 25-30).   L. Tertiary, Barbados.

P. perforatus Lefèvre, 1933b, p. 418 (figured in Lefèvre, 1933c, text-figs. 25-30).   L. Tertiary, Barbados.

P. piriformis Lefèvre, 1933b, p. 417 (figured in Lefèvre, 1933c, text-figs. 17-18).   L. Tertiary, Barbados.

P. piriformis Lef., 1933b var. compactus Lefèvre, 1933b, p. 417 (figured in Lefèvre, 1933c, text-figs. 19-20).   L. Tertiary, Barbados.

P. rossicus (Deflandre, 1940b), pp. 266-7, text-figs. 1-4   (as Lithoperidinium).   Eocene, France. ---, Deflandre, 1945b, cards 817-8.

P. sphaericus Lefèvre, 1933b, pp. 416-7 (figured in Lefèvre, 1933c, text-figs. 13-14). L. Tertiary, Barbados.

P. sphaericus Lef., 1933b var. minor Lefèvre, 1933c, p. 224, text-fig. 24. L. Tert., Barbados.

PERIDINIUM Ehrenberg   (Modern genus and type species).

P. cinctum Ehrenberg (Modern species doubtfully recorded by Ehrenberg, 1854, pl. 34 no. 12 fig. 3, no. 8 fig. 1, from U. Cretaceous-Eocene, Germany).

P. conicum (Gran) Ostenfeld and Schmidt. (Modern species recorded by Deflandre, 1936c, p. 26, pl. 4 figs. 4-6,   from U. Cretaceous, France).

P. damasii Lejeune-Carpentier, 1942, pp. 185-6, text-figs. 9-14.   U. Cretaceous, Belgium.

? P. diamantum Churchill and Sarjeant, 1963, pp. 34-6, pl. 1 fig. 19, text-fig. 3.   Post-Pleistocene, Australia.

P. galeatum Lejeune-Carpentier, 1942, pp. 186-8, text-figs. 5-20.   U. Cretaceous, Baltic.

P. hansonianum Traverse, 1955, pp. 77-9, fig. 13 no. 147.   Oligocene, U.S.A.

P. illustrans O. Wetzel, 1933, p. 167, pl. 2 fig. 15.   U. Cretaceous, Germany.

P. cf. pedunculatum Schütt (Modern species) forma divaricans O. Wetzel, 1933, pp. 165-6, text-fig. 2.   U. Cretaceous, Baltic.

P. pyrophorum Ehrenberg, 1838a, pl. 1 figs. 1, 4.   U. Cretaceous, Germany.

P. subconicoides Lejeune-Carpentier, 1942, pp. 183-5, text-figs. 1-8.   U. Cretaceous, Belgium.

PHANERODINIUM Deflandre, 1937b, p. 110.

* P. cayeuxi (Deflandre, 1935a), pp. 229, pl. 6 figs. 2, 3   (as Palaeoperidinium). U. Cretaceous,
      France.   (Figured and named without description in Deflandre, 1934, p. 967, text-fig. 5).
      ---, Deflandre, 1937b, p. 110-2.

P. cayeuxi (Defl. 1935a) var. laeve Lejeune-Carpentier, 1951, pp. 310-22, text-fig. 6.
      U. Cretaceous, Belgium.

P. fourmarieri Lejeune-Carpentier, 1951, p. 311, text-fig. 7.   U. Cretaceous, Belgium.

P. setiferum Deflandre, 1937b, pp. 112-4, text-fig. 5.   U. Cretaceous, Baltic.

PLATYCYSTIDIA Cookson and Eisenack, 1960a, p. 12.

* P. diptera Cookson and Eisenack, 1960a, p. 14, pl. 3 fig. 22.   U. Cretaceous, Australia.

PLEUROZONARIA O. Wetzel, 1933, p. 29.

* P. globulus O. Wetzel, 1933, p. 29, pl. 4 fig. 12.   U. Cretaceous, Baltic.

PLURIARVALIUM Sarjeant, 1962a, p. 260.

* P. osmingtonense Sarjeant, 1962a, p. 262, pl. 1 fig. 5, text-fig. 6.   U. Jurassic, England.

PODOLAMPAS Stein (Modern genus and type species).

P. bipes (Modern species recorded by Deflandre, 1935a, p. 229, pl. 7 fig. 1, from U. Cret., France).

P. palmipes Stein (Modern species recorded by W. Wetzel, 1922, p. 60, from U. Cretaceous, Baltic).

POLYEDRYXIUM Deunff, 1954d, p. 1065, emend. Jansonius, 1962, pp. 86-7.

P. bathyaster Deunff, 1961b, p. 216. M. Devonian, Canada.   (Figured and named without
      description in Deunff, 1954d, text-fig. 3).

P. cuboides Deunff, 1955a, p. 147, text-fig. 19.   M. Devonian, Canada.

* P. deflandrei Deunff, 1961b, p. 216.   M. Devonian, Canada.   (Figured and named without
      description in Deunff, 1954d, text-fig. 8).

P. deflandrei Dff., 1961b, var. major Deunff, 1955a, pl. 1 fig. 3.   M. Devonian, Canada.
      No description;   validity doubtful.

P. diabolicum Deunff, 1961b, p. 216.   M. Devonian, Canada.   (Figured and named without
      description in Deunff, 1954d, text-fig. 4).

P. evolutum Deunff, 1955a, p. 147, pl. 4 fig. 7.   M. Devonian, Canada.

P. lelayi Deunff, 1957, pp. 7-8, text-fig. 5.   M. Devonian, Canada.

P. membranaceum Deunff, 1961b, p. 217.   M. Devonian, Canada.   (Figured and named without
      description in Deunff, 1955a, text-fig. 20).

P. mirum Deunff, 1957, p. 8, text-fig. 13.   M. Devonian, Canada.

P. pharaonis Deunff, 1961b, p. 217.   M. Devonian, Canada.   (Figured and named without
      description in Deunff, 1955a, text-fig. 13).

140

P. piveteaui Deunff, 1955a, p. 147, pl. 4 fig. 1.   M. Devonian, Canada.

P. pruvosti Deunff, 1955a, p. 147, pl. 1 fig. 1.   M. Devonian, Canada.

P. pulchrum Deunff, 1957, p. 8, text-fig. 9.   M. Devonian, Canada.

P. tectum Deunff, 1961b, p. 216.   M. Devonian, Canada.   (Figured and named without
    description in Deunff, 1954d, text-fig. 2).

P. venustum Deunff, 1955a, p. 147, pl. 2 fig. 2.   M. Devonian, Canada.

POLYEDROSPHAERIDIUM Timofeyev, 1962.   No diagnosis ; validity doubtful.

P. hidusense Timofeyev, 1962, pl. 4 fig. 1.   L. Camb., U.S.S.R.   No description; validity doubtful.

POLYSTEPHANEPHORUS Sarjeant, 1961c, p. 1096.

* P. calathus (Sarjeant, 1961a), p. 104, pl. 14 fig. 7, text-fig. 7 (as Polystephanoshpaera).
    U. Jurassic, England.   ---, Sarjeant, 1961c, p. 1096.

P. paracalathus (Sarjeant, 1960a), pp. 143-4, pl. 6 fig. 4, text-fig. 3b (as Polystephano-
    sphaera).   M. Jurassic, England.   ---, Sarjeant, 1961c, p. 1096.

P. urnaformis (Cookson, 1953), p. 118, pl. 2 figs. 41-3 (as Cannosphaeropsis).   Oligocene,
    Australia.   Polystephanosphaera urnaformis Sarjeant, 1960a, p. 140.   ---, Sarjeant,
    1961c, p. 1096.

PRISCOGALEA Deunff, 1961, p. 40.

* P. barbara Deunff, 1961, p. 41, pl. 1 fig. 5.   L. Ordovician, Sahara.

P. columellifera Deunff, 1961, p. 41, pl. 1 fig. 3.   L. Ordovician, Sahara.

P. cortinula Deunff, 1961, p. 41, pls. 1 figs. 8, 10, 12.   L. Ordovician, Sahara.

P. cuvillieri Deunff, 1961, p. 41, pl. 1 fig. 2.   L. Ordovician, Sahara.

P. furcata Deunff, 1961, p. 41, pl. 1 fig. 11.   L. Ordovician, Sahara.

P. multarea Deunff, 1961, p. 41, pl. 1 fig. 5.   L. Ordovician, Sahara.

P. multiclaustra Deunff, 1961, p. 41, pl. 2 fig. 4.   L. Ordovician, Sahara.

P. simplex Deunff, 1961, p. 41, pl. 1 fig. 9.   L. Ordovician, Sahara.

PRISCOTHECA Deunff, 1961a, pp. 42-3.

P. complanata Deunff, 1961a, p. 43, pl. 3 fig. 7.   L. Ordovician, Sahara.

P. minima Deunff, 1961a, p. 43, pl. 3 fig. 4.   L. Ordovician, Sahara.

P. prismatica Deunff, 1961a, p. 43, pl. 3 fig. 5.   L. Ordovician, Sahara.

* P. raia Deunff, 1961a, p. 43, pl. 3 fig. 2.   L. Ordovician, Sahara.

P. tumida Deunff, 1961a, p. 43, pl. 3 fig. 6.   L. Ordovician, Sahara.

PROTARCHAEOSACCULINA Naumova, 1961, p. 112.

* P. atava Naumova, 1961, p. 112.   Pre-Cambrian, U.S.S.R.

PROTOOCRIDOSPHAERIDIUM Timofeyev, 1962.   No diagnosis; validity doubtful.

P. elandi Timofeyev, 1962, pl. 4 fig. 2.   M. Cambrian, Sweden.   No description; validity doubtful.

PROTOTREMATOSPHAERIDIUM Timofeyev, 1962.   No diagnosis; validity doubtful.

P. holtedahli Timofeyev, 1962, pl. 3 fig. 1.   Pre-Camb., Norway.   No description; validity doubtful.

PSEUDOCERATIUM Gocht, 1957, p. 166.

PSEUDOCERATIUM subgen.   Eopseudoceratium Neale and Sarjeant, 1962, p. 446.

* P. gochti Neale and Sarjeant, 1962, pp. 446-8, pl. 20 figs. 3, 4, text-fig. 5.   L. Cretaceous, England.

PSEUDOCERATIUM subgen.   Pseudoceratium Neale and Sarjeant, 1962, pp. 448-9.

P. gochti Pocock, 1962, p. 79, pl. 14 figs. 213-4.   L. -U. Cretaceous, Canada.   (This is a junior homonym of P. gochti Neale and Sarjeant, 1962; a taxonomic note by Pocock, proposing a new name, is in preparation).

P. ludbrooki (Cookson and Eisenack, 1958), pp. 52-4, pl. 5 figs. 7-8.   L. Cretaceous, Australia (as Ceratocystidiopsis).   ---, Eisenack, 1961b, p. 299.

? P. nudum Gocht, 1957, p. 168, pl. 18 figs. 3-4, 6.   L. Cretaceous, Germany.

* P. pelliferum Gocht, 1957, pp. 166-8, pl. 18 fig. 102, text-figs. 1-3.   L. Cretaceous, Germany.

P. turneri Cookson and Eisenack, 1958, p. 55, pl. 5 figs. 2-6.   L. Cretaceous, Australia and Papua.

PSEUDODEFLANDREA Alberti, 1959a, pp. 91-2.

* P. gigantea Alberti, 1959a, p. 92, text-fig. 1.   Oligocene, Germany.

PTEROCYSTIDIOPSIS Deflandre, 1935a, p. 234.

? P. angulosa Deflandre, 1941b, pp. 23-4, pl. 6 figs. 6-10.   U. Jurassic, France.

P. ornata Deflandre, 1937c, pp. 91-2, pl. 18 figs. 1-3.   U. Cretaceous, France.

* P. stephaniana Deflandre, 1935a, p. 234, pl. 9 fig. 2.   U. Cretaceous, France.

PTERODINIUM Eisenack, 1958c, p. 395.

* P. aliferum Eisenack, 1958c, pp. 395-6, pl. 24 fig. 6, text-fig. 6.   L. Cretaceous, Germany.

P. cornutum Cookson and Eisenack, 1962b, p. 490, pl. 3 figs. 1-6.   L. -U. Cretaceous, Australia.

P. magnoserratum Cookson and Eisenack, 1962b, pl. 3 figs. 7-8.   L. -U. Cretaceous, Australia.

PTEROSPERMOPSIMORPHA Timofeyev, 1962. No diagnosis; validity doubtful.

P. kelar Timofeyev, 1962, pl. 4 fig. 3.   M. Cambrian, Sweden.   No description; validity doubtful.

PTEROSPERMOPSIS W. Wetzel, 1952, p. 411.

142

P. aureolata Cookson and Eisenack, 1958, p. 49, pl. 9 figs. 10-12.   L. -U. Cretaceous, Australia.

P. australiensis Deflandre and Cookson, 1955, p. 286, pl. 3 fig. 4, text-figs. 52-3.
        L. Cretaceous, Australia.   (Figured and named without description in Deflandre
        and Cookson, 1954, text-figs. 13-14).

P. barbarae Górka, 1963, pp. 74-5, pl. 11 fig. 3.   U. Cretaceous, Poland.

P. chinaica Timofeyev, 1962, pl. 1 fig. 2.   Pre-Cambrian, China.   No description; val. doubtful.

* P. danica W. Wetzel, 1952, p. 412, pl. * fig. 16, text-fig. 34.   U. Cretaceous, Baltic.

P. eurypteris Cookson and Eisenack, 1958, p. 49, pl. 9 figs. 9, 13.   L. Cretaceous, Australia.

P. ginginensis Deflandre and Cookson, 1955, pp. 287-8, text-fig. 49.   U. Cretaceous, Australia.

P. harti Sarjeant, 1960c, pp. 402-3, pl. 14 fig. 16, text-fig. 3a.   U. Jurassic, England.

P. helios Sarjeant, 1959, p. 342, pl. 13 fig. 9.   M. Jurassic, England.

P. macroptera Döring, 1961, pp. 111-2, pl. 16 figs. 5-8, text-fig. 1.   U. Jurassic, Germany.

P. microptera Deflandre and Cookson, 1955, p. 288, pl. 6 fig. 8.   Paleocene-Eocene, Australia.

P. onondagaensis Deunff, 1955a, p. 148, text-fig. 27.   M. Devonian, Canada.

P. pastielsi Durand in Deflandre and Deflandre-Rigaud, 1958, cards 1687-8, 4 figs.   Eocene,
        Belgium.

P. pluriparietes Döring, 1961, p. 111, pl. 16 figs. 1-4.   U. Jurassic, Germany.

? P. vancampoae Rossignol, 1962, p. 134, pl. 2 fig. 1.   Pleistocene, Israel.

PULVINOSPHAERIDIUM Eisenack, 1954a, p. 210, emend.   Deunff, 1954c, pp. 305-6.

* P. pulvinellum Eisenack, 1954a, p. 210, pl. 1 fig. 10.   L. Silurian, Sweden.

PXYIDIELLA Cookson and Eisenack, 1958, p. 51.

* P. pandora Cookson and Eisenack, 1958, p. 52, pl. 6 figs. 10-22.   U. Jurassic, Australia
        and Papua.

P. scrobiculata (Deflandre and Cookson, 1955), p. 291, pl. 3 fig. 3, text-fig. 7 (as Leiosphaera).
        U. Cretaceous, - Eocene, Australia.   Leiosphaeridia scrobiculata Eisenack, 1958a,
        p. 9.   ---, Cookson and Eisenack, 1958, p. 52.

QUISQUILITES Wilson and Urban, 1963, p. 18.

* Q. buckhornensis Wilson and Urban, 1963, pp. 18-19, pl. 1 figs. 1-12.   U. Devonian, U.S.A.

RAPHIDODINIUM Deflandre, 1936c, pp. 184-5.

* R. fucatum Deflandre, 1936c, pp. 185-6, pl. 10 figs. 1-7.   U. Cretaceous, France.

RHOMBODELLA Cookson and Eisenack, 1962b, p. 496.

* R. natans Cookson and Eisenack, 1962b, p. 496, pl. 7 figs. 12-13.   L. -U. Cretaceous,
        Australia.

RHOMBODINIUM subgen. of Wetzeliella, q.v.

RHYNCHODINIOPSIS Deflandre, 1935a, p. 231.

* R. aptiana Deflandre, 1935a, p. 231, pls. 5 fig. 10; 8 figs. 7-10.   U. Cretaceous, France.

ROTTNESTIA Cookson and Eisenack, 1961b, pp. 41-2.

* R. borussica (Eisenack, 1954b), pp. 62-3, pl. 9 figs. 5-7   (as Hystrichosphaera (Hystrichosph-
          aeropsis) borussica,   Oligocene, East Prussia.   ---, Cookson and Eisenack, 1961b, p. 42.

R. simplicia Cookson and Eisenack, 1961b, pp. 42, 44, pl. 2 figs. 3-4, text-figs. le-f.   Eocene,
          Australia.

SAMLANDIA Eisenack, 1954b, p. 76.

S. angustivela (Deflandre and Cookson, 1955), p. 290, pl. 7 figs. 4-5   (as Membranilarnax).
          Eocene, Australia.   ---, Eisenack, 1963b, p. 102.

* S. chlamydophora Eisenack, 1954b, p. 76, pl. 11 figs. 12-15.   Oligocene, East Prussia.

SCHEMATOPHORA Deflandre and Cookson, 1955, p. 262.

* S. speciosa Deflandre and Cookson, 1955, pp. 262-3, pls. 6 figs. 11-13; 7 fig. 11.
          Eocene-?Miocene, Australia.   (Figured and named without description, by
          Deflandre and Cookson, 1954, p. 1237).

SCHIZOCYSTIA Cookson and Eisenack, 1962a, p. 270.

S. laevigata Cookson and Eisenack, 1962a, pp. 270-1, pl. 37 figs. 13-14.   U. Cretaceous,
          Australia.

* S. rugosa Cookson and Eisenack, 1962a, p. 270, pl. 37 figs. 11-12.   U. Cretaceous, Australia.

SCRINIODINIUM Klement, 1957, pp. 409-10.

SCRINIODINIUM subgen. Endoscrinium Klement, 1960, p. 18.

S. apatelum Cookson and Eisenack, 1962b, p. 249, pl. 37 figs. 12-13.   U. Jurassic, Australia.

S. campanula Gocht, pp. 61-2, pls. 4 fig. 6; 5 fig. 1.   L. Cretaceous, Germany.

* S. galeritum (Deflandre, 1938e), p. 167, pl. 5 figs. 7-9, text-fig. 1   (as Gymnodinium).
          U. Jurassic, France.   ---, Klement, 1957, p. 410.

S. galeritum (Defl., 1938e) subsp. galeritum Klement, 1960, pp. 23-5, pl. 1 figs. 4-6,
          text-figs. 4-5. U. Jurassic, France.

S. galeritum(Defl.,1938e)subsp.fornicatum Klement,1960,pp. 25-6,pl. 1 figs.7-12. U. Jur., German

S. galeritum(Defl.,1938e)subsp.reticulatum Klement,1960,pp.26-7,pl.2 figs.1-2. U. Jur.,Germany

S. luridum (Deflandre, 1938e), p. 166, pl. 5 figs. 4-6.   (as Gymnodinium).   U. Jurassic, France.
          ---, Klement, 1957, pp. 409-10.

S. oxfordianum Sarjeant, 1962b, pp. 485-6, pl. 69 figs. 13-14.   U. Jurassic, England.

S. subvallare Sarjeant, 1962a, pp. 262-3, pl. 1 fig. 10, text-fig. 7.   U. Jurassic, England.

SCRINIODINIUM subgen. Scriniodinium Klement, 1960, p. 18.

S. attadalense (Cookson and Eisenack, 1958), p. 25, pl. 1 fig. 7   (as Gymnodinium).
        L. Cretaceous, Australia.   ---, Klement, 1957, p. 410.

S. ceratophorum Cookson and Eisenack, 1960b, p. 249, pl. 37 fig. 7.   U. Jurassic, Australia.

* S. crystallinum (Deflandre, 1938e), p. 165, pl. 5 figs. 1-3 (as Gymnodinium).   U. Jurassic,
        France.   ---, Klement, 1957, pp. 409-10.

S. dictyotum Cookson and Eisenack, 1960b, pp. 248-9, pl. 37 figs. 8-9.   U. Jurassic, Australia.

S. galeatum Cookson and Eisenack, 1960a, pp. 3-4, pl. 1 figs. 16-18.   U. Cretaceous, Australia.

S. parvimarginatum (Cookson and Eisenack, 1958), pp. 24-5, pl. 1 fig. 6   (as Gymnodinium).
        U. Jurassic, Australia.   ---, Klement, 1957, p. 410.

S. playfordi Cookson and Eisenack, 1960b, p. 248, pl. 37 fig. 6.   U. Jurassic, Australia.

S. scutellum Eisenack, 1958c, p. 385, pl. 24 fig. 3.   L. Cretaceous, Germany.

S. trabeculosum Gocht, 1959, pp. 62-3, pls. 4 fig. 5; 8 fig. 2.   L. Cretaceous, Germany.

SIMSANGIA Baksi, 1962, p. 18.

* S. trispinosa Baksi, 1962, p. 18, pl. 3 fig. 34.   Oligocene, Assam, India.

SIRMIODINIUM Alberti, 1961, p. 22.

* S. grossi Alberti, 1961, p. 22, pls. 7 figs. 5-7; 12 fig. 5.   L. Cretaceous, Germany.

SPINIDINIUM Cookson and Eisenack, 1962b, p. 489.

* S. styloniferum Cookson and Eisenack, 1962b, p. 489, pl. 1 figs. 1-5.   L. -?U. Cretaceous,
        Australia.

SPONGODINIUM Deflandre, 1936c, pp. 169-70.

* S. delitiense (Ehrenberg, 1838a), pl. 1 fig. 6   (as Peridinium).   U. Cretaceous, Germany.
        ---, Deflandre, 1936c, pp. 170-1.

?S. solidum Alberti, 1961, pp. 31-2, pl. 3 figs. 17-18.   L. Cretaceous, Germany.

STAPLINIUM Jansonius, 1962, p. 87.

S. centrigerum (Deunff, 1955a), p. 147, pl. 2 fig. 3   (as Polyedryxium).   M. Devonian, Canada.
        ---, Jansonius, 1962, p. 87.

S. decorum (Deunff, 1955a), pp. 146-7, pl. 2 fig. 1   (as Polyedryxium).   M. Devonian, Canada.
        ---, Jansonius, 1962, p. 87.

* S. hexaeder Jansonius, 1962, p. 87, pl. 16 figs. 36-7.   L. Triassic, Canada.

S. simplex(Deunff, 1955a), p. 147, pl. 2 fig. 4   (as Polyedryxium).   M. Devonian, Canada.
        ---, Jansonius, 1962, p. 87.

STEPHANELYTRON Sarjeant, 1961a, p. 109.

S. caytonense Sarjeant, 1961a, p. 110, pl. 15 fig. 16, text-fig. 11.   U. Jurassic, England.

* S. redcliffense Sarjeant, 1961a, pp. 109-10, pl. 15 fig. 11, text-fig. 10. U. Jurassic, England.

S. scarburghense Sarjeant, 1961a, p. 111, pl. 15 figs. 12-13. U. Jurassic, England.

STEPHODINIUM Deflandre, 1936a, p. 58.

S. australicum Cookson and Eisenack, 1962b, p. 491, pl. 2 figs. 5-10. U. Cretaceous, Australia.

* S. coronatum Deflandre, 1936a, p. 58, text-fig. 103. U. Cretaceous, France.

S. pellucidum Deflandre, 1943a, pp. 505, 507, text-figs. 12-16. U. Cretaceous, France.

STICTOSPHAERIDIUM Timofeyev, 1962   No diagnosis; validity doubtful.

S. podolense Timofeyev, 1962, pl. 3 fig. 2. Pre-Camb., U.S.S.R. No description; validity doubtf

STYLODINIOPSIS Eisenack, 1954a, p. 75.

* S. maculatum Eisenack, 1954a, pp. 75-6, pl. 12 figs. 12-13. Oligocene, East Prussia, U.S.S.R.

SVALBARDELLA Manum, 1960, p. 21.

* S. cooksoniae Manum, 1960, pp. 21-2, plate figs. 1-3, text-fig. 2. L. Tertiary, Spitsbergen.

SYMPLASSOSPHAERIDIUM Timofeyev, 1959, p. 26. Type species not designated.

S. incrustatum Timofeyev, 1959, p. 27, pl. 1 fig. 10. L. Ordovician, U.S.S.R.

S. subcoalitum Timofeyev, 1959, p. 27, pl. 1 fig. 12. U. Cambrian, U.S.S.R.

S. tumidulum Timofeyev, 1959, p. 27, pl. 1 fig. 11. U. Cambrian, U.S.S.R.

SYSTEMATOPHORA Klement, 1960, pp. 61-2.

* S. areolata Klement, 1960, pp. 62-5, pl. 9 figs. 1-8, text-figs. 32-5. U. Jurassic, Germany.

?S. austini (Merrill, 1895), p. 16, text-fig. 11 (as ?Geodia). L. Cretaceous, Texas, U.S.A.
      ---, Sarjeant, 1964 (in press).

S. complicata Neale and Sarjeant, 1962, pp. 455-6, pl. 19 figs. 7-8, text-fig. 9. L. Cretaceous,
      England.

S. fasciculigera Klement, 1960, pp. 65-6, pls. 9 figs. 11-2; 10 fig. 8. U. Jurassic, Germany.

S. orbifera Klement, 1960, pp. 66-7, pls. 9 fig. 9-10; 10 fig. 7. U. Jurassic, Germany.

S. schindewolfi (Alberti, 1961), pp. 38-9, pl. 10 figs. 1-3, 6-7 (as Hystrichosphaerina).
      U. Cretaceous, Germany. ---, Neale and Sarjeant, 1962, p. 455 (by implication).

S. turonica (Alberti, 1961), p. 39, pl. 10 figs. 4a-b (as Hystrichosphaerina). U. Cretaceous,
      Germany. ---, Neale and Sarjeant, 1962, p. 455 (by implication).

S. valensii (Sarjeant, 1960a), pp. 142-3, pl. 6 figs. 5-7, text-fig. 3c (as Polystephanosphaera).
      U. Jurassic, England. ---, Sarjeant, 1961c, p. 1096.

TAENIOPHORA Klement, 1960, pp. 67-8.

* T. iunctispina Klement, 1960, pp. 68-9, pl. 10 figs. 1-6. U. Jurassic, Germany.

T. iunctispina subsp. iunctispina Klement, 1960, p. 69, pl. 10 figs. 1-4.   U. Jurassic, Germany.

T. iunctispina subsp. filamentosa Klement, 1960, p. 70, pl. 10 figs. 5-6.   U. Jurassic, Germany.

TASMANITES Newton, 1875, p. 339, emend. Schopf, Wilson and Bentall, 1944, pp. 11-18.

T. avelinoi Sommer, 1953, pp. 24-5, pls. 1 fig. 3; 2 fig. 3, text-fig. 3.   M. Devonian, Brazil.

T. chigagoensis (Reinsch, 1884), vol. 2, p. 6, pl. 72A fig. 76   (as Sporangites).   U. Devonian,
        U.S.A.   ---, Schopf, Wilson and Bentall, 1944, p. 18.

T. derbyi Sommer, 1953, pp. 26-7, pls. 1 fig. 6, 2 fig. 4, text-fig. 6.   M. Devonian, Brazil.

T. eisenacki Utech, 1962, pp. 90-1, text-figs. 1a-b.   L. Triassic, Germany.

T. euzebioi Sommer, 1953, p. 26, pl. 1 fig. 5, text-fig. 5.   M. Devonian, Brazil.

T. hartti Sommer, 1953, p. 27, pl. 1 fig. 7, text-fig. 7.   M. Devonian, Brazil.

T. huronensis (Dawson, 1871a), p. 257, text-figs. 1-3   (as Sporangites).   U. Devonian, U.S.A.
        Bion (Ovum?) solidum Eisenack, 1931, p. 109 Leiosphaera solida Eisenack, 1938a, pp. 24,
        26.   Leiosphaera huronensis Krausel, 1941, pp. 126-7.   ---, Schopf, Wilson and
        Bentall, 1944, p. 18.   ---, Emend. Winslow, 1962, pp. 81-3.

T. lamegoi Sommer, 1956b, pp. 457-8, pl. 1 figs. 2-4; pl.2 fig. 1.   Devonian, Brazil.

T. martinssoni Eisenack, 1958a, p. 6, pl. 1 figs. 10-13, text-figs. 2, 3.   Baltic drift,
        Ordovician pebble.

T. medius (Eisenack, 1931), p. 109, pl. 5 fig. 1   (as Bion (Ovum?).   Baltic drift, Silurian
        pebble.   Leiosphaera media Eisenack, 1938a, p. 26.   ---,Eisenack, 1958a, p. 6.

T. mosesi Sommer, 1956b, pp. 458-9, pls. 1 figs. 6-8, 2 fig. 5.   Devonian, Brazil.

T. mourai Sommer, 1953, pp. 25-6, pl. 1 fig. 4, text-fig. 4.   M. Devonian, Brazil.

T. noremi Eisenack, 1962, pp. 63-4, pl. 2 figs. 1-4.   L. Carboniferous, U.S.A.

T. primigenus (Naumova, 1950), p. 187, pl. 4 fig. 15 (as Perisaccus).   Ord.,U.S.S.R. ---, comb.nov.

* T. punctatus Newton, 1875, p. 389, pl. 10 figs. 1-9.   M. Permian, Tasmania.

T. roxoi Sommer, 1953, pp. 23-4, pls. 1 fig. 2; 2 fig. 2; text-fig. 2.   M. Devonian, Brazil.

T. salustianoi Sommer, 1953, p. 27, pl. 1 fig. 8, text-fig. 8.   M. Devonian, Brazil.

T. sinuosus Winslow, 1962, pp. 83-4, pl. 20 figs. 1-3, text-fig. 20.   U. Devonian, U.S.A.

T. sommeri Winslow, 1962, p. 84, pls. 20 figs. 4, 4a, 9; 21 fig. 2; text-figs. 10-12.
        U. Devonian, U.S.A.

T. tapajonensis Sommer, 1953, p. 23, pl. 1 fig. 1; 2 fig. 1, text-fig. 1.   M. Devonian, Brazil.

T. tardus Eisenack, 1957, pp. 243-4, pl. 20 figs. 4-6.   L. Jurassic, Germany.

T. trematus Eisenack, 1962a, pp. 61-2, pl. 3 fig. 1.   L. Ordovician, Sweden.

T. verrucosus Eisenack, 1962a, pp. 62-3, pls. 2 fig. 5; 3 figs. 4-6.   ?Ordovician, Baltic.

TENERIDINIUM Krutzsch, 1962, p. 41.

* T. magnoides Krutzsch, 1962, p. 42, pl. 10 figs. 1-7, text-fig. 1a.   Eocene, Germany.

TENUA Eisenack, 1958c, p. 410.

T. hystricella Eisenack, 1958c, p. 411, pl. 23 figs. 5-7.   L. Cretaceous, Germany.

* T. hystrix Eisenack, 1958c, p. 410, pl. 23 figs. 1-4, text-fig. 10.   L. Cretaceous, Germany.

TETRABRACHIOPHORA Eisenack, 1954b, pp. 76-7.

* T. natans Eisenack, 1954b, pp. 76-7, pl. 11 fig. 6.   Oligocene, East Prussia, U.S.S.R.

THALASSIPHORA Eisenack and Gocht, 1960, p. 51 .

* T. pelagica (Eisenack, 1938c), p. 187 (as Bion).   Oligocene, East Prussia.   Pterospermopsis
      pelagica Eisenack, 1954b, pp. 71-2, pl. 12 figs. 17-18.   ---, Eisenack and Gocht,
      1960, pp. 513-4.

T. velata (Deflandre and Cookson, 1955), p. 291, pl. 8 fig. 8   (as Pterocystidiopsis).
      L. Tertiary, Australia.   ---, Eisenack and Gocht, 1960, pp. 514-5.

TOOLONGIA Cookson and Eisenack, 1960a, p. 14.

* T. medusoides Cookson and Eisenack, 1960a, p. 14, pl. 3 figs. 11-12.   U. Cretaceous,
      Australia.

TRACHYDIACRODIUM Timofeyev, 1959, p. 60, emend.   Deflandre and Deflandre-Rigaud, 1961,
      p. 8.

T. coarctatum Timofeyev, 1959, p. 60, pl. 5 fig. 4.   L. Ordovician, U.S.S.R.

L. dentatum (Naumova, 1950), p. 182, pl. 2 fig. 12   (as Azonomonoletes).   L. Ordovician,
      Baltic U.S.S.R.   ---, comb. nov.

T. involutivum (Timofeyev, 1959), pp. 60-1, pl. 5 fig. 5 (as Trachyrytidodiacrodium).
      M. Cambrian, U.S.S.R.   ---, Deflandre and Deflandre-Rigaud, 1961, p. 8.

T. legiminiforme Timofeyev, 1959, p. 60, pl. 5 fig. 3.   L. Ordovician, U.S.S.R.

T. maximum Timofeyev, 1959, p. 60, pl. 5 fig. 2.   L. Ordovician, U.S.S.R.

* T. productum Timofeyev, 1959, p. 60, pl. 5 fig. 1.   L. Ordovician, U.S.S.R.

T. signatum (Timofeyev, 1959), p. 61, pl. 5 fig. 6   (as Trachyzonodiacrodium).   L. Ordovician,
      U.S.S.R.   ---, Deflandre and Deflandre-Rigaud, 1961, p. 8.

TRACHYMINUSCULA ° Naumova (in Naumova and Pavlovski, 1961, p. 182).

T. microrugosa ° Naumova ? (in Naumova and Pavlovski, 1961, p. 182, fig. 1)   Pre-
      Cambrian, Scotland.

TRACHYSPHAERIDIUM Timofeyev, 1959, p. 28.   Type species not designated.

T. attenuatum Timofeyev, 1959, p. 29, pl. 2 fig. 3.   L. Ordovician, U.S.S.R.

T. patellare Timofeyev, 1959, p. 29, pl. 2 fig. 2.   L. Ordovician, U.S.S.R.

T. uspenskyi Timofeyev, 1959, p. 29, pl. 2 fig. 4.   L. -M. Ordivician, U.S.S.R.

TREMATOSPHAERIDIUM Timofeyev, 1959, p. 27.

*T. decoratum Timofeyev, 1959, pl. 1 fig. 13.   U. Cambrian,U.S.S.R.

TRIANGULOPSIS Döring, 1961, p. 113.

* T. discoidalis Döring, 1961, p. 114, pl. 17 figs. 1-3.   U. Jurassic, Germany.

L. trilobatus (Balme, 1957), p. 33, pl. 8 figs. 91-2   (as Zonalapollenites).   U. Jurassic,
      Australia.   ---, Döring, 1961, p. 114.

TRIBLASTULA O. Wetzel, 1933, p. 54.

T. nuda O. Wetzel, 1961, p. 340, pl. 2 fig. 4.   U. Cretaceous, Germany.

T. quasicribrata O. Wetzel, 1961, p. 340, pl. 2 fig. 3.   U. Cretaceous, Germany.

T. tubulata O. Wetzel, 1961, p. 340, pl. 2 fig. 4.   U. Cretaceous, Germany.

* T. utinensis O. Wetzel, 1933, pp. 54-5, pl. 6 figs. 5-6.   U. Cretaceous, Baltic.   (A full
      redescription of this species is given by Evitt 1961c, p. 395, pls. 6 figs. 6-8;
      7 figs. 4-6).

TRICHODINIUM Eisenack and Cookson, 1960, p. 5.

T. intermedium Eisenack and Cookson, 1960, p. 6,pl. 2 figs. 5-6.   L. -U. Cretaceous, Australia.

T. paucispinum Eisenack and Cookson, 1960, pp. 5-6, pl. 2 fig. 7.   U. Cretaceous, Australia.

* T. pellitum Eisenack and Cookson, 1960, p. 5, pl. 2 fig. 4.   L. Cretaceous, Australia.

TRIGONOPYXIDIA Eisenack, 1961b, p. 316.

* T. ginella (Cookson and Eisenack, 1960a), p. 11, pl. 3 figs. 18-20   (as Trigonopyxis).
      U. Cretaceous, Australia.   ---, Eisenack, 1961b, p. 316   (by implication).

TYTTHODISCUS Norem, 1955b, pp. 694-5.

* T. californiensis Norem, 1955b, p. 695, pl. 68 figs. 1a-c.   Eocene-Pliocene, U.S.A.

T. chondrotus Norem, 1955b, p. 695, pl. 68 figs. 2a-c.   Miocene, U.S.A.

T. suevicus Eisenack, 1957, p. 241-3, pls. 19 figs. 1-3; 20 figs. 1-3.   L. Jurassic, Germany.

T. suevicus Eis., 1957 var. macroporus Eisenack, 1957, p.243, pl.2 fig.3.   L. Jur., Germany.

T. vanderhammeni Sole de Porta, 1959, p. 63, text-fig. 1.   Oligocene, Colombia.

VALENSIELLA Eisenack, 1963b, pp. 100-1.

V. amandopolitana (Valensi, 1955b), p. 590, pls. 2 figs. 7; 5 fig. 1 (as Membranilarnax).
      M. Jurassic, France.   Favilarnax amandopolitanum Sarjeant, 1963a, pp. 720-1.
      ---, Eisenack, 1963b, p. 102.

?V. clathroderma (Deflandre and Cookson, 1955), p. 290, pl. 7 fig. 6, text-fig. 5.   (as
      Membranilarnax).   Eocene, Australia.   ---, Eisenack, 1963c, p. 102.

*V. ovula (Deflandre, 1947d), pp. 9-10, text-figs. 22-3, (as Membranilarnax). M. Jur., France.
Favilarnax ovulum Sarjeant, 1963a, p. 720. ---, Eisenack, 1963b, pp. 100-1.

VAVOSOSPHAERIDIUM Timofeyev, 1959, p. 30.

* V. michailovskyi Timofeyev, 1959, p. 30, pl. 2 fig. 8.   L. Ordovician, U.S.S.R.

VERYHACHIUM Deunff, 1958, pp. 26-7, emend. Downie & Sarjeant, 1963, p. 93. (Name first published by Deunff, 1954c, pp. 305-6, but type species not validly described until 1958).

V. ambiguum Deunff, 1955a, p. 146, pl. 3 fig. 2.   M. Devonian, Canada.

V. asymmetricum Deunff, 1961b, p. 217.   M. Devonian, Canada.   (Figured and named without
description in Deunff, 1954d, text-fig. 15).

V. balticum (Eisenack, 1951), p. 190, pl. 3 figs. 10-11 (as Hystrichosphaeridium).
L. Ordovician, Estonia, U.S.S.R.   ---, Deunff, 1954c, p. 306.

V. belgicum (Stockmans and Willière, 1960), p. 3-4, pl. 2 figs. 26-7, 29 (as Polyedryxium).
U. Devonian, Belgium.   ---, Stockmans and Willière, 1962a, p. 50.

V. brevitrispinosum Staplin, 1961, p. 412, pl. 49 fig. 1.   U. Devonian, Canada.

V. bulbiferum (Deflandre, 1945a), pp. 29-30, pl. 2 figs. 10-11 (as Micrystridium).   M. Silurian,
France.   ---, Deunff, 1954c, p. 306.

V. centrigerum Deunff, 1957, p. 8, text-fig. 4.   M. Devonian, Canada.

V. ceratioides Stockmans and Willière, 1962a, p. 53, text-fig. 10.   U. Devonian, Belgium.

? V. clava Deunff, 1958, p. 31, pl. 4 fig. 40.   M. Ordovician, France.

V. crucistellatum Deunff, 1955a, p. 146, pl. 3 fig. 3.   M. Devonian, Canada.

V. cucruse Timofeyev, 1962, pl. 12 fig. 1.   U. Ord., Estonia. No description; validity doubtful.

V. delmeri Stockmans and Willière, 1963, p. 453, pl. 1 fig. 17, text-fig. 5. Silurian, Belgium.

V. downiei Stockmans & Willière, 1962a, pp. 47-8, pl. 2 figs. 20-2, text-fig. 2. U. Dev., Belgium.

V. downiei var. haumani Stockmans and Willière, 1963, p. 452, text-fig. 3. Sil., Belgium.

V. duodeciaster Staplin, 1961, p. 414, pl. 49 fig. 7.   U. Devonian, Canada.

V. eisenacki Deunff, 1961b, p. 217.   M. Devonian, Canada.   (Figured and named without
description in Deunff, 1954d, text-fig. 7).

V. elongatum Downie, 1963, p. 637, pl. 92 fig. 10.   M. Silurian, England.

V. europaeum Stockmans and Willière, 1960, p. 3, pl. 2 fig. 25.   U. Devonian, Belgium.

V. exasperatum Deunff, 1955a, p. 146, pl. 3 fig. 4.   M. Devonian, Canada.

V. exile Timofeyev, 1962, pl. 12 fig. 2. U. Sil., U.S.S.R. No description; validity doubtful.

V. flagelliferum Wall & Downie, 1963, p. 779, pl. 112 figs. 3-5, text-figs. 4a-d. L. Permian,
England.

V. florigerum Deunff, 1957, p. 9 fig. 8.   M. Devonian, Canada.

V. formosum Stockmans and Willière, 1960, p. 2, pl. 2 fig. 28.   U. Devonian, Belgium.

V. furcillatum Deunff, 1955a, p. 146, text-fig. 18.   M. Devonian, Canada.

V. geometricum (Deunff, 1945a), pp. 26-7, pl. 2 figs. 2-5   (as Hystrichosphaeridium).
   M. Silurian, France.   ---, Deunff, 1954c, p. 306.   (Figured and named, without
   description,in Deflandre 1942b, text-fig. 9).

V. hebetatum Deunff, 1957, p. 10, text-fig. 11.   M. Devonian, Canada.

V. heterogonum Deunff, 1955a, p. 146, pl. 4 fig. 4.   M. Devonian, Canada.

V. hyalodermum (Cookson, 1956), pp. 188-9, pl. 1 figs. 12-16   (as Palaeotetradinium).
   U. Cretaceous, Australia.   ---, Downie and Sarjeant, 1963, p. 94.

V. irregulare Jekhowsky, 1961, pp. 208-210, pl. 1 figs. 1-21.   Permo-Triassic, Yugoslavia.

V. irregulare Jekh. 1961 forma irregulare Jekhowsky, 1961, p. 208, pl. 1 figs. 10-17.   Permo-
   Triassic, Yugoslavia.

V. irregulare Jekh. 1961 forma pirula Jekhowsky, 1961, p. 208, pl. 1 figs. 18-21.   Permo-
   Triassic, Yugoslavia.

V. irregulare Jekh. 1961 forma subhexaedron Jekhowsky, 1961, p. 208, pl. 1 figs. 1-3.   Permo-
   Triassic, Yugoslavia.

V. irregulare Jekh, 1961 forma subtetraedron Jekhowsky, 1961, p. 208, pl. 1 figs. 4-9.
   Permo-Triassic, Yugoslavia.

V. lairdi (Deflandre, 1946c), card 1112, 1 text-fig.   (as Hystrichosphaeridium).   M. Silurian,
   Canada.   ---, Deunff, 1954c, p. 306.

V. ledanoisi Deunff, 1957, p. 9, fig. 6.   M. Devonian, Canada.

V. legrandi Stockmans and Willière, 1962a, p. 54, pl. 1 figs. 3-4, text-figs. 11a-b.
   U. Devonian, Belgium.

V. libratum Deunff, 1957, p. 9, fig. 7.   M. Devonian, Canada.

V. limaciforme Stockmans and Willière, 1963, pp. 453-4, pl. 1 figs. 12, 14-15, 19, text-fig. 6.
   Silurian, Belgium.

?V. macroceras Deunff, 1958, pp. 30-1, pls. 3 figs. 33-8; 4 figs. 39, 41.   M. Ordovician,
   France.

V. mamillatum Deunff, 1961b, p. 217.   U. Devonian, Canada.   (Figured and named,without
   description,in Deunff, 1954d, text-fig. 11).

V. mensulum (O. Wetzel, 1933), pp. 49-50, pl. 4 fig. 32   (as Hystrichosphaera).   U. Cretaceous,
   Baltic.   Hystrichosphaeridium mensulum Deflandre, 1937c, p. 31.   ---, Downie and
   Sarjeant, 1963, p. 94.

V. micropolygonale (Stockmans and Willière, 1960), p. 4, pl. 1 fig. 12   (as Micrhystridium).
   U. Devonian, Belgium.   ---, Stockmans and Willière, 1962b, p. 52.

V. minor Staplin, 1961, pl. 49 fig. 9, p. 414.   U. Devonian, Canada.

V. minutum Downie, 1958, p. 344, pl. 17 fig. 4, text-fig. 3c.   L. Ordovician, England.

V. mucronatum Stockmans and Willière, 1963, pp. 456-7, pls. 1 fig. 20; 3 fig 6; text-figs. 10-11. Silurian, Belgium.

V. nasicum (Stockmans and Willière, 1960), p. 3, pl. 1 fig. 3   (as Polyedryxium).   U. Devonian, Belgium.   ---, Stockmans and Willière, 1962a, p. 52.

V. octoaster Staplin, 1961, pp. 413-4, pl. 49 figs. 3-4.   U. Devonian, Canada.

V. oligospinosum (Eisenack, 1934), p. 64, pl. 4 figs. 15-18   (as Ovum hispidum).   Baltic drift, Sil pebble.   Hystrichosphaeridium oligospinosum Eisenack, 1938a, p. 12.   ---, Deunff, 1954c, p. 306.

V. polyaster Staplin, 1961, p. 413, pl. 49 fig. 20.   U. Devonian, Canada.

V. polyaster Stap., 1961, var. hexaster Staplin, 1961, p. 413, pl. 49 fig. 19.   U. Dev., Canada.

V. pseudopharaonis Stockmans and Willière, 1962a, pp. 49-50, pl. 1 fig. 2, text-fig. 5. U. Devonian, Belgium.

V. reductum Deunff, 1958 , p. 27, pl. 1 figs. 1, 3, 8, 10-12, 14, 16-17, 22-23   (as V. trisulcum var. reductum). M. Ordovician, France.   ---, Jekhowsky, 1961, pp. 210-212.

V. reductum Dff. 1958 forma breve Jekhowsky, 1961, p. 212, pl. 2 figs. 38-44.   Permo-Triassic, Europe and Africa.

V. reductum Dff. 1958, var. concavum Cookson and Eisenack, 1962b, p. 492, pl. 4 fig. 17. U. Cretaceous, Australia.

V. reductum Dff. 1958 forma globula Jekhowsky, 1961, p. 212 (figured by Deunff, 1958, pl. 1 figs. 22-3).   Ordovician, France.

V. reductum Dff. 1958 var. reductum Jekhowsky, 1961, p. 212, pl. 2 figs. 33-37.   Permo-Triassic, Europe and Africa.

V. reductum Dff. 1958 forma trispinosoides Jekhowsky, 1961, p. 212, pl. 2 figs. 22-32.   Permo-Triassic, Europe and Africa.

V. remotum Deunff, 1955a, p. 146, pl. 4 fig. 8.   M. Devonian, Canada.

V. rhomboidium Downie, 1959, pp. 62-3, pl. 12 fig. 10.   M. Silurian, England.

? V. riburgense Brosius and Bitterli, 1961, p. 39, pl. 2 figs. 7-12, text-figs. 4a-d, 5a-d. M. Triassic, Switzerland.

? V. riburgense Bros. & Bit., 1961   forma irregularis Brosius and Bitterli, 1961, p. 39, pl. 2 figs. 10-12, text-fig. 4.   M. Triassic, Switzerland.

V. staurasteroides (Deflandre, 1945a), pp. 25-6, pl. 2 figs. 7-9   (as Hystrichosphaeridium). M. Silurian, France.   (Figured and named without description in Deflandre, 1942b, text-fig. 10).   ---, Deunff, 1954c, p. 306.

V. stelligerum Deunff, 1957, p. 10, fig. 10.   M. Devonian, Canada.

V. stelligerum Dff., 1957 var. robustum Deunff, 1958, p. 28, pl. 8 fig. 74. M. Ord., France.

V. tetraedron Deunff, 1961b, p. 217.   M. Devonian, Canada.   (Figured and named without description in Deunff, 1954d, text-fig. 9).

V. tetraxis (Sarjeant, 1960b), pp. 401-2, pl. 14 figs. 2-4, text-fig. 1p (as Micrhystridium). U. Jurassic, England. ---, Downie and Sarjeant, 1963, p. 94.

V. trisphaeridium Downie, 1963, p. 637, pl. 92 fig. 7. M. Silurian, England.

V. trispinoramosum Stockmans & Willière, 1962b, pp. 83-4, pl. 1 fig.1, text-fig.1. U. Dev., Belg.

V. trispinosum (Eisenack, 1938a), pp. 14, 16, text-figs. 2-3 (as Hystrichosphaeridium). Baltic drift, Silurian pebble. ---, Deunff, 1954c, p. 306.

* V. trisulcum Deunff, 1958, p. 27, pl. 1 figs. 4-13. M. Ord., France. (Figured but not described by Deunff, 1951, text-fig. 3, under the name of Hystrichosphaeridium trisulcum).

V. trisulcum Dff., 1958, var. venetum Deunff, 1958, pp. 27-8, pl. 1 figs. 2, 20. M. Ord., France.

V. valensii (Valensi, 1953), pp. 60-1, pl. 10 fig. 28. (as Micrhystridium polyedricum forma reducta). M. Jurassic, France. ---, Downie and Sarjeant, 1963, pp. 93-4.

V. vandenbergheni Stockmans and Willière, 1962b, pp. 86-7, pl. 2 figs. 11, 13, text-figs. 5a-b. U. Devonian, Belgium.

V. vanmeeli Stockmans & Willière, 1962a, p. 51, pl. 2 fig. 27, text-fig.7. U. Dev., Belgium.

V. visbyense (Eisenack, 1959a), pp. 200-1, pl. 16 figs. 12-14, text-fig. 7 (as Baltisphaeridium). U. Silurian, Sweden. ---, Downie and Sarjeant, 1963, p. 94.

V. wenlockium Downie, 1959, p. 63, pl. 12 figs. 9, 11 (as V. tetraedron var. wenlockium). M. Silurian, England. ---, Stockmans and Willière, 1962c, pp. 28-9.

VULCANISPHAERA Deunff, 1961a, p. 42.

* V. africana Deunff, 1961a, p. 42, pl. 2 figs. 1, 2. L. Ordovician, Sahara.

V. nebulosa Deunff, 1961a, p. 42, pl. 2 figs. 3, 5. L. Ordovician, Sahara.

WANAEA Cookson and Eisenack, 1958, p. 57.

W. clathrata Cookson and Eisenack, 1958, p. 58, pl. 9 figs. 6-8. U. Jurassic, Australia and Papua.

W. digitata Cookson and Eisenack, 1958, pl. 9 figs. 2-5. U. Jurassic, Australia.

W. fimbriata Sarjeant, 1961a, pp. 112-13, pl. 15 fig. 14, text-fig. 13. U. Jurassic, England.

* W. spectabilis (Deflandre and Cookson, 1955), p. 293, pl. 3 figs. 12-14 (as Epicephalopyxis). L. Cretaceous, Papua. ---, Cookson and Eisenack, 1958, pp. 57-8.

WENDIELLA Timofeyev, 1962. No diagnosis; validity doubtful.

W. gyperboreum Timofeyev, 1962, pl. 3 fig. 1. Pre-Cambrian, U.S.S.R. No description; validity doubtful.

W. sinicum Timofeyev, 1962, pl. 2 fig. 2. Pre-Cambrian, China. No description; validity doubtful.

WETZELIELLA Eisenack, 1938c, pp. 186-7.

WETZELIELLA subgen. Dracodinium Gocht, 1955, pp. 87 (as genus Dracodinium; subgeneric status proposed by Eisenack, 1961b, p. 306).

* <u>W. solida</u> (Gocht, 1955), pp. 88-91, text-figs. 3-5 (as <u>Dracodinium</u>). Oligocene, Germany.
---, Eisenack, 1961b, p. 306 (by implication).

WETZELIELLA subgen. <u>Rhombodinium</u> Gocht, 1955, pp. 85 (as genus <u>Rhombodinium</u>; subgeneric status proposed by Alberti, 1961, p. 9).

* <u>W. draco</u> (Gocht, 1955), pp. 85-7, text-fig. 1 (as <u>Rhombodinium</u>). Oligocene, Germany.
---, Alberti, 1961, pp. 9-10.

<u>W. draco</u>(Gocht,1955)forma <u>freienwaldensis</u> Gocht,1955,p.87,text-fig.2. Olig.,Germany.

<u>W. minuscula</u> Alberti, 1961, pp. 10-11, pls. 1 fig. 10, 12 fig. 4. Eocene, Germany.

<u>W. rhomboidea</u> Alberti, 1961, p. 10, pls. 1 figs. 1-5, 12 fig. 9. Eocene, Germany.

WETZELIELLA subgen. <u>Wetzeliella</u> Alberti, 1961, p. 7.

* <u>W. articulata</u> Eisenack, 1938c, pp. 186-7, text-fig. 4 , emend. Eisenack, 1954b, pp. 55-7, pls. 7 figs. 1-10; 8 figs. 14-16. Oligocene, East Prussia, U.S.S.R.

<u>W. clathrata</u> Eisenack, 1938c, p. 187, text-fig. 5. Oligocene, East Prussia, U.SS.R.

<u>W. exinulata</u> Vozzhennikova,1960,pl.3 fig.3. No diag.;validity doubtful.Eoc.,Siberia,U.S.S.R.

<u>W. glabra</u> Cookson, 1956, pp. 186-7, pl. 2 figs. 1-5. Eocene, Australia.

<u>W. homomorpha</u> Deflandre and Cookson, 1955, p. 254, pl. 5 fig. 7, text-fig. 19. Eocene, Australia.

<u>W. irregularis</u> Cookson and Eisenack, 1958, pp. 28-9, pl. 10 figs. 1-2. U. Jurassic, Australia.

<u>W. irtyschensis</u> Alberti, 1961, p. 8, pls. 1 figs. 11-12; 12 fig. 8. Oligocene, U.S.S.R.

<u>W. lineidentata</u> Deflandre and Cookson, 1955, pp. 253-4, pl. 5 fig. 5, text-figs. 17-18.
L. Tertiary, Australia. (Figured and named, without description, in Deflandre and Cookson, 1954, text-fig. 2).

<u>W. neocomica</u> Gocht, 1957, pp. 172-6, pls. 19 figs. 1-4, 20 figs. 4, 6, 7, text-figs. 7-8, 15-16. L. Cretaceous, Germany.

? <u>W. neocomica</u> Gocht, 1957 forma <u>circulata</u> Gocht, 1957, p. 178, text-fig. 14.
L. Cretaceous, Germany.

? <u>W. neocomica</u> Gocht, 1957 forma <u>convexa</u> Gocht, 1957, p. 178, pl. 20 figs. 1-2.
L. Cretaceous, Germany.

? <u>W. neocomica</u> Gocht, 1957 forma <u>cruciformis</u> Gocht, 1957, pp. 176-7, pls. 19 fig. 5, 20 fig. 3, text-figs. 9. 10. L. Cretaceous, Germany.

? <u>W. neocomica</u> Gocht, 1957 forma <u>dedecosa</u> Gocht, 1957, p. 177, text-fig. 11.
L. Cretaceous, Germany.

? <u>W. neocomica</u> Gocht, 1957 forma <u>pteridia</u> Gocht,1957,p.178,pl.20 fig.5.L. Cret., Germany.

? <u>W. neocomica</u> Gocht, 1957 forma <u>subovalis</u> Gocht, 1957, p. 177, text-figs. 12-13.
L. Cretaceous, Germany.

<u>W. ovalis</u> Eisenack, 1954b, p. 59, pl. 8 figs. 1-7. Oligocene, East Prussia, U.S.S.R.

<u>W. parva</u> Alberti, 1961, pp. 8-9, pls. 1 figs. 14-18; 12 figs. 10-12. Eocene, Germany.

W. samlandica Eisenack, 1954b, p. 59, pl. 8 figs. 11-12.   Oligocene, East Prussia, U.S.S.R.

W. similis Eisenack, 1954b, pp. 58-9, pl. 8 figs. 8-10.   Oligocene, East Prussia, U.S.S.R.

W. symmetrica Weiler, 1956, pp. 132-5, pl. 11 figs. 1-3, text-figs. 2-5.   Oligocene, Germany.

W. symmetrica Weil., 1956, subsp. incisa Gerlach, 1961, pp. 156-9, pl. 25 fig. 9. Olig., Germany.

W. symmetrica Weil., 1956 subsp. symmetrica Gerlach, 1961, pp. 155-6, pl. 25 figs. 7-8.
      Oligocene, Germany.

WETZELODINIUM Deflandre, 1936c, p. 168.

* W. tentaculatum (O. Wetzel, 1933), pp. 171-2, pl. 2 fig. 23, text-fig. 4   (as Polykrikos).
      U. Cretaceous, Baltic.   ---, Deflandre, 1936c, pp. 168-9.

WILSONASTRUM Jansonius, 1962, pp. 88-9.

* W. colonicum Jansonius, 1962, p. 89, pl. 16 figs. 42-9, 58, text-fig. 3g.   U. Permian-
      L. Triassic, Canada, Australia and Netherlands.

XENICODINIUM Klement, 1960, pp. 53-4.

* X. densispinosum Klement, 1960, p. 54, pl. 5 figs. 14-15.   U. Jurassic, Germany.

XENIKOON Cookson and Eisenack, 1960a, pp. 14-16.

* X. australis Cookson and Eisenack, 1960a, p. 16, pl. 3 figs. 16-17.   U. Cretaceous, Australia.

ZONOOIDIUM Timofeyev, 1958, p. 282.   Type species not designated.

Z. disciforme Timofeyev, 1958, p. 283, pl. 1 fig. 25. M. Cambrian, U.S.S.R.

Z. guttiforme Timofeyev, 1958, p. 282, pl. 1 figs. 15-23. L. Cambrian, U.S.S.R.

Z. mirabile Timofeyev, 1958, pp. 282-3, pl. 1 fig. 24. L. Cambrian, U.S.S.R.

Z. piriforme Timofeyev, 1958, p. 283, pl. 1 fig. 28. M. Cambrian, U.S.S.R.

Z. scutellatum Timofeyev, 1958, p. 283, pl. 1 figs. 26-7. U. Cambrian, U.S.S.R.

Z. strobiliforme Timofeyev, 1958, p. 282, pl. 1 figs. 11-4. L. Cambrian, U.S.S.R.

ZONOSPHAERIDIUM Timofeyev, 1959, p. 30.   Type species not designated.

Z. absolutum Timofeyev, 1959, p. 31, pl. 2 fig. 11.   L. Ordovician, U.S.S.R.

Z. actinomorphum Timofeyev, 1959, p. 30, pl. 2 fig. 9.   L. Ordovician, U.SS.R.

Z. limpatum Timofeyev, 1959, p. 30, pl. 2 fig. 10.   L. Ordovician, U.S.S.R.

Z. obscurum Timofeyev, 1959, p. 31, pl. 2 fig. 12.   L. Ordovician, U.S.S.R.

Z. speciosum Timofeyev, 1959, p. 31, pl. 2 fig. 12.   L. Ordovician, U.S.S.R.

INVALID AND REJECTED TAXA

The list which follows contains reference to all generic and infrageneric taxa which are not currently employed. It includes all invalid and rejected taxa and all combinations not now employed. In the former case, reference is given to the paper in which rejection was proposed; in the latter, the current allocation of the taxon is given and the synonymy may be determined by reference to the index of valid taxa. In a number of cases, taxa were originally wrongly allocated to genera of which there are not now considered to be any fossil representatives, or to genera belonging to other taxonomic groups outside the scope of this work. In these cases, the generic name will not appear in the list of valid taxa.

ACANTHORYTIDODIACRODIUM Timofeyev, 1959, p. 79; rejected by Deflandre and Deflandre-Rigaud, 1961, p. 9.

A. acre Timofeyev, 1959; now Acanthodiacrodium.

A. apertum Timofeyev, 1959; now Acanthodiacrodium.

A. biplicatum Timofeyev, 1959; now Acanthodiacrodium.

A. decipiens Timofeyev, 1959; now Acanthodiacrodium.

A. dichotomum Timofeyev, 1959; now Acanthodiacrodium.

A. diffusum Timofeyev, 1959; now Acanthodiacrodium.

A. echinatum Timofeyev, 1959; now Acanthodiacrodium.

A. erinaceum Timofeyev, 1959; now Acanthodiacrodium.

A. flabellatum Timofeyev, 1959; now Acanthodiacrodium.

A. hippocrepiforme Timofeyev, 1959; now Acanthodiacrodium.

A. lanatum Timofeyev, 1959; now Acanthodiacrodium.

A. lentiforme Timofeyev, 1959; now Acanthodiacrodium.

A. micronulatum Timofeyev, 1959; now Acanthodiacrodium.

A. nidiusculum Timofeyev, 1959; now Acanthodiacrodium.

A. oblongatum Timofeyev, 1959; now Acanthodiacrodium.

A. orthoploceum Timofeyev, 1959; now Acanthodiacrodium.

A. papilliforme Timofeyev, 1959; now Acanthodiacrodium.

A. patulum Timofeyev, 1959; now Acanthodiacrodium.

A. prolatum Timofeyev, 1959; now Acanthodiacrodium.

A. prolongatum Timofeyev, 1959; now Acanthodiacrodium.

A. rigidulum Timofeyev, 1959; now Acanthodiacrodium.

A. scaberrimum Timofeyev, 1959; now Acanthodiacrodium.

A. seronitum Timofeyev, 1959; now Acanthodiacrodium.

A. tectum Timofeyev, 1959; now Acanthodiacrodium.

A. trinatum Timofeyev, 1959; now Acanthodiacrodium.

A. typicum Timofeyev, 1959; now Acanthodiacrodium.

A. unigeminum Timofeyev, 1959; now Acanthodiacrodium.

A. varium Timofeyev, 1959; now Acanthodiacrodium.

A. vestitum Timofeyev, 1959; now Acanthodiacrodium.

A. vulgare Timofeyev, 1959; now Acanthodiacrodium.

A. zonatum Timofeyev, 1959; now Acanthodiacrodium.

ACANTHOZONODIACRODIUM Timofeyev, 1959, p. 87; rejected by Deflandre and
    Deflandre-Rigaud, 1961, p. 9.

A. duplex Timofeyev, 1959; now Acanthodiacrodium.

A. hipocrateriforme Timofeyev, 1959; now Acanthodiacrodium.

Archaeletes anticus Naumova, 1950; now Baltisphaeridium.

A. antiqua Naumova, 1950; typographic variant of A. anticus, now Baltisphaeridium.

A. conspersus Naumova, 1950; now Baltisphaeridium.

A. excisus Naumova, 1950; now Baltisphaeridium.

A. membrasnaceus Naumova, 1950; now Cymatiogalea.

A. mutabilis Naumova, 1950; now Baltisphaeridium.

A. scabei Naumova, 1950; now Baltisphaeridium.

A. serratus Naumova, 1950; now Baltisphaeridium.

A. spectatisimus Naumova, 1950; now Baltisphaeridium.

A. spinellosus Naumova, 1950; now Baltisphaeridium.

A. trivialis Naumova, 1950; now Leiosphaeridia.

ANHYSTRICHOSPHAERA Deflandre.   Unpublished manuscript name mentioned by
    West, 1961, p. 452.

A. multiplex Deflandre.   Unpublished manuscript name mentioned by West, 1961, p. 452.

Areoligera danica W. Wetzel, 1952; now Baltisphaeridium.

ASPERATOPSOPHOSPHAERA Shepeleva and Timofeyev, 1963; mention only, without figures or text description.

Azonomonoletes aciferus Naumova, 1950; now Acanthodiacrodium.

A. aculatus Naumova, 1950; typographic variant of A. aculeatus, now Lophodiacrodium.

A. aculeatus Naumova, 1950; now Lophodiacrodium.

A. argutus Naumova, 1950; now Dasydiacrodium.

A. brevispinus Naumova, 1950; now Acanthodiacrodium.

A. communis Naumova, 1950; now Leiosphaeridia.

A. curvispinus Naumova, 1950; now Acanthodiacrodium.

A. dentatus Naumova, 1950; now Trachydiacrodium.

A. denticulatus Naumova, 1950; now Acanthodiacrodium.

A. denudatus Naumova, 1950; typographic variant of A. dentatus, now Trachydiacrodium.

A. echinatus Naumova, 1950; now Acanthodiacrodium.

A. gibberosus Naumova, 1950; now Lophodiacrodium.

A. hirbus Naumova, 1950; typographic variant of A. hirtus, now Acanthodiacrodium.

A. imperfectus Naumova, 1950; now Dasydiacrodium.

A. meonanthus Naumova, 1950; now Acanthodiacrodium.

A. notadus Naumova, 1950; typographic variant of A. notatus, now Lophodiacrodium.

A. notatus Naumova, 1950; now Lophodiacrodium.

A. parvimammus Naumova, 1950; now Lophodiacrodium.

A. parvispinus Naumova, 1950; now Lophodiacrodium.

A. punctulosus Naumova, 1950; now Leiosphaeridia.

A. quadrangalaris Naumova, 1950; typographic variant of A. quadrangularis, now Acanthodiacrodium.

A. quadrangularis Naumova, 1950; now Acanthodiacrodium.

A. rotundus Naumova, 1950; now Lophodiacrodium.

A. simplissimus Naumova, 1950; now Acanthodiacrodium.

A. sinuoitus Naumova, 1950; now Lophodiacrodium.

158

A. spinellosus Naumova, 1950; now Acanthodiacrodium.

A. striatus Naumova, 1950; now Lophodiacrodium.

A. subrotundus Naumova, 1950; now Acanthodiacrodium.

A. subscabrum Naumova, 1950; now Acanthodiacrodium.

A. subscarbum Naumova, 1950; typographic variant of A. subscabrum, now Acanthodiacrodium.

A. subspinellosus Naumova, 1950; now Lophodiacrodium.

A. torulosus Naumova, 1950; now Lophodiacrodium.

A. tuberculatus Naumova, 1950; now Lophodiacrodium.

A. varius Naumova, 1950; now Acanthodiacrodium.

Baltisphaeridium clavigerum (Deflandre, 1937c), Downie and Sarjeant, 1963; now
           Hystrichosphaeridium.

B. divergens (Eisenack, 1954b), Downie and Sarjeant, 1963; now Cordosphaeridium.

B. eisenackium (Deunff, 1958), Downie and Sarjeant, 1963; typographic variant of
           B. eisenackianum.

B. hirsutoides var. asteroidea (Maslov, 1956), Eisenack, 1959a; now B. asteroideum.

B. lobospinosum (Gocht in Weiler, 1956), Downie and Sarjeant, 1962; now Chiropteridium.

B. longispinosum (Eisenack, 1931), forma robusta Eisenack, 1959a; now B. robustum Eisenack,
           1963e, non Sannemann, 1955.

B. micracanthum Eisenack, 1959, in Downie and Sarjeant, 1962; typographic variant of
           B. micranthum.

B. microspinosum (Eisenack, 1954a), Downie, 1959; now Lophosphaeridium.

B. octospinum (Staplin, 1961), Downie and Sarjeant, 1962; typographic variant of
           B. octospinosum.

B. ramuliferum (Deflandre, 1937c), Downie and Sarjeant, 1962; now Achomosphaera.

B. spiniscens (Timofeyev, 1959), Downie and Sarjeant, 1962; typographic variant of B. spinescens.

B. vigivitispinosum (Staplin, 1961), Downie and Sarjeant, 1962; typographic variant of
           B. vigintispinosum.

B. westi Deflandre.   Unpublished manuscript name mentioned by West, 1961, p. 452,
           and Churchill and Sarjeant, 1963, p. 48.

BAVLINELLA Shepeleva and Timofeyev, 1963; mention only, without figures or text description.

Bion fluctuans Eisenack, 1938b; rejected by Eisenack, 1944, p. 105.

B. medius Eisenack, 1931; now Tasmanites.

B. megacystis Eisenack, 1938b; now Leiosphaeridia.

B. microcystis Eisenack, 1938b; now Leiosphaeridia.

B. navis Eisenack, 1938b; now Leiofusa.

B. pelagicum Eisenack, 1938c; now Thalassiphora.

B. solidum Eisenack, 1931; rejected by Eisenack, 1958a, p. 5.

Cannosphaeropsis calathus in Sarjeant, 1960a; species never published under this name, now Polystephanephorus.

C. fenestrata Deflandre and Cookson, 1955; now Aiora.

C. urnaformis Cookson, 1953; now Polystephanephorus.

CAYEUXISTYLUS Graindor, 1957, p. 2077.   Not valid; no figures given, no species attributed to the genus.

Ceratium (Euceratium) operculatum O. Wetzel, 1933; now Odontochitina.

Ceratocystidiopsis incerta Deflandre-Rigaud, 1954; now Odontochitinopsis.

C. ludbrooki Cookson and Eisenack, 1958; now Pseudoceratium.

C. molesta Deflandre, 1937c; now Odontochitinopsis.

CODONIA Cookson and Eisenack, 1960a, p. 11; junior homonym, altered to Codoniella in Cookson and Eisenack, 1961a, p. 75.

C. campanulata Cookson and Eisenack, 1960a; now Codoniella.

Cymatiosphaera cingulata O. Wetzel, 1933; now Hystrichosphaera.

C. el gassiensse Deunff, 1961a; typographical variant of Cymatiosphaera el gassiensis, corrected by the author on reprints.

C. krauseli Stockmans and Willière, 1960; now Duvernaysphaera.

DASYRYTIDODIACRODIUM Timofeyev, 1959, p. 92; rejected by Deflandre and Deflandre-Rigaud, 1961, p. 10.

D. angulatum Timofeyev, 1959; now <u>Dasydiacrodium.</u>

D. asymmetricum Timofeyev, 1959; now <u>Dasydiacrodium.</u>

D. gibbum Timofeyev, 1959; now <u>Dasydiacrodium.</u>

D. inaequilaterale Timofeyev, 1959; now <u>Dasydiacrodium.</u>

D. mutilatum Timofeyev, 1959; now <u>Dasydiacrodium.</u>

D. sewergini Timofeyev, 1959; now <u>Dasydiacrodium.</u>

D. stellare Timofeyev, 1959; now <u>Dasydiacrodium.</u>

<u>Deflandrea bakeri</u> (Deflandre and Cookson) forma <u>pellucida</u> Deflandre and Cookson, 1955; now <u>D. pellucida.</u>

D. minor Cookson and Eisenack, 1960a, non Alberti, 1959b, junior homonym, altered to <u>D. balmei</u> by Cookson and Eisenack, 1962b.

D. parva Cookson and Eisenack, 1958; now <u>Ascodinium.</u>

<u>Dictyocha elegans</u> Ehrenberg, 1844; now <u>Actiniscus.</u>

D. pentasterias Ehrenberg, 1841; now <u>Actiniscus.</u>

D. stella Ehrenberg, 1838; now <u>Actiniscus.</u>

DICTYOPYXIS Cookson and Eisenack, 1960b, p. 255; junior homonym, altered to <u>Dictyopyxidia</u> by Eisenack, 1961b, p. 316.

D. areolata Cookson and Eisenack, 1960b; now <u>Dictyopyxidia.</u>

<u>Dictyospyris chlamydea</u> Rüst, 1885; now <u>Cymatiosphaera.</u>

DIORNATOSPHAERA Downie, 1958, p. 345; rejected by Deflandre and Deflandre-Rigaud, 1961, pp. 4, 8.

D. angusta Downie, 1958; now <u>Lophodiacrodium.</u>

D. constricta Deunff, 1961a; now <u>Acanthodiacrodium.</u>

D. divisa Deunff, 1961a; now <u>Acanthodiacrodium.</u>

D. ignorata Deunff, 1961a; now <u>Acanthodiacrodium.</u>

D. lineata Deunff, 1961a; now <u>Acanthodiacrodium.</u>

D. phaseola Deunff, 1961a; now <u>Acanthodiacrodium.</u>

<u>D. tuber</u> Deunff, 1961a; now <u>Lophodiacrodium</u>.

<u>Epicephalopyxis spectabilis</u> Deflandre and Cookson, 1955; now <u>Wanaea</u>.

FAVILARNAX Sarjeant, 1963a, p. 720; rejected by Sarjeant, 1964 (in press).

<u>F. amandopolitanum</u> (Valensi, 1955b), Sarjeant, 1963a; now <u>Valensiella</u>.

<u>F. ovulum</u> (Deflandre, 1947d), Sarjeant, 1963a; now <u>Valensiella.</u>

GALEA Maier, 1959, pp. 305-6; rejected by Gerlach, 1961, p. 198, and Eisenack, 1962b, p. 94.

<u>G. densicomata</u> Maier, 1959; now <u>Baltisphaeridium</u>.

<u>G. galea</u> Maier, 1959; now <u>Baltisphaeridium</u>.

<u>G. koryka</u> Maier, 1959; now <u>Baltisphaeridium</u>.

<u>G. levis</u> Maier, 1959; now <u>Baltisphaeridium</u>.

<u>G. lynchnea</u> Maier, 1959; now <u>Baltisphaeridium</u>.

<u>G. mespilana</u> Maier, 1959; now <u>Baltisphaeridium</u>.

<u>G. twistringensis</u> Maier, 1959; now <u>Baltisphaeridium</u>.

<u>G. xiphea</u> Maier, 1959; now <u>Hystrichosphaeridium</u>.

?<u>Geodia austini</u> Merrill, 1895; now <u>Systematophora</u>.

?<u>G. cretacea</u> Merrill, 1895; now <u>Baltisphaeridium</u>.

?<u>G. hilli</u> Merrill, 1895; now <u>Hystrichosphaeridium</u>.

?<u>G. irregulare</u> Merrill, 1895; now <u>Hystrichosphaeridium</u>.

?<u>G. spinicurvata</u> Merrill, 1895; now <u>Baltisphaeridium</u>.

?<u>G. spinipansata</u> Merrill, 1895; now <u>Hystrichosphaeridium</u>.

?<u>G. texana</u> Merrill, 1895; now <u>Baltisphaeridium</u>.

<u>Gonyaulax helicoida</u> Eis. and Cooks. subsp. <u>cassidata</u> Eisenack and Cookson, 1960; now <u>G. cassidata</u>.

<u>G. ornata</u> (Eisenack, 1935), Klement, 1960; now <u>Ctenidodinium</u>.

162

Gymnodinium attadalense Cookson and Eisenack, 1958; now Scriniodinium.

G. crystallinum Deflandre, 1938e; now Scriniodinium.

G. galeritum Deflandre, 1938e; now Scriniodinium.

G. luridum Deflandre, 1938e; now Scriniodinium.

G. parvimarginatum Cookson and Eisenack, 1958; now Scriniodinium.

Hystrichosphaera asteroidea Maslov, 1958; now Baltisphaeridium.

H. biformis Wiesner, 1936; now Hystrichosphaeridium.

H. borussica Eisenack, 1954b; now Rottnestia.

H. bulbosa (Ehrenberg, 1838), O. Wetzel, 1933; now Hystrichosphaeridium.

H. cruciata O. Wetzel, 1933; now Hystrichosphaeridium.

H. inconspicua Deflandre, 1935a; now Micrhystridium.

H. intermedia O. Wetzel, 1933; now Baltisphaeridium.

H. longispinosa (Eisenack, 1931), O. Wetzel, 1932; now Baltisphaeridium.

H. longispinosa (Eis. 1931) var. pumilis O. Wetzel, 1932; now Micrhystridium pumile.

H. mensula O. Wetzel, 1933; now Veryhachium.

H. penicillata (Ehrenberg, 1843), O. Wetzel, 1933; now Hystrichosphaeridium.

H. penicillata (Ehr. 1843) forma coronata O. Wetzel, 1933; now Areoligera coronata.

H. penicillata (Ehr. 1843) forma medusettiformis O. Wetzel, 1933; now Areoligera medusettiformis.

H. penicillata (Ehr. 1843) forma rhizopodiphora O. Wetzel, 1933; now Areoligera rhizopodiphora.

H. pilosa (Ehrenberg, 1843), O. Wetzel, 1933; now Baltisphaeridium.

H. salpingophora Deflandre, 1935a; now Hystrichosphaeridium.

H. tenuicapillata O. Wetzel, 1933; now Areoligera.

H. tenuicapillata O. Wetzel, 1933 forma irregularis O. Wetzel, 1933; typical form of genus (!), now Areoligera tenuicapillata.

H. tenuicapillata O. Wetzel, 1933 forma turbilineata O. Wetzel, 1933; now Areoligena turbilineata.

H. tubifera (Ehrenberg, 1838), O. Wetzel, 1933; now Hystrichosphaeridium.

H. xanthiopyxides O. Wetzel, 1933; now Baltisphaeridium.

HYSTRICHOANGULATUM Wilson and Hoffmeister; name proposed in a paper read to the
Geological Society of America, 1954. Not subsequently validated by publication.

HYSTRICHOCORPULENTUM Wilson and Hoffmeister; name proposed in a paper read to the
Geological Society of America, 1954. Not subsequently validated by publication.

Hystrichosphaeridium aculeatum Timofeyev, 1959; now Baltisphaeridium.

H. aemulum Deflandre, 1938e; now Cannosphaeropsis.

H. annulatum Timofeyev, 1959; now Baltisphaeridium.

H. apiculatum Timofeyev, 1959; now Baltisphaeridium.

H. armatum Deflandre, 1937c; now Baltisphaeridium.

H. arrectum Timofeyev, 1959; now Baltisphaeridium.

H. ashdodense Rossignol, 1962; now Baltisphaeridium.

H. asteroideum (Maslov, 1956), Deflandre and Deflandre-Rigaud, 1958; now Baltisphaeridium.

H. bacifer (Eisenack, 1934), Eisenack, 1938a; now Bacisphaeridium.

H. balticum Eisenack, 1951; now Veryhachium.

H. biformoides Eisenack, 1954b; now Baltisphaeridium.

H. bimarginatum Timofeyev, 1959; now Baltisphaeridium.

H. bohemicum (Eisenack, 1934), Eisenack, 1938a; now Baltisphaeridium.

H. brevifurcatum Eisenack, 1954a; now Baltisphaeridium.

H. brevispinosum (Eisenack, 1931), Eisenack, 1938a; now Baltisphaeridium.

H. brevispinosum (Eis., 1931) var. nanum Deflandre, 1945a; now Baltisphaeridium nanum.

H. brevispinosum (Eis., 1931) var. wenlockensis Downie, 1958; now Baltisphaeridium wenlockense.

H. castaneum (Eisenack, 1934), Eisenack, 1938a; now Baltisphaeridium.

H. caulleryi Deflandre, 1938e; now Cannosphaeropsis.

H. centrocarpum Deflandre and Cookson, 1955; now Baltisphaeridium.

H. circumscissum Timofeyev, 1959; now Baltisphaeridium.

H. claviculorum Deflandre, 1938e; now Baltisphaeridium.

H. claviferum (Wilkinson, 1849), Deflandre, 1946a; now Baltisphaeridium.

H. cognitum Timofeyev, 1959; now Baltisphaeridium.

H. colligerum Deflandre and Cookson, 1955; now Baltisphaeridium.

H. conspicuum Timofeyev, 1959; now Baltisphaeridium.

H. corollatum Timofeyev, 1959; now Baltisphaeridium.

H. cristatum Downie, 1959; now Baltisphaeridium.

H. danicum (W. Wetzel, 1952), W. Wetzel, 1955; now Baltisphaeridium.

H. denticulatum Courteville in Deflandre, 1946a; now Baltisphaeridium.

H. dictyophorum Cookson and Eisenack, 1958; now Baltisphaeridium.

H. differtum Sannemann, 1955; now Baltisphaeridium.

H. digitatum Eisenack, 1938a; now Baltisphaeridium.

H. dignum Sannemann, 1955; now Baltisphaeridium.

H. diktyoplokus Klumpp, 1953; now Cordosphaeridium.

H. diploporum Eisenack, 1951; now Baltisphaeridium.

H. divergens Eisenack, 1954b; now Baltisphaeridium.

H. echinoides Maier, 1959; now Baltisphaeridium.

H. ehrenbergi Deflandre, 1947d; now Baltisphaeridium.

H. eisenacki Sannemann, 1955; now Baltisphaeridium.

H. eisenackianum Deunff, 1958; now Baltisphaeridium.

H. elegantulum Lejeune-Carpentier, 1940; rejected by Deflandre, 1946d, p. 111.

H. eoinodes Eisenack, 1958c; now Cordosphaeridium.

H. eoplanktonicum Eisenack, 1955; now Baltisphaeridium.

H. erraticum Eisenack, 1954a; now Baltisphaeridium.

H. ferox Deflandre, 1937c; now Baltisphaeridium.

H. fimbriatum (White, 1842), Deflandre, 1936a; now Baltisphaeridium.

H. floripes Deflandre and Cookson, 1955; now Cordosphaeridium.

H. fluctuans (Eisenack, 1938a), Pastiels, 1948; rejected by Eisenack, 1944, p. 105.

H. franconium Sannemann, 1955; now Baltisphaeridium.

H. geometricum Deflandre, 1945a; now Veryhachium.

H. geometricum Pastiels, 1948, non Deflandre, 1945a; now Baltisphaeridium.

H. gotlandicum Eisenack, 1954a; now Baltisphaeridium.

H. heteracanthum Deflandre and Cookson, 1955; now Baltisphaeridium.

H. hippocrepicum Timofeyev, 1959; now Baltisphaeridium.

H. hirsutoides Eisenack, 1951; now Baltisphaeridium.

H. hirsutum (Ehrenberg, 1838a), Deflandre, 1937c; now Baltisphaeridium.

H. hirtum Ehrenberg, in W. Wetzel, 1952; invalid alteration of H. hirsutum, now Baltisphaeridium.

H. horridum Deflandre, 1937c; now Baltisphaeridium.

H. huguonioti Valensi, 1955a; now Baltisphaeridium.

H. hystrichoreticulatum Eisenack, 1938a; now Baltisphaeridium.

H. inconspicuum Timofeyev, 1959; now Baltisphaeridium.

H. inodes Klumpp, 1953; now Cordosphaeridium.

H. integrum Sannemann, 1955; now Baltisphaeridium.

H. intermedium (O. Wetzel, 1933), Deflandre, 1937c; now Baltisphaeridium.

H. israelicanum Rossignol, 1962; now Baltisphaeridium.

H. lairdi Deflandre, 1946c; now Veryhachium.

H. lewisi Deunff, 1954; now Baltisphaeridium.

H. lobospinosum Gocht in Weiler, 1956; now Chiropteridium.

H. longifurcatum Firtion, 1952; now Baltisphaeridium.

H. longispinosoides Sannemann, 1955; now Baltisphaeridium.

H. longispinosum (Eisenack, 1931), Eisenack, 1938a; now Baltisphaeridium.

H. longofilum Maier, 1959; now Baltisphaeridium.

H. lucidum Deunff, 1958; now Baltisphaeridium.

H. machaerophorum Deflandre and Cookson, 1955; now Baltisphaeridium.

H. malleoferum (White, 1842), Deflandre, 1937c; now Baltisphaeridium.

H. mariannae Philippot, 1949; now Baltisphaeridium.

H. mensulum (O. Wetzel,1933), Deflandre, 1937c; now Veryhachium.

H. meson Eisenack, 1955; now Baltisphaeridium.

H. microfurcatum Deunff, 1957; now Baltisphaeridium.

H. microspinosum Eisenack, 1954a; now Lophosphaeridium.

H. microtriaina Klumpp, 1953; now Cordosphaeridium.

H. monacanthum Deunff, 1951; now Deunffia.

H. multifurcatum Deflandre, 1937c; now Baltisphaeridium.

H. multipilosum (Eisenack, 1931), Eisenack, 1938a; now <u>Baltisphaeridium</u>.

H. mutabile Sannemann, 1955; now <u>Baltisphaeridium</u>.

H. nudatum Timofeyev, 1959; now <u>Baltisphaeridium.</u>

H. ohioensis Winslow, 1962; now <u>Baltisphaeridium</u>.

H. oligacanthum W. Wetzel, 1952; now <u>Baltisphaeridium</u>.

H. oligofurcatum Eisenack, 1954a; now <u>Baltisphaeridium</u>.

H. oligospinosum (Eisenack, 1934), Eisenack, 1938a; now <u>Veryhachium</u>.

H. ordovicum Timofeyev, 1959; now <u>Baltisphaeridium</u>.

H. palmatum Deflandre and Courteville, 1939; now <u>Baltisphaeridium</u>.

H. parvispinum (Deflandre, 1937c), Cookson and Eisenack, 1958; now <u>Baltisphaeridium</u>.

H. pateum Timofeyev, 1959; now <u>Baltisphaeridium</u>.

H. pattei Valensi, 1948; now <u>Baltisphaeridium</u>.

H. paucifurcatum Cookson and Eisenack, 1961b; now <u>Baltisphaeridium</u>.

H. pilosum (Ehrenberg, 1843), Deflandre, 1937c; now <u>Baltisphaeridium</u>.

H. piriferum Eisenack, 1954a; now <u>Baltisphaeridium</u>.

H. placacanthum Deflandre and Cookson, 1955; now <u>Baltisphaeridium</u>.

H. plicatum Maier, 1959; now <u>Baltisphaeridium</u>.

H. polygonale (Eisenack, 1931), Eisenack, 1938a; now <u>Baltisphaeridium</u>.

H. polytrichium Valensi, 1947, in Downie, 1957; typographical variant of <u>H. polytrichum</u>
    now <u>Baltisphaeridium</u>.

H. polytrichum Valensi, 1947; now <u>Baltisphaeridium</u>.

H. pseudhystrichodinium Deflandre, 1937c; now <u>Baltisphaeridium</u>.

H. pterophorum Deflandre and Courteville, 1939; now <u>Cymatiosphaera</u>.

H. pumile (O. Wetzel, 1932), Deflandre, 1937c; now <u>Micrhystridium</u>.

H. quadriradiatum Timofeyev, 1959; now <u>Baltisphaeridium</u>.

H. ramuliferum Deflandre, 1937c; now <u>Achomosphaera</u>.

H. ramusculosum Deflandre, 1945a; now <u>Baltisphaeridium</u>.

H. rehdense Maier, 1959; now <u>Baltisphaeridium</u>.

H. rigens Timofeyev, 1959; now <u>Baltisphaeridium</u>.

H. rjabinini Timofeyev, 1959; now <u>Baltisphaeridium</u>.

H. robustum Sannemann, 1955; now <u>Baltisphaeridium</u>.

H. saalfeldiensis Eisenack in Hundt, 1940, p. 235, text-figs. 1-2 of p. 326, U. Silurian,
Germany. (Note: the characters of this species are not clear and the type is
lost. Eisenack (personal communication to W.A.S.S.) considers that the species
should be abandoned).

H. saturnium Maier, 1959; now <u>Baltisphaeridium</u>.

H. scaffoldi Baksi, 1962; now <u>Connosphaeropsis</u>.

H. setigerfurcatum Timofeyev, 1959; now <u>Baltisphaeridium</u>.

H. sexradiatum Timofeyev, 1959; now <u>Baltisphaeridium</u>.

H. spiciferum Deunff, 1955a; now <u>Baltisphaeridium</u>.

H. spinellosum Eisenack; mentioned by Timofeyev, 1956a, p. 132, but no such species
has been published by Eisenack.

H. spinescens Timofeyev, 1959; now <u>Baltisphaeridium</u>.

H. spinosum (White, 1842), Deflandre, 1937c; now <u>Baltisphaeridium</u>.

H. staurasteroides Deflandre, 1945a; now <u>Veryhachium</u>.

H. stellaeforme Timofeyev, 1959; now <u>Baltisphaeridium</u>.

H. stimuliferum Deflandre, 1938e; now <u>Baltisphaeridium</u>.

H. striolatum Deflandre, 1937c; now <u>Baltisphaeridium</u>.

H. striatoconus Deflandre and Cookson, 1955; now <u>Baltisphaeridium</u>.

H. sylheti Baksi, 1962; now <u>Baltisphaeridium</u>.

H. tenuicapillatum (O. Wetzel, 1933), W. Wetzel, 1955; now <u>Areoligera</u>.

H. tiara Klumpp, 1953; now <u>Baltisphaeridium</u>.

H. tridactylites Valensi, 1955a; now <u>Baltisphaeridium</u>.

H. trifurcatum (Eisenack, 1931), Eisenack, 1938a; now <u>Baltisphaeridium</u>.

H. trispinosum Eisenack, 1938a; now <u>Veryhachium</u>.

H. trisulcum Deunff, 1951; now <u>Veryhachium</u>.

H. tschunense Timofeyev, 1962; now <u>Baltisphaeridium</u>.

H. tuberatum Downie, 1958; now <u>Baltisphaeridium</u>.

H. tuberosum Sannemann, 1955; now <u>Baltisphaeridium</u>.

H. veliferum Downie, 1958; now <u>Baltisphaeridium</u>.

H. venustum Sannemann, 1955; now <u>Baltisphaeridium</u>.

H. vestitum Deflandre, 1938e; now <u>Baltisphaeridium</u>.

H. whitei Deflandre and Courteville, 1939; now Baltisphaeridium.

H. xanthiopyxides (O. Wetzel, 1933); Deflandre, 1937c; now Baltisphaeridium.

H. xanthiopyxides (O. We. 1933) var. granulosum Deflandre, 1937c; now Baltisphaeridium granulosum.

H. xanthiopyxides (O. We. 1933) var. parvispinum Deflandre, 1937c; now Baltisphaeridium parvispinum.

H. zonale Timofeyev, 1959; now Baltisphaeridium.

HYSTRICHOSPHAERINA Alberti, 1961, p. 38; rejected by Neale and Sarjeant, 1962, p. 455.

H. schindewolfi Alberti, 1961; now Systematophora.

H. turonica Alberti, 1961; now Systematophora.

KISSELJOVIA Vozzhennikova, 1961, p. 1461. Mention only- no adequate diagnosis, no named species. May be a typographic variant of Kiselevia.

LEIOSPHAERA Eisenack, 1938a, p. 12; rejected by Eisenack, 1958a, pp. 2-5.

L. aurata Deflandre, 1945a; now Leiosphaeridia.

L. dictyota Eisenack, 1938a; now Dictyotidium.

L. globosa (White, 1842), Deflandre, 1946a; now Leiosphaeridia.

L. granulata Eisenack, 1938a; now Leiosphaeridia.

L. huronensis (Dawson, 1871a), Krausel, 1941; now Tasmanites.

L. hyalina Deflandre, 1941b; now Leiosphaeridia.

L. media (Eisenack, 1931), Eisenack, 1938a; now Tasmanites.

L. megacystis (Eisenack, 1938b), Eisenack, 1938a; now Leiosphaeridia.

L. microcystis (Eisenack, 1938b), Eisenack, 1938a; now Leiosphaeridia.

L. reticulata Eisenack, 1938a; now Leiosphaeridia.

L. retigera Deflandre, 1945a; now Leiosphaeridia.

L. scrobiculata Deflandre and Cookson, 1955; now Pyxidiella.

L. solida (Eisenack, 1931), Eisenack, 1938a; rejected by Eisenack, 1958, p. 5.

Leiosphaeridia britannica Deflandre. Unpublished manuscript name mentioned by West, 1961, p. 452.

L. chytroeides Sarjeant, 1962b; now Chytoeisphaeridia.

L. eisenackia (Timofeyev, 1959), Downie and Sarjeant, 1963; typographic variant of L. eisenacki.

L. granulifera (Staplin, 1961), Downie and Sarjeant, 1963; non existent species quoted in error.

L. granulosa (Staplin, 1961), Downie and Sarjeant, 1963; now Lophosphaeridium.

L. microgranulifera (Staplin, 1961), Downie and Sarjeant, 1963; typographic variant of
       L. microgranifera.

LEIOSPHAERIDIUM Timofeyev, 1959, p. 27; rejected by Downie and Sarjeant, 1963, pp. 87-8.

?L. belloyense Jansonius, 1962; now Leiosphaeridia.

L. discum Timofeyev, 1962; now Leiosphaeridia.

L. eisenacki Timofeyev, 1959; now Leiosphaeridia.

L. fastigatirugosum Staplin, 1961; now Leiosphaeridia.

L. muitschum Timofeyev, 1962; now Leiosphaeridia.

L. pestovi Timofeyev, 1962; now Leiosphaeridia.

Lithodinia jurassica Eis. 1935 var. ornata Eisenack, 1935; now Ctenidodinium ornatum.

LITHOPERIDINIUM Deflandre, 1933, pp. 265-73; rejected by Deflandre, 1945b, cards 806-9.

L. oamaruense Deflandre, 1933; now Peridinites.

L. rossicum Deflandre, 1940b; now Peridinites.

LOPHOMARGINATA Naumova, 1961, p. 113; mentioned only, without figures or text description.

LOPHORYTIDODIACRODIUM Timofeyev, 1959, p. 62; rejected by Deflandre and Deflandre-
       Rigaud, 1961, pp. 4, 8-9.

L. abnorme Timofeyev, 1959; now Lophodiacrodium.

L. atavum Timofeyev, 1959; now Lophodiacrodium.

L. bilaterale Timofeyev, 1959; now Lophodiacrodium.

L. bubnoffi Timofeyev, 1958; now Lophodiacrodium.

L. ellipticum Timofeyev, 1959; now Lophodiacrodium.

L. filiforme Timofeyev, 1959; now Lophodiacrodium.

170

L. gibbosum Timofeyev, 1959; now Lophodiacrodium.

L. inane Timofeyev, 1959; now Lophodiacrodium.

?L. intertextum Timofeyev, 1959; now Lophodiacrodium.

L. introrsum Timofeyev, 1959; now Lophodiacrodium.

L. lutkevischi Timofeyev, 1959; now Lophodiacrodium.

L. maljavkinae Timofeyev, 1959; now Lophodiacrodium.

L. meniscatum Timofeyev, 1959; now Lophodiacrodium.

L. monomorphum Timofeyev, 1959; now Lophodiacrodium.

L. obversum Timofeyev, 1959; now Lophodiacrodium.

L. palmatum Timofeyev, 1959; now Lophodiacrodium.

L. primarium Timofeyev, 1959; now Lophodiacrodium.

L. rotundum Timofeyev, 1959; now Lophodiacrodium.

L. salebrosum Timofeyev, 1959; now Lophodiacrodium.

L. tosnaense Timofeyev, 1959; now Lophodiacrodium.

L. totum Timofeyev, 1959; now Lophodiacrodium.

L. tuberculatum Timofeyev, 1959; now Lophodiacrodium.

L. turulosum Timofeyev, 1959; now Lophodiacrodium.

L. valdaicum Timofeyev, 1959; now Lophodiacrodium.

LOPHOZONODIACRODIUM Timofeyev, 1959, p. 67; rejected by Deflandre and Deflandre-
        Rigaud, 1961, pp. 4, 8.

L. doliumsimile Timofeyev, 1959; now Lophodiacrodium.

L. oblatum Timofeyev, 1959; now Lophodiacrodium.

L. spectabile Timofeyev, 1959; now Lophodiacrodium.

L. tumidum Timofeyev, 1959; now Lophodiacrodium.

MEMBRANILARNAX O. Wetzel, 1933, p. 51; rejected by Eisenack, 1959c, pp. 327-32,
        and 1963b, pp. 98-9.

M. amandopolitanum Valensi, 1955b; now Valensiella.

M. angustivelum Deflandre and Cookson, 1955; now Samlandia.

M. leptodermum Cookson and Eisenack, 1958; now Membranilarnacia.

M. liradiscoides O. Wetzel, 1933; now ?Membranilarnacia.

M. marinum Kufferath, 1950; now ? Membranilarnacia.

M. ovulum Deflandre, 1947d; now Valensiella.

?M. pirus Deunff, 1958; now ?Membranilarnacia.

M. pterococcoides O. Wetzel, 1933; now Membranilarnacia.

M. pterospermoides O. Wetzel, 1933; now ?Membranilarnacia.

MEMBRANOPHORIDIUM Gerlach, 1961, pp. 198-9; rejected by Brosius, 1963, pp. 47-8.

M. aspinatum Gerlach, 1961; now Chiropteridium.

M. multispinatum Gerlach, 1961; junior synonym of Chiropteridium dispersum, rejected
        by Brosius, 1963, p. 48.

M. partispinatum Gerlach, 1961; now Chiropteridium.

Mesocena heptagona Ehrenberg, 1841; now Actiniscus.

Micrhystridium alloiteaui Deunff, 1955a; now Baltisphaeridium.

M. areolatum Deflandre, 1941b; now Cymatiosphaera.

M. breviciliatum Staplin, 1961; now Baltisphaeridium.

M. bulbiferum Deflandre, 1945a; now Veryhachium.

M. crassiechinatum Staplin, 1961; now Baltisphaeridium.

M. dictyophorum Valensi, 1953; now Cymatiosphaera.

M. duvernayensis Staplin, 1961; now Baltisphaeridium.

M. echinosum Staplin, 1961; now Baltisphaeridium.

M. exilissimum Deflandre, 1947d; now Cymatiosphaera.

M. fucosum Valensi, 1955a; now Hystrichosphaeridium.

M. gilsonii Kufferath, 1950; now Baltisphaeridium.

M. micropolygonale Stockmans and Willière, 1960; now Veryhachium.

M. octospinosum Staplin, 1961; now Baltisphaeridium.

M. paucispinum Deunff, 1954d; now Baltisphaeridium.

M. paulinae Valensi, 1953; now Hystrichosphaeridium.

172

M. pavimentum Deflandre, 1945a; now Cymatiosphaera.

M. placophorum Valensi, 1948; now Cymatiosphaera.

M. polyedricum Val. 1953, var. reducta Valensi, 1953; now Veryhachium valensii.

M. reticulatum Deflandre, 1935; now Cymatiosphaera.

M. sannemanni Deunff, 1958; now Baltisphaeridium.

M. sericum Deunff, 1954d; now Baltisphaeridium.

M. spinoglobosum Staplin, 1961; now Baltisphaeridium.

M. tetraxis Sarjeant, 1960b; now Veryhachium.

M. tomaeeuse Stockmans and Willière, 1950, in Downie and Sarjeant, 1963; typographical
    variant of M. tornacense.

M. veligerum Deflandre, 1937c; now Ceratocorys.

M. vigintispinosum Staplin, 1961; now Baltisphaeridium.

MICRORUGOSINA Naumova, 1961, p. 116.   Mention only; no figure or text description.

MONOTREMATUM Timofeyev; generic name stated by Timofeyev, 1963, p. 475, as
    described in Timofeyev, 1961a, but not in fact described in that paper.   Place
    of publication, if any, not known to the authors.

MULTIPLICISPHAERIDIUM Staplin, 1961, p. 410; rejected by Eisenack, 1962b, p. 96,
    and Downie and Sarjeant, 1963, pp. 85-7.

M. deunffi Jansonius, 1962; now Baltisphaeridium.

M. ramispinosum Staplin, 1961; now Baltisphaeridium.

M. spicatum Staplin, 1961; now Baltisphaeridium.

?M. sprucegrovensis Staplin, 1961; now Baltisphaeridium.

M. truncatum Staplin, 1961; now Baltisphaeridium.

Nannoceratopsis deflandrei Evitt, 1961b; junior synonym of ?N. gracilis rejected by
    Evitt, 1962, pp. 1129-230.

Odontochitina silicorum Deflandre, 1935a; junior synonym of O. operculata rejected by
    Deflandre and Cookson, 1955, p. 292.

Ooidium sablincaene Timofeyev, 1958; typographical variant of O. sablincaense.

Ovum hispidum bohemicum Eisenack, 1934; now Baltisphaeridium bohemicum.

O. hispidum brevispinosum Eisenack, 1931; now Baltisphaeridium brevispinosum.

O. hispidum bulbosum (Ehrenberg, 1838a), Lohmann, 1904; now Hystrichosphaeridium bulbosum.

O. hispidum castaneum Eisenack, 1934; now Baltisphaeridium castaneum.

O. hispidum furcatum (Ehrenberg, 1838a), Lohmann, 1904; now Hystrichosphaera furcata.

O. hispidum fusiformis Eisenack, 1934; now Leiofusa fusiformis.

O. hispidum hirsutum (Ehrenberg, 1838a), W. Wetzel, 1922; now Baltisphaeridium hirsutum.

O. hispidum longispinosum Eisenack, 1931; now Baltisphaeridium longispinosum.

O. hispidum multipilosum Eisenack, 1931; now Baltisphaeridium multipilosum.

O. hispidum oligospinosum Eisenack, 1934; now Veryhachium oligospinosum.

O. hispidum penicillatum (Ehrenberg, 1843), Lohmann, 1904; now Hystrichosphaeridium penicillatum.

O. hispidum pilosum (Ehrenberg, 1843), Lohmann, 1904; now Baltisphaeridium pilosum.

O. hispidum polygonale Eisenack, 1931; now Baltisphaeridium polygonale.

O. hispidum ramosum (Ehrenberg, 1838a), Lohmann, 1904; now Hystrichosphaera ramosa.

O. hispidum trifurcatum Eisenack, 1931; now Baltisphaeridium trifurcatum.

O. hispidum tubiferum (Ehrenberg, 1838a), Lohmann, 1904; now Hystrichosphaeridium tubiferum.

Palaeoceratium operculatum (O. Wetzel, 1933), O. Wetzel, 1948a; now Odontochitina operculata.

Palaeohystrichophora dispersa Cookson and Eisenack, 1958; now Diconodinium.

P. multispina Deflandre and Cookson, 1955; now Diconodinium.

P. pellifera Cookson and Eisenack, 1958; now Diconodinium.

Palaeoperidinium cayeuxi Deflandre, 1935a; now Phanerodinium.

P. nuciforme Deflandre, 1938a; now Gonyaulax.

P. spinosissimum Deflandre, 1938e; now Palaeohystrichophora.

174

Palaeotetradinium hyalodermum Cookson, 1956; now Veryhachium.

PALHISTIODINIA Deflandre, 1938e, p. 185;   rejected by Evitt, 1961c, p. 402.

P. arcana Deflandre, 1938e; rejected by Evitt, 1961c, p. 402.

PENTAGONUM Vozzhennikova, 1961, p. 1461.   Mention only; no adequate diagnosis,
    no named species.

Peridinium delitiense Ehrenberg, 1838a; now Spongodinium.

P. tricuspis O. Wetzel, 1933; now Lejeunia.

P. ventriosum O. Wetzel, 1933; now Palaeoperidinium.

Perisaccus primigenus Naumova, 1950; now Tasmanites.

Polyedryxium belgicum Stockmans and Willière, 1960; now Veryhachium.

P. centrigerum Deunff, 1955; now Staplinium.

P. decorum Deunff, 1955; now Staplinium.

P. nasicum Stockmans and Willière, 1960; now Veryhachium.

P. simplex Deunff, 1955; now Staplinium.

Polykrikos tentaculatus O. Wetzel, 1933; now Wetzelodinium.

POLYSTEPHANOSPHAERA Sarjeant, 1960a, pp. 140-2; rejected by Sarjeant, 1961c, pp. 1095-

P. calathus Sarjeant, 1961a; now Polystephanephorus.

P. paracalathus Sarjeant, 1960a; now Polystephanephorus.

P. urnaformis (Cookson, 1953), Sarjeant, 1960a; now Polystephanephorus.

P. valensii Sarjeant, 1960a; now Systematophora.

PROTOLEIOSPHAERIDIUM Timofeyev, 1959, p. 25; rejected by Downie and Sarjeant,
    1963, p. 88.

P. cambriensis Timofeyev, 1959; now Leiosphaeridia.

P. conglutinatum Timofeyev, 1959; now Leiosphaeridia.

P. cryptogranulosum Staplin, 1961; now Leiosphaeridia.

P. diaphanium Staplin, 1961; now Leiosphaeridia.

P. faveolatum Timofeyev, 1959; now Leiosphaeridia.

P. granulosum Staplin, 1961; now Lophosphaeridium.

P. indefinitum Timofeyev, 1959; now Leiosphaeridia.

P. major Staplin, 1961; now Leiosphaeridia.

P. microgranifer Staplin, 1961; now Leiosphaeridia.

P. microsaetosum Staplin, 1961; now Leiosphaeridia.

P. minutum Staplin, 1961; now Leiosphaeridia.

P. nervatum Timofeyev, 1959; now Leiosphaeridia.

P. orbiculatum Staplin, 1961; now Leiosphaeridia.

P. papillatum Staplin, 1961; now Leiosphaeridia.

P. parvigranulosum Staplin, 1961; now Leiosphaeridia.

P. sorediforme Timofeyev, 1959; now Leiosphaeridia.

P. wimani Timofeyev, 1960; now Leiosphaeridia.

?Pseudoceratium tetracanthum Gocht, 1957; now Muderongia.

Pterocystidiopsis Deflandre and Cookson, 1955; now Thalassiphora.

Pterospermopsis pelagica (Eisenack, 1938a), Eisenack, 1954b; now Thalassiphora.

Pulvinosphaeridium oligoprojectum Downie, 1959; junior synonym of P. pulvinellum, rejected by Downie, 1963, p. 638.

Scriniodinium trabeculosum Gocht, 1959; now Gardodinium.

SPHAEROSOMATITES Rothpletz, 1880, pp. 453-6; rejected by Deflandre, 1945a, pp. 20-1.

S. mesocenoides Rothpletz, 1880; rejected by Deflandre, 1945a, pp. 20-1.

S. reticulatus Rothpletz, 1880; rejected by Deflandre, 1945a, pp. 20-1.

S. spiculosus Rothpletz, 1880; rejected by Deflandre, 1945a, pp. 20-1.

S. spinosus Rothpletz, 1880; rejected by Deflandre, 1945a, pp. 20-1.

S. verrucosus Rothpletz, 1880; rejected by Deflandre, 1945a, pp. 20-1.

SPINIFERITES Mantell, 1850, p. 190; rejected by Sarjeant, 1964 (in press).

S. palmatus (White, 1842), Mantell, 1854; now Hystrichosphaeridium recurvatum.

S. ramosus (Ehrenberg, 1838a), Mantell, 1854; now Hystrichosphaera.

S. reginaldi (Mantell, 1844), Mantell, 1854; now Baltisphaeridium.

Sporangites chicagoensis Reinsch, 1884; now Tasmanites.

S. huronensis Dawson, 1871a; now Tasmanites.

Sporites intersignatus Thiergart, 1944; rejected by Eisenack, 1957, p. 247.

S. parvulus Thiergart, 1944; rejected by Eisenack, 1957, p. 247.

S. schandelahensis minor Thiergart, 1944; rejected by Eisenack, 1957, p. 24.

S. schandelahensis spinosus Thiergart, 1944; rejected by Eisenack, 1957, p. 247.

S. tectus Thiergart, 1944; rejected by Eisenack, 1957, p. 247.

?Trachelomonas cretacea O. Wetzel, 1933; now Palaeostomocystis.

T. volvocina Ehrenberg, 1854; now Palaeostomocystis.

TRACHYDISCINA Naumova, 1961, p. 113; Mention only, without figures or text description.

TRACHYRYTIDODIACRODIUM Timofeyev, 1959, p. 60; rejected by Deflandre and Deflandre-Rigaud, 1961, pp. 4, 8.

T. involutivum Timofeyev, 1959; now Trachydiacrodium.

TRACHYZONODIACRODIUM Timofeyev, 1959, p. 61; rejected by Deflandre and Deflandre-Rigaud, 1961, pp. 4, 8.

T. signatum Timofeyev, 1959; now Trachydiacrodium.

TRIGONOPYXIS Cookson and Eisenack, 1960a, p. 11; junior homonym, rejected by Eisenack, 1961b, p. 316.

T. ginella Cookson and Eisenack, 1960a; now Trigonopyxidia.

Veryhachium bacifer (Eisenack, 1934), Deunff, 1954c; now Bacisphaeridium.

V. brevitispinosum Staplin, 1961, in Downie and Sarjeant, 1963; typographical variant of V. brevitrispinosum.

V. duodeciaster Staplin, 1961; now Micrhystridium.

V. monacanthum (Deunff, 1951), Deunff, 1954c; now Deunffia.

V. sedecimspinosum Staplin, 1961; now Baltisphaeridium.

V. trisulcum Deunff, 1958 var. reductum Deunff, 1958; now V. reductum.

V. tetraedron Deunff, 1961b var. wenlockium Downie, 1959; now V. wenlockium.

Vulcanisphaera africanum Deunff, 1961a; typographic variant, in plate caption, of Vulcanisphaera africana.

Xanthidium bulbosum Ehrenberg, 1838a; now Hystrichosphaeridium.

X. crassipes Reade, 1839; now Hystrichosphaeridium.

?X. difforme Pritchard, 1845; now Baltisphaeridium.

X. delitziense Ehrenberg, Rüst 1885; now Hystrichosphaera furcata.

X. fimbriatum H.H. White, 1842; now Baltisphaeridium.

X. furcatum Ehrenberg, 1838a; now Hystrichosphaerid.

X. globosum H.H. White, 1842; now Leiosphaeridia.

X. hirsutum Ehrenberg, 1838a; now Baltisphaeridium.

X. hirtum Ehrenberg, quoted by W. Wetzel, 1952; junior synonym of X. hirsutum; now Baltisphaeridium.

X. malleoferum H.H. White, 1842; now Baltisphaeridium.

X. palmatum H.H. White, 1842, Bronn, 1848; now Hystrichosphaeridium recurvatum.

X. penicillatum Ehrenberg, 1843; now Hystrichosphaeridium.

X. pilosum Ehrenberg, 1843; now Baltisphaeridium.

X. ramosum Ehrenberg, 1838a; now Hystrichosphaera.

X. reginaldi Mantell, 1844; now Baltisphaeridium.

X. spinosum H.H. White, 1842; now Baltisphaeridium.

X. tubiferum Ehrenberg, 1838a; now Hystrichosphaeridium.

X. tubiferum Ehr. 1838a subsp. complex, H.H. White, 1842; now Hystrichosphaeridium complex.

X. tubiferum Ehr. 1838a subsp. palmaforme, H.H. White, 1842; invalid alternative name for
      X. tubiferum recurvatum, now Hystrichosphaeridium recurvatum.

X. tubiferum Ehr. 1838a subsp. palmatum, H.H. White, 1842; invalid alternative name for
      X. tubiferum recurvatum, now Hystrichosphaeridium recurvatum.

X. tubiferum Ehr. 1838a subsp. recurvatum H.H. White, 1842; now Hystrichosphaeridium
      recurvatum.

X. tubiferum Ehr. 1838a subsp. simplex H.H. White, 1842; now Hystrichosphaeridium simplex.

X. tubiferum Ehr. 1838a subsp. spiculatum H.H. White, 1844b; now Baltisphaeridium spiculatum.

Zonalapollenites dampieri Balme, 1957; now Applanopsis.

ADDENDUM

In Section 111, index to dinoflagellate and acritarch taxa, certain species
reallocated to new genera are quoted as "Sarjeant 1964 (in press)". These
taxonomic proposals are made in two papers published after the period covered
by the Bibliography but before its publication.   The two papers in
question are:-

SARJEANT, W.A.S.

* 1964a – Hystrichosphere synonyms: Favilarnax Sarjeant junior
                    to Valensiella Eisenack.   J. Paleont, vol. 38,
                    no. 1, pp. 172-3.

        * 1964b – Taxonomic notes on hystrichospheres and acritarchs.
                    J. Paleont, vol. 38, no. 1, pp. 173-7.

180